# Quantitative Analysis

# About the Author

Ray U. Brumblay received his A.B. degree from Indiana University and his Ph.D. degree from the University of Wisconsin. For five years he taught at the Indiana University Extension Division in its Calumet Center at East Chicago, Indiana. After a period in the army, he joined the faculty of the University of Wisconsin at Milwaukee, where he is now Professor of Chemistry and Chairman of the Chemistry Department.

The author is a member of Sigma Xi and the American Chemical Society, and has contributed to *Analytical Chemistry*.

COLLEGE OUTLINE SERIES

# QUANTITATIVE ANALYSIS

*Ray U. Brumblay*

**Professor of Chemistry**
**University of Wisconsin**

BARNES & NOBLE, INC.  NEW YORK
PUBLISHERS · BOOKSELLERS · SINCE 1873

Printed in the United States of America

# Preface

This book is intended to provide in brief form the information usually contained in a one-semester course in quantitative analysis. In addition, a few well-established ideas and methods are included. Activities are given relatively more space than is usual in most textbooks because they are fundamental and should be applied to problems in analytical chemistry more frequently than they are. Thermogravimetric analysis is a basic method of evaluating a standard procedure, the heating of a substance to constant weight. It deserves some mention. The over-all intention is to state the fundamentals of analytical chemistry, and whenever possible, illustrate them with problems. The solutions to problems are broken down into simple steps to aid the student in following the reasoning involved.

In order for the student to study the subject matter in this book profitably an acquaintance with simple algebra and elementary chemistry is essential. Other books in the "College Outline Series" that can be of aid in understanding quantitative analysis principles are:

> *College Algebra*
> *First Year College Chemistry*
> *Chemistry Problems and How to Solve Them*
> *Physical Chemistry*

*Physical Chemistry* treats much of the theoretical material applied in analytical chemistry from a different angle and usually with a more rigorous mathematical approach. The different viewpoint it provides can be quite helpful in giving the student a better insight into ideas encountered in analytical chemistry.

# Table of Contents

# Tabulated Bibliography
# of Standard Textbooks

This *College Outline* is keyed to standard textbooks in two ways.

1. If you are studying one of the following textbooks, consult the cross references here listed to find which pages of this *Outline* summarize the appropriate chapter of your text. (Roman numerals refer to the textbook chapters; Arabic figures refer to the corresponding pages of this *Outline*.)

2. If you are using this *Outline* as your basis for study and need a fuller treatment of a topic, consult the pages of any of the standard textbooks as indicated in the Quick Reference Table on pp. xiv–xvii.

Ayers, *Quantitative Chemical Analysis*, 1958, Harper.
I (1–3); II (4–10); III (97–98); IV (28–31); V (31–39); VI (97–121); VII (186–190); VIII (21–27); IX (17–20); X (175–185, 191–194); XI (158–174); XII (178–180); XIII (180–183); XIV (183–185); XV (31–47); XVI (28–30); XVII (47–49); XVIII (52–55); XIX (55–59); XX (215–219); XXI (59–61, 217–218); XXII (144–148); XXIII (61–63); XXV (179); XXVI (11–15); XXVII (66–82); XXIX (97–121); XXX (69–73, 119–120, 178–179); XXXI (186–194, 124–130); XXXII (84–96); XXXIII (84–96, 140–144); XXXIV (84–96, 144–151); XXXV (151–156); XXXVI (84–96, 137–142); XXXVII (195–207); XXXVIII (89–90, 134–137); XXXIX (168, 208–211); XL (163–164, 211–213); XLI (11–12, 18–20, 43, 45–46, 47–49, 54–55); XLII (4–11); XLIII (52–59, 169–171, 215–219); XLIV (70–71, 130–133); XLV (122–128, 191–194); XLVI (137–156); XLVII (204–206).

Benedetti-Pichler, *Essentials of Quantitative Analysis*, 1956, Ronald.
I (1–3); II (21–27); III (30–46, 68); IV (4–16); VI (4–11); VII (9–20, 25); X (195–207); XI (82, 195–208, 211, 212); XII (66–83, 129, 137, 168, 208–211); XIII (44, 182); XV (66–83); XVI (66–83); XVII (17–20); XVIII (17–20); XIX (17–20); XX (17–20, 28–51, 158–185); XXI (45, 47–49, 54–55, 59, 143, 175–185); XXIII (4–16); XXIV (4–16); XXV (52–65, 169–173, 176); XXVI (97–121, 130–137, 178); XXVII (28–51, 122–130, 189); XXVIII (176–178, 191–194); XXIX

(59–61, 87–94, 140–148, 217–218); XXX (87–94, 138–140, 144–148); XXXI (151–156); XXXIV (195–206); XXXV (215–219).

Blaedel and Meloche, *Elementary Quantitative Analysis*, 1957, Row, Peterson. I (1–3); II (1–3, 17–20, 28–51, 66–83); IV (28–51); V (21–27); VII (4–11); VIII (4–16, 18–20, 43, 54, 59); IX (28–51); X (18, 215–219); XI (28–51); XII (28–51); XIII (52–65); XIV (66–83); XV (12–16, 122–157); XVI (122–157); XVII (97–121); XVIII (122–157, 178); XIX (84–96); XX (122–157); XXI (195–214); XXII (195–214).

Daggett and Meldrum, *Quantitative Analysis*, 1955, Heath. I (1–3); II (21–27); III (4–11); IV (66–69, 97–115); V (84–111, 175–177, 191–194); VI (28–51, 97–121, 186–188); VII (17–20, 28–30, 53–54); VIII (52–65, 176); IX (28–51); X (158–174, 208–213); XI (11–16); XII (66–83, 84–96); XIII (28–36, 122–130); XIV (97–121); XV (84–96, 137–157); XVI (11–14, 125–128). Experiments: I (4–11); II (4–11); III (12–14); IV (12–14); V (12–14); VI (52–55); VII (55–59); VIII (61–63); IX (176); X (122–126); XI (122–126, 129); XII (126–128); XIII (133–136); XIV (131–133); XV (178); XVI (137–144); XVII (137–144); XVIII (144–148); XIX (151–156); XXI (148–151); XXIV (215–219); XXV (169–173).

Day and Underwood, *Quantitative Analysis*, 1958, Prentice-Hall. (Textbook) I (1–3); II (21–27); III (66–74); IV (66–74, 97–103); V (97–121); VI (84–96); VII (84–96, 137–157); VIII (84–96); IX (122–128, 175–178, 186–195); X (28–30); XI (30–42, 175–178); XII (42–51); XIII (175–185); XIV (52–65, 168–173, 215–219); XV (100–103, 160–161); XVI (158–174); XVII (208–212); XVIII (195–206).

Day and Underwood, *Quantitative Analysis Laboratory Manual*, 1958, Prentice-Hall. I (11–16, 47–55); II (17–20); III (4–11); IV (66–83, 130–137, 178); V (136–155); VI (122–130, 188–194); VII (52–65); VIII (169–173, 215–219); IX (100–116, 158–174, 208–212); X (183–185, 195–214).

Diehl and Smith, *Quantitative Analysis*, 1952, Wiley. I (1–3); II (11–16, 17–20, 54–55); III (4–11); IV (28–30); V (30–36); VI (47–65, 215–219); VII (9–16); VIII (97–124); IX (66–73, 130–137, 178); X (84–96); XI (71–74, 136–156); XII (122–130, 176–178, 186–194); XIII (195–207); XIV (175–185); XV (158–174); XVI (169–174); XVII (215–219); XVIII (100–116); XIX (21–27).

Fischer, *Quantitative Chemical Analysis*, 1956, Saunders. 1 (1–3, 30–36, 39–40, 99–111); II (2–4); III (4–11); IV (11–20); V (21–27); VI (17–20, 28–30, 45–65); VII (52–65, 165–174, 215–219); VIII (30–47); IX (11–15, 66–81); X (97–121, 130–137, 178–180, 183–185); XI (97–121);

XII (87–88, 122–130); XIII (176–178, 186–194); XIV (84–96); XV (84–96, 137–156); XVI (151–156); XVII (195–208); XVIII (195–208); XIX (158–174); XX (208–212).

Griffin, *Inorganic Quantitative Analysis*, 1954, Blakiston.
I (1–3, 76–79); II (11–15, 17–20, 45–47, 180–183); III (21–27); IV (4–11); V (12–15); VI (175–185); VII (66–73); VIII (97–121); IX (130–131, 178); X (78–79, 138–139, 144); XI (84–96); XII (137–151); XIII (138–139, 151–156); XIV (30–41, 110–111); XV (43–46); XVI (52–64, 176–179, 215–219); XVII (122–130, 188–190); XVIII (90–91, 134–137); XIX (158–174); XX (195–214).

Hamilton and Simpson, *Quantitative Chemical Analysis*, 1958, Macmillan.
I (1–3); II (21–24); III (11–20, 45); IV (4–11); V (21–27); VI (28–51, 66–83, 97–121); VII (11–16); VIII (97–121); IX (66–83, 97–127); X (84–96); XI (66–83); XII (137–150); XIII (87–91, 137–150); XIV (150–156); XV (122–130); XVI (186–190); XVII (28–51, 175–185); XVIII (52–65); XIX (17–20, 61–63, 215–217); XX (84–94, 158–174, 208–213); XXI (195–208); XXIII (54–63, 134–137, 169–173, 176–178, 204–206, 215–219).

Kolthoff and Sandell, *Textbook of Quantitative Inorganic Analysis*, 1952, Macmillan.
I (1–3); II (28–30); III (28–30); IV (97–121); V (30–43); VI (175–185); VII (42–51); VIII (43–46); IX (44–46); X (158–174); XII (10–16, 54); XIII (4–11); XIV (47–49, 180–182); XV (21–27); XVII (52–55); XVIII (59–61); XIX (48–49); XX (40–41, 55–59); XXI (48–49); XXII (61–64, 113–115); XXIII (215–219); XXIV (61–64); XXV (217–219); XXVII (158–174); XXVIII (66–83); XXIX (97–121); XXX (28–37, 66–78, 122–130, 175); XXXI (84–96); XXXII (195–214); XXXIII (9–10, 11–15); XXXIV (69–71, 130–131); XXXV (122–123, 126–128, 188–190); XXXVI (139–141, 144–148); XXXVII (137–148); XXXVIII (137–148); XXXIX (151–156); XLI (195–206); XLII (207–213); XLIII (169–173); XLIV (202–206); XLV (215–219).

MacNevin and Sweet, *Quantitative Analysis*, 1952, Harper.
I (1–3); II (4–11); III (11–12, 47–49); IV (11, 55–59); V (52–55); VI (59–61); VII (176–178); VIII (215–217); IX (11–15); X (66–79); XI (97–121); XII (54, 70, 130–131); XIII (130–131, 178); XIV (88–94, 136–144); XV (144–148); XVI (151–156); XVII (122–126); XVIII (179); XIX (179); XX (195–207); XXI (100–116); XXII (100–116, 134–136); XXIII (158–173); XXIV (183–185); XXV (191–194); XXVI (4–11).

Mellon, *Quantitative Analysis*, 1955, Crowell.
I (1–3, 29); II (17–20); III (4–11); IV (11–16); V (17–20); VI (175–185); VII (175–185); VIII (28–51, 186–194); IX (158–174); X (175–185); XI (175–185); XII (66–83); XIII (97–121); XIV (84–96); XV

(81–82, 186–194); XVII (195–207); XVIII (84–96, 207–214); XIX (207–214); XXI (4–16, 47–48); XXII (21–27); XXIII (4–11); XXIV (11–16); XXV (122–127); XXVI (137–156); XXVII (122–124, 126–128); XXVIII (43–49, 54–59, 158–180); XXIX (195–208); XXX (208–213); XXXI (61–64, 131–133, 136–145, 169–173, 215–219); XXXIII (9–10, 21–30, 66–96, 158–174).

Olson, Koch, and Pimentel, *Introductory Quantitative Chemistry*, 1956, Freeman.
I (1–3); II (4–11); III (11–12); IV (28–30, 66–71); V (21–27); VI (31–36); VII (31–42, 97–116); VIII (42–47); IX (47–65); X (66–83); XI (97–112); XII (112–120); XIII (11–14, 122–137, 191); XIV (84–96); XV (175–185); XVI (144–156, 183–185, 215–219); XVII (195–214); XVIII (158–174, 180–186, 195–214).

Pierce, Haenisch, and Sawyer, *Quantitative Analysis*, 1958, Wiley.
I (1–3); II (11–12); III (4–11); IV (11–14, 17–20, 47–50, 53–55); V (28–30, 66–80); VI (21–27); VII (97–121); VIII (28–51); IX (28–51, 97–121); X (84–96); XI (84–96); XII (66–83); XIII (130–137, 178–179); XIV (137–150); XV (151–157); XVI (137–150); XVII (122–137, 186–194); XVIII (28–51); XIX (52–65, 176–178); XX (215–219); XXI (195–207); XXII (84–96, 134, 208–213); XXIII (158–174).

Rieman, Neuss, and Naiman, *Quantitative Analysis*, 1951, McGraw-Hill.
I (1–3, 21–27); II (11–12, 19–20, 45–49, 54); III (4–11); IV (11–15); V (66–81); VI (31–42, 124–126); VII (84–96); VIII (97–121); IX (70–71, 106, 116–120, 130–132); X (101–116, 131–134, 178); XI (84, 88, 92, 93); XII (137–148); XIII (84–96); XIV (112–116, 151); XV (151–156); XVI (29, 47, 217); XVII (43–46); XVIII (52–55, 124–129); XIX (55–59, 40–41); XX (148–150); XXI (195–214); XXII (94–95); XXIII (61–63); XXIV (112–116); XXV (176–178); XXVI (158–174); XXVII (215–219); XXVIII (179); XXIX (100–116, 134, 211–212); XXX (183–185).

Swift, *Introductory Quantitative Analysis*, 1950, Prentice-Hall.
I (11–12); II (4–11); III (66–71); IV (11–15); V (31–39, 122–130); VI (84–91); VII (90–92, 137–144); VIII (91–92, 95–96, 139–144); IX (106–116, 151–156); X (97–121, 70–71, 130–134, 178); XI (28–51); XII (45–49, 54); XIII (52–55); XIV (55–59, 183–185); XV (158–174); XVI (17–20); XVII (17–20); XVIII (175–185).

Van Peursem and Imes, *Elementary Quantitative Analysis*, 1953, McGraw-Hill.
I (1–3); II (17–20); III (4–11); IV (11–16); V (28–42); VI (42–51); VII (39–42); VIII (66–73, 195–206); IX (97–121); X (158–168); XI (84–96); XII (21–27); XIII (28–30); XIV (66–83); Units: I (4–11); II (212); III (17–20, 29–30, 52–61); IV (11–16); V (122–130); VI

(130–137, 178); VII (137–156); VIII (215–219); IX (158–173); X (31–39, 106–113, 116–119); XI (116–120); XII (84–95); XIII (195–214); Part IV (11, 12–15, 18–19, 45, 47–49, 54, 124, 143–144).

Walton, *Elementary Quantitative Analysis*, 1958, Prentice-Hall.
   I (1–3, 21–27, 28–30); II (4–11); III (52–54, 124–126); IV (43–48, 52–61); V (28–36); VI (61–63, 178, 217); VII (158–171); VIII (11–14, 66–69); IX (124–130); X (97–121, 130–136); XI (97–121); XII (183–194); XIII (178); XIV (84–96); XV (137–151); XVI (151–155); XVII (186–194, 215–219); XVIII (195–207).

Willard, Furman, and Bacon, *A Short Course in Quantitative Analysis*, 1957, Van Nostrand.
   I (1–3); II (11–16, 54–55); III (4–11); IV (11–16, 66–71); V (21–27); VI (69–81, 178–179); VII (97–121); VIII (137–142); IX (151–156); X (84–96); XI (186–194, 124–128); XII (28–51); XIII (52–65); XIV (158–174, 215–219); XV (195–214).

Willard, Furman, and Bricker, *Elements of Quantitative Analysis*, 1956, Van Nostrand.
   I (1–3); II (17–20, 45, 54); III (4–11); IV (21–27); V (28–43, 97–98); VI (11–14, 66–82); VII (31–36, 122–130); VIII (186–194); IX (69–71, 130–137, 178); X (97–121); XI (69–74, 84–86, 94–95); XII (137–151); XIII (137–144); XIV (137–144); XV (151–156); XVI (84–96); XVII (28–49); XVIII (52–65); XIX (43–47, 175–178); XX (215–219); XXI (158–174); XXII (158–174); XXIII (180–183); XXIV (183–185); XXV (178–180); XXVI (195–207); XXVII (208–213).

# Quick Reference Table

*See preceding pages*

*for list of titles.*

| Day & Underwood *Lab.* | Day & Underwood *Text* | Diehl & Smith | Fischer | Griffin | Hamilton & Simpson |
|---|---|---|---|---|---|
| | 1–5 | 1–5 | 23–30 | 1–5 | 1–8 |
| 1–31 39–61 | | 22–70 146–167 | 31–75 95–112 195–216 | 6–22 39–73 | 14–74 |
| 32–38 | | 8–22 | 64–75 96–97 | 5–8 | 22–28 |
| | 6–24 | 471–485 | 77–91 | 23–38 | 75–91 |
| | 175–186 195–249 261–286 | 71–101 | 3–21 96–125 161–192 | 253–279 | 92–116 327–347 |
| 109–118 | | 102–134 | 126–160 | 280–316 | 208–302 348–365 |
| | 25–50 | 135–146 | 205–216 | 88–101 | 138–310 |
| | 97–171 | 226–272 | 311–340 | 172–206 | 198–207 |
| | 37–96 | 168–203 209–220 450–470 | 237–274 | 102–147 | 138–156 |
| 62–108 | | 203–208 220–226 273–319 | 217–236 275–291 341–384 | 148–171 207–252 317–328 | 157–197 209–287 |
| 136–139 | 277–281 307–334 | 406–435 | 425–435 | 339–352 | 397–412 |
| 154–157 | 250–260 | 377–405 | 24, 98 403–406 | 74–87 | 315–327 |
| | 177–194 | 320–345 | 170–172 292–310 | | 303–310 323–327 |
| 128–136 139–157 | 289–306 335–404 | 346–376 | 387–417 436–460 | 329–338 353–372 | 412–464 |
| 119–127 | 270–277 | 436–449 | 149–154 | 296–316 | 366–394 473–533 |

# Quick Reference Table

*See preceding pages*

| Chapter in This Outline | Topic | Kolthoff & Sandell | MacNevin & Sweet | Mellon | Olson, Koch, & Pimentel |
|---|---|---|---|---|---|
| 1 | Introduction | 1–6 | 1–4 | 3–11 | 1–5 |
| 2 | Tools of Analytical Chemistry | 183–260 498–520 | 5–38 61–75 216–221 | 24–58 347–358 383–397 | 6–39 122–132 245–260 |
| 3 | Samples and Sampling | 149 241–248 700–701 | 232–233 | 9 12–23 59–63 | 2–3 |
| 4 | Precision, Accuracy, and Errors | 261–295 | 39–40 | 359–382 | 58–70 |
| 5 | Gravimetric Analysis Theory | 12–74 106–149 | 38–40 42–60 154–161 | 90–124 234–243 | 40–48 71–121 |
| 6 | Typical Gravimetric Analyses | 296–403 | 23–60 | 453–491 | 36–39 139–153 |
| 7 | Volumetric Analysis Theory | 415–426 | 76–84 | 171–194 | 48–57 154–172 |
| 8 | Oxidation-Reduction Theory | 463–481 | 127–132 | 221–233 | 294–329 383–388 |
| 9 | Neutralization Theory | 427–447 | 76–84 99–114 184–196 | 195–220 | 173–244 |
| 10 | Typical Volumetric Analyses | 521–609 | 84–98 115–153 | 398–460 | 260–293 360–373 376–380 |
| 11 | Electrolytic Separations and Analyses | 150–171 404–411 | 197–202 | 125–147 491–497 | 334 394–397 |
| 12 | General Methods of Separation | 75–105 | 203–207 | 67–162 | 330–388 411–414 |
| 13 | Complex Formation Methods | 448–461 | 208–215 | 65–66 237–240 453–460 510–512 | 135–138 376–383 |
| 14 | Analysis by Instrumental Measurements | 482–497 613–663 | 162–196 | 244–338 501–558 | 389–434 |
| 15 | Analysis of Complex Substances | 364–403 667–727 | 58–59 | 559–598 | 352 373–376 380–383 |

xvi

# to Standard Textbooks (Continued)

*for list of titles.*

| Pierce, Haenisch, & Sawyer | Rieman, Neuss, & Naiman | Swift | Van Peursem & Imes | Walton | Willard, Furman, & Bacon | Willard, Furman, & Bricker |
|---|---|---|---|---|---|---|
| 1–2 | 1–3 | | 1–6 | 1–2 | 1–5 | ix–xi |
| 3–94 | 18–58 | 1–35<br>44–62<br>320–331 | 20–48<br>209–225<br>341–365 | 13–53<br>131–145 | 6–38 | 11–62<br>99–108 |
| 82–89 | 13–14 | 401–417 | 7–19 | | 13, 15 | 20–27 |
| 123–140 | 3–13 | 438–443 | 167–182 | 7–11 | 44–51 | 63–73 |
| 98–122 | 73–86<br>247–263<br>264–288 | 295–320<br>332–373 | 49–99<br>183–194<br>313–316 | 2–12<br>54–107 | 142–159 | 109–121<br>299–322<br>354–355 |
| 200–233<br>414–435 | 234–246<br>264–289<br>335–360<br>393–395 | 332–373 | 228–239 | 58–93<br>108–122 | 17–18<br>160–173 | 323–361 |
| 141–176<br>191–199 | 59–69<br>70–73<br>81–86 | 36–217 | 195–208<br>226–227<br>247–256 | 145–154 | 38–43<br>52–60<br>116–130 | 119–121 |
| 200–233<br>414–435 | 89–106<br>172–179<br>191–211<br>318–333 | 104–217 | 132–165<br>326–330 | 234–262 | 89–103<br>104–115 | 204–215<br>276–298 |
| 141–176<br>191–199 | 107–151 | 218–294 | 111–131<br>316–325 | 189–217 | 52–88 | 74–99<br>140–150<br>168–203 |
| 235–334 | 153–171<br>180–190<br>212–233<br>294–297<br>335–360 | 36–294 | 240–293<br>301–312 | 155–188<br>225–234<br>263–297 | 89–103<br>134–141 | 122–130<br>151–167<br>216–275 |
| 436–456 | 372–395 | 374–400 | 132–142 | 123–130 | 184–192 | 401–443 |
| | 445–454 | 368–371<br>418–434 | 91–99 | 218–224 | 60–63 | 3–10<br>444–482 |
| 319–334 | 361–371 | 297–298<br>310 | 95–96 | 298–305 | 131–134 | 131–139<br>376–381 |
| 401–435 | 299–317<br>427–444 | | 100–110<br>331–339 | 312–329 | 193–204 | 483–519 |
| 382–398 | 397–426 | 187–188<br>211–215 | 294–300 | 306–311 | 174–184 | 382–400<br>422–443 |

# 1

# Introduction

Analytical chemistry is concerned with identifying the constituents of a substance and finding how much of each constituent is in the substance. Identifying the constituents is called qualitative analysis. Finding how much of one or more constituents is present in a given amount of the substance is called quantitative analysis. Quantities are usually measured in weight and are calculated as per cent by weight of the original material, although, in dealing with liquids, volumes are frequently employed.

Progress in scientific research depends almost entirely on quantitative measurements. This is indicated by the fact that chemistry made little advancement until quantitative weight experiments produced knowledge of the nature of combustion and the laws of chemical action. Then chemistry as a science advanced rapidly, and it continues to advance only as rapidly as quantitative measurements can furnish answers to research problems. Advances in instrumental methods have accelerated analytical work greatly but have not replaced strictly chemical methods. This is true because each instrument requires calibration and checking, made possible only by using established analytical methods.

The analytical chemist reaches out into all fields of knowledge for principles which he can apply to improve his work or accomplish his objective. One of his most useful tools is mathematics. Although higher mathematics is often required to establish the validity of an equation, or to derive it, the calculations made by the student of analytical chemistry seldom require more than a knowledge of simple algebra. It is largely through calculations, the working of problems, that one becomes familiar with most of the basic principles of analytical chemistry.

Not everyone who studies analytical chemistry becomes an analytical chemist. For most people, study of the subject is for the

1

purpose of becoming familiar with the possibilities the subject offers in helping to solve problems that one may face in related fields.

## Types of Chemical Analysis

There are several ways of classifying the methods applied in analytical chemistry. The two largest groups are organic analysis and inorganic analysis. The former is quite specialized; the latter is applicable to a wide variety of elements and their compounds. It is inorganic analysis with which this book is generally concerned.

**Complete Analysis.** If all elements in a material, even those in trace quantities, are determined quantitatively, the analysis is said to be complete.

**Partial Analysis.** A partial analysis is the quantitative determination of one or more constituents in a sample, such as the determination of the per cent of phosphorus in phosphate rock or the per cent of iron in iron ore.

**Proximate Analysis.** The determination of the per cent of one or more constituents in a sample all of which react alike with a certain treatment is called a proximate analysis. The separation and determination of the per cent of $R_2O_3$ in a limestone (p. 215) is a common example of a proximate analysis.

**Ultimate Analysis.** If the per cent of each element in a substance is determined, the process is called an ultimate or elemental analysis. This type is usually applied to the analysis of organic compounds in order to aid in establishing the formula of the substance. It seldom includes determination of the per cent of trace elements.

**Types by Sample Size.** Analytical methods are sometimes labelled according to the size of the sample taken for analysis.

Macro methods apply to samples 0.1 g or larger.

Semimicro methods apply to samples approximately 0.01 g to 0.1 g.

Micro methods apply to samples approximately 0.001 g to 0.01 g (1–10 mg).

Ultramicro methods apply to samples approximately 1 to 10 micrograms, designated by the symbols $\mu$g or $\gamma$ (gamma). A microgram is 0.001 mg.

## Types of Methods of Determination

There are almost an unlimited number of types of methods used in making determinations, but only a few are general enough to deserve mention here.

**Gravimetric (Weight-Measuring) Methods.** A constituent or some compound of it is weighed to find the per cent of the constituent. Several general procedures are applied in gravimetric methods.

Precipitation of a solid, filtering it off, drying it, and weighing it can in many instances give a value which is related to the weight of the constituent sought.

Volatilization of a material which has a relatively high vapor pressure or low decomposition temperature may be useful in measuring the portion of a sample that can be driven off by heat.

Electrolysis is often applied to separating an element or a compound in a weighable form.

**Volumetric (Volume-Measuring) Methods.** The measurement of a volume of a substance, or of a reagent, is often made to determine the per cent of a constituent. The volume of reagent as a solution added is usually measured in an instrument called a buret (p. 12). The process of adding the reagent from a buret is called titration. A method involving a titration is therefore called a titrimetric method. The analysis of gases is also generally a volumetric method.

**Instrumental Methods.** Methods of determining a constituent by measuring some physical property with an instrument are called instrumental methods. Some are based on light measurements and are called optical methods, and some are based on measurement of electrical phenomena and are called by various names depending on what electrical property is measured. Some of the better known electrical methods are conductometric (measurement of conductance), polarography (measurement of polarization due to concentration), and potentiometric (measurement of voltage or potential at an electrode, as in a pH meter).

It would be ideal for the student to become familiar with all the types of methods in common use. However, this becomes increasingly difficult with the rapid introduction of new methods that has taken place in recent years. In addition, some of the newer instrumental methods are so technical and specialized as to be beyond the scope of an elementary course in analytical chemistry. It is necessary therefore to limit this book to the most widely used methods and to those which seem to be based on general rather than on specific principles.

# 2

# The Tools of Analytical Chemistry

The tools of analytical chemistry are instruments for measuring accurately the mass or volume of a material. In gravimetric analysis the mass of a substance is measured directly. In volumetric analysis the mass of a substance is measured indirectly by measuring the volume of a liquid solution containing a known concentration of a reagent.

## Gravimetric Tools

**The Balance.** Because the results of every analysis depend upon the weighing of a quantity of material, the chemical balance is the most important instrument in analytical chemistry. It compares the mass of an object with the known mass of weights. The weight of an object is the pull of gravity on it, a force which varies from place to place on earth. The mass of an object is the amount of material in the object, measured as the force required to change its velocity ($f = ma$, Newton's second law). Weighing with a balance actually gives the mass of the object although chemists call such values weights.

CONSTRUCTION OF THE BALANCE. The analytical balance is an equal arm lever of the first class; that is, the fulcrum lies between the points of application of force.

The parts of the chemical balance, as shown in Fig. 1, are as follows:

$A$ The beam

$B$ Agate or sapphire bearing, supports the fulcrum

$D_1,D_2$ Stirrups with plane agate bearing and knife edge, support the pans

$E_1,E_2$ Pans for objects and weights

$F$ Agate fulcrum, supports the beam

$G_1,G_2$ Balance-adjusting screw nuts

$H$ Beam rest knob, raises or lowers beam and fulcrum by controlling $K_1,K_2$

4

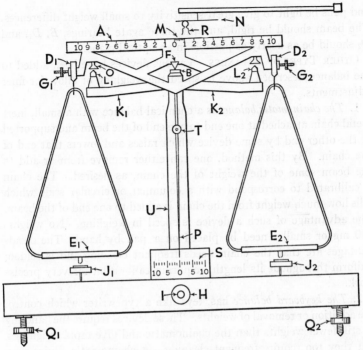

Fig. 1. The Chemical Balance.

*I*   Pan support knob, raises or lowers the pan supports $J_1, J_2$

$J_1, J_2$   Pan supports, hold pans from swinging when no balancing operation is taking place

$K_1, K_2$   Beam rest arms, controlled by *H*

$L_1, L_2$   Beam rest studs

*M*   Rider scale or beam scale

*N*   Rider carrier

*O*   Suction cup, starts beam and pointer swinging

*P*   Pointer

$Q_1, Q_2$   Leveling screws

*R*   Rider, a weight for adding up to 10 mg to either pan

*S*   Scale or pointer scale

*T*   Center of gravity adjusting weight

*U*   Main supporting column or post

The delicate parts of the balance should be enclosed in a case for protection from dust. In a good balance it is essential that the beam and pans be light to give great sensitivity to small weight differences. The beam should be rigid, and the three agate bearings, $B$, $D_1$, and $D_2$ should be as nearly as possible in an optical plane.

OTHER TYPES OF BALANCES. Various devices have been added to the balance described above to speed the weighing or allow for finer adjustments.

1. *The chainomatic balance* is a chemical balance with a small, inert metal chain attached at one end to one end of the beam and supported at the other end by some device which raises and lowers that end of the chain. By this method, one can either remove from or add to the beam some of the weight of the chain, as desired. The chain is calibrated to correspond with a columnar or circular scale which tells how much weight from the chain is added to one end of the beam. The advantage of such a device is speed in weighing. No weights 100 mg or smaller need be placed on a pan by hand. The disadvantages are that the chain needs frequent cleaning and is seldom uniform throughout its length, requiring calibration for very precise work.

2. *The keyboard balance* has keys like a typewriter which control the addition or removal of weights. These devices require the handling of still fewer weights than the chainomatic and give rapid weighings, but they too require frequent cleaning. A chainomatic device may be added to a keyboard balance to further increase speed.

3. *The single-pan balance* has weights added or removed by turning dials. It gives phenomenal speed in weighing where not too great precision is required. Its beam is balanced with weights (equal to the capacity of the balance) that are suspended over the pan at one end, and counterweights suspended at the other. The object is placed on the pan, and dials are turned until a weight equal to that of the object has been removed from the beam above the pan. The beam is then again in balance. An optical device and a damping mechanism (see 4 below) make it unnecessary to add or remove any weight smaller than 100 mg with these dials. The main disadvantage of the single-pan balance is the need for frequent adjustment.

4. *The damped balance* has a device that slows swinging and brings the balance directly to the zero point. Either magnetic or air damping devices are used.

5. *The micro balance* differs from the chemical balance only in fineness of construction and adjustment. Its operation is essentially the same, greater care being necessary on the part of the operator.

**Weighing with the Chemical Balance.** The principle in weighing is to place the object to be weighed on the left pan of the balance and then add weights of known mass to the right pan until weights and object balance each other.

METHOD OF SWINGS. This is the method most commonly used by students.

*Zero Point and Rest Point.* The center of gravity of the combination that includes the beam, the pans, and the pointer is adjusted so that it is slightly below the fulcrum. This allows the pointer to swing back and forth like a pendulum if the fulcrum is set on its bearing and the pans are released and given a slight motion. Friction of air and bearings causes the amplitude of pointer swings to be reduced with each swing. Where the pointer stops when there are no weights on the pans is called the zero point; where it stops when there are weights on the pans is called the rest point. A balance is seldom so perfectly aligned as to have its zero point in the center of the pointer scale. The zero point is found as follows. First, the pan supports are lowered (knob $I$). Then, with knob $H$, the fulcrum is set gently on its bearing by lowering the beam rest arms ($K_1, K_2$). A slight pull is exerted on the beam by the suction cup ($O$) so that the beam support stud ($L_2$) is lowered. This starts the pointer swinging. Three consecutive readings of maximum swing of the pointer to one side and two to the other are read on the scale, the first swing being omitted. An average of the three readings on one side is taken, and an average of the two readings on the other side is taken. Then an average of these two averages is taken to find the zero point.

**Example.** Where the center of the pointer scale is 0, each end is 10, and swings to the left are negative while swings to the right are positive.

Maximum pointer swings

| To left | | To right | |
|---|---|---|---|
| 1st swing | $-5.3$ | 1st swing omitted | |
| 2nd swing | $-5.1$ | 2nd swing | 4.8 |
| 3rd swing | $-4.9$ | 3rd swing | 4.4 |
| | $-15.3$ | | 9.2 |

$$\frac{-15.3}{3} = -5.1. \qquad \frac{9.2}{2} = 4.6.$$

$$\frac{-5.1 + 4.6}{2} = -0.25.$$

One quarter of a scale division left of center is the zero point.

*Sensitivity.* The smallest weight that can be measured by a balance is called its sensitivity. This term is often confused with sensibility.

*Sensibility.* The number of scale divisions the zero point or rest point is changed when one milligram is added to one pan of the balance is its sensibility. This value decreases with increasing loads on the pans.

*Sensibility in Weighing.* When an object is being weighed, weights and rider (see *R*, Fig. 1) are adjusted so that the pans are nearly in balance. The rest point is found by the method of weighing being used. The difference between the rest point and the zero point is divided by the sensibility to find the change in weight needed to balance the instrument.

$$\frac{\text{rest point} - \text{zero point}}{\text{sensibility}} = \begin{array}{l} \text{number of milligrams the rider should be} \\ \text{changed to balance the instrument.} \end{array}$$

**Example.** If the zero point is $+0.5$, the rest point is $-2.7$, and the sensibility of the balance is 3, what weight change is needed for balancing?

$$\frac{-2.7 - 0.5}{3} = -1.07.$$

The change required is 1.1 mg (to the nearest 0.1 mg). The negative sign indicates that there is excess of weight on the right side which can probably be compensated for by moving the rider 1.1 mg to the left on the beam.

METHOD OF SHORT SWINGS. This method differs from the method of swings in that the zero point and rest point are found by averaging only one reading on the scale to the left with one to the right, in the same order each time in any series of weighings. The advantage is a saving in time; the disadvantage, a slight loss in precision.

SINGLE DEFLECTION METHOD. This is the fastest reliable method of weighing on an ordinary chemical balance. Its precision is about equal to the method of short swings and its speed is considerably greater.

In weighing by this method the balance is adjusted so that the left side of the beam is slightly heavier than the right side. This is done either by hanging a tare (any object of a definite mass) on the left pan or by adjusting the balancing nuts (see Fig. 1). To find the zero point the beam rest arms are lowered before the pan supports, thus allowing the pointer to swing as soon as the pan supports are pulled away from under the pans. With the beam slightly off balance, the pointer swings first to the right, and the farthest point on the scale to which it swings is called the zero point. The object is then placed on the left pan and weights are placed on the right pan until the rest point, found in the same way as the zero point, is the same as the zero point.

METHOD OF GAUSS, TRANSPOSITION, OR DOUBLE WEIGHING. This method is used to eliminate error due to unequal arm length of the beam.

The object is first placed on one pan and weighed, then transposed to the other pan and weighed again. If both balance arms are equal, then exactly equal weights will be found. If not, then an average of the two weights gives a reasonably accurate value. For a true evaluation, the square root of the product of the two weights should be taken.

METHOD OF SUBSTITUTION. This method is commonly used for calibrating weights.

The object is placed on one pan, some counterweight such as shot is placed on the other pan, and the instrument is brought to balance by adjusting the counterweights. Then the object is removed and weights are put on the same pan until a balance is reached. The sum of these weights is of course the weight of the object.

**Errors in Weighing.** Errors in weighing are generally small, but in precise work they must be recognized and proper corrections must be made.

BUOYANCY IN AIR. According to Archimedes' principle, any object is lighter in air than in a vacuum. The density of air varies with the temperature and pressure but averages about 0.0012 g per ml. The weights, as well as the object being weighed, are buoyed up by the air. Since atomic weights and others in tables are generally on a weight *in vacuo* basis, a correction is often needed, especially where objects of large volume are weighed. The true weight (weight *in vacuo*) is found from the equation:

$$\text{True weight} = \text{weight in air} + 0.0012 \left( \frac{\text{wt. in air}}{\text{density of object}} - \frac{\text{wt. in air}}{\text{density of weights}} \right)$$

where 0.0012 is taken as the density of air in g per ml.

A form of the above equation that is probably more usable is:

$$TW = W_A \left[ 1 + 0.0012 \left( \frac{1}{D_O} - \frac{1}{D_W} \right) \right]$$

where:      $TW$ is the true weight,
         $W_A$ is the weight of the object in air,
         $D_O$ is the density of the object,
         $D_W$ is the density of the weights.

**Example.** A quantity of water at 25° C having a density of 0.9972 was found to weigh 24.913 g in air. Calculate its weight *in vacuo* (true weight) if the weights used were brass of density 8.4 and the air had a density of 0.0012 g per ml.

$$\text{True weight} = 24.913 \left[ 1 + 0.0012 \left( \frac{1}{0.9972} - \frac{1}{8.4} \right) \right]$$
$$= 24.913[1 + 0.0012(0.88375)]$$
$$= 24.939.$$

ADSORPTION OF MOISTURE. To compensate for the moisture an object adsorbs during weighing, treat a similar object in the same way and use it as a counterweight during the weighing. Both objects should adsorb equally and practically cancel any errors of this kind. A desiccant may be used in the balance case, but it will only partially eliminate moisture and may encourage corrosion of metal balance parts.

TEMPERATURE OF THE OBJECT. The object must not be much warmer than the air in the balance case. A warmer object may cause upward currents of air which decrease apparent weights, and may warm one arm of the beam, making that arm longer.

ELECTRIFICATION. Rubbing glass equipment charges it electrically, causing errors that are considerable. During dry weather, electrification is most troublesome. Some radioactive material or ultraviolet light in the balance case helps charges to leak away. Ten minutes of waiting after the object is placed on the pan usually reduces this effect sufficiently.

**Weights.** Weights are precision-made of brass or stainless, nonmagnetic alloys. The necessity for their being reliable is obvious. The Bureau of Standards calibrates weights of analytical grade, but weights thus calibrated are used only for checking weights in common use.

ABSOLUTE WEIGHT METHOD. For accuracy, the deviation of each weight from a standard must be determined. The easiest way is to check each weight in the set to be calibrated against the corresponding piece in a set calibrated by the Bureau of Standards.

RELATIVE METHOD. Choosing one weight within the set to be calibrated as a standard and comparing all others to it gives sufficient reliability to weights for most uses.

The first step in this procedure is to weigh the smallest weights with the rider. Then the small weights are used to weigh the larger weights. Any "corrections" in the weights found by this method are to be used in the weighing of larger pieces. After all weights are "corrected," the values found for each one are redistributed on the basis that the weight chosen as standard is correct. Redistribution is accomplished by dividing the "corrected" values of all weights by the "corrected" value of the standard weight.

**Example.** The one gram weight taken as the standard was found to weigh 1.0080 g when weighed with the smaller weights. This is called its "corrected" weight. If the "corrected" weight of the 0.5 g weight is 0.5030, what is the redistributed weight of the 1 g piece and of the 0.5 g piece?

$$\frac{1.0080}{1.0080} = 1.0000 \text{ g, the redistributed weight of the 1 g piece.}$$

$$\frac{0.5030}{1.0080} = 0.4990 \text{ g, the redistributed weight of the 0.5 g piece.}$$

The redistributed weights are those used when making weighings. The "corrected" weights are never used for weighing since they are values obtained by assuming the rider weight to be correct. The redistributed weights are calculated to the nearest 0.1 mg.

**The Weighing Bottle.** The weighing bottle is a thin-walled glass container with a ground glass stopper. Samples are generally dried and weighed in it. The bottle containing the sample may be weighed, some sample poured out, and the bottle weighed again; the difference in weight will be the weight of the sample poured out. This last process is known as weighing by difference. By this method only one more weighing than the number of samples is required.

**The Desiccator.** The desiccator (see Fig. 2, p. 12) is a utensil required for storing samples and equipment, such as crucibles, before they are weighed. It provides an atmosphere with a relative humidity that is easily reproducible. Desiccants (drying agents) such as calcium chloride, sulfuric acid, phosphorus pentoxide, calcium sulfate, magnesium perchlorate, and others are used in desiccators.

## Volumetric Tools

Titration is the gradual addition of a liquid reagent from a measuring instrument to a known or unknown quantity of material until chemi-

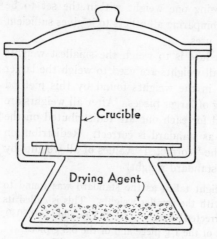

Fig. 2.   A Desiccator.

cally equivalent quantities have been mixed. The measuring instrument most often employed for delivering the liquid reagent is called a buret.

**The Buret.** Burets are long tubes of uniform bore, with graduations along most of their length and with a device at the lower end for controlling the outflow of liquid. See Fig. 3.

For any but the roughest work, burets need calibration. This is done by filling the buret to the 0.00 mark, draining out 10 ml into a tared (weighed) weighing bottle, weighing the water delivered, and dividing the weight found by the density of water at that temperature to find the true volume delivered. By finding the true volume delivered at other volume levels, each time starting the delivery at the 0.00 mark, corrections, if any, can be made for any part of the buret that does not deliver the rated capacity.

**The Pipet.** Pipets are tubes used for transferring or measuring solutions.

TRANSFER PIPET. Transfer pipets (see Fig. 3) are tubes with a bulb in the center and a ring marked above the bulb to indicate the volume of liquid that will be delivered by the pipet if it is filled to this mark at a certain temperature.

Calibration of transfer pipets is accomplished by weighing the water delivered into a weighing bottle, as in the calibration of the buret.

MEASURING PIPET. Measuring pipets (see Fig. 3) are long tubes, marked off over most of their lengths, with a tip restricted to reduce the rate of delivery of liquid. They are seldom used for accurate work but can be calibrated in the same way as a buret. They may be marked to the tip or over only the straight part of the tube, as shown in Fig. 3.

**The Volumetric Flask.** The volumetric flask is flat bottomed and pear shaped, and has a long narrow neck. The neck has a ring around it to indicate the point to which the flask must be filled for it to contain its rated volume at a given temperature. See Fig. 3.

Calibration is done by weighing the dried empty flask, filling it to the mark with water, weighing the filled flask, making corrections

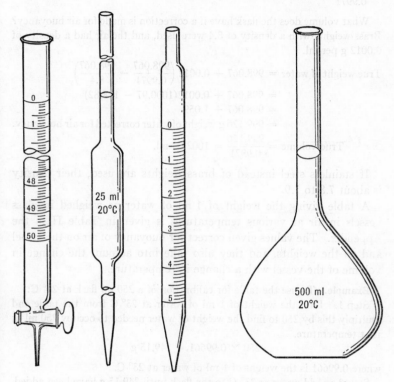

Buret    Transfer Pipet    Measuring Pipet      Volumetric Flask

Fig. 3. Volumetric Apparatus.

for buoyancy of air, and dividing the corrected weight of water by its density to give the true volume contained by the flask. If the flask must have a mark which indicates exactly its rated volume, this point can be found by putting more or less water into the flask, weighing it again, estimating where the new mark should be, and testing to see if the estimate is correct. A gummed label can be used for the new mark.

**Example.** An empty flask weighed 143.371 g. Filled to the mark it weighed 1141.438 g at 25° C. If the density of water is 0.9971 at 25° C, what volume does the flask have, disregarding air buoyancy?

1141.438 − 143.371 = 998.067 g weight of water.

$\dfrac{998.067}{0.9971}$ = 1000.97 ml the flask contains, uncorrected for air buoyancy.

What volume does the flask have if a correction is made for air buoyancy? Brass weights with a density of 8.4 were used, and the air had a density of 0.0012 g per ml.

$$\text{True weight of water} = 998.067 + 0.0012 \left( \frac{998.067}{0.9971} - \frac{998.067}{8.4} \right)$$
$$= 998.067 + 0.0012(1000.97 - 118.82)$$
$$= 998.067 + 1.059$$
$$= 999.126 \text{ g weight of water corrected for air buoyancy.}$$
$$\text{True volume} = \frac{999.126}{0.9971} = 1002.03 \text{ ml.}$$

If stainless steel instead of brass weights are used, their density is about 7.8 to 7.9.

A table giving the weight of 1 ml of water as weighed in glass vessels in air at various temperatures is given in Table II in the Appendix. The values given correct for buoyancy of air on the vessel and on the weights, and they also take into account the change in volume of the vessel with a change in temperature.

**Example.** To use the table for calibration of a 250 ml flask at 23° C:

Step 1. Find the weight of 1 ml of water at 23° C from the table and multiply this by 250 to find the weight of water needed to occupy 250 ml at that temperature.

$$250 \times 0.99661 = 249.15 \text{ g}$$

where 0.99661 is the weight of 1 ml of water at 23° C.

Step 2. Add water at 23° C to the flask until 249.15 g have been added, and then mark the neck of the flask at a point level with the meniscus. This mark is the calibration mark, which is as accurate as the work of the operator.

**Reading Volumetric Glassware.** The concave surface of the liquid in volumetric glassware is called the meniscus. When a measurement is taken, the eye must be held level with the bottom of the meniscus to avoid errors of parallax. See Fig. 4. If solutions used are colored and the meniscus cannot be seen, the top of the solution is read. If the liquid used does not wet the glass, the meniscus is inverted and the top of the meniscus is read.

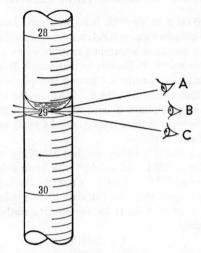

Fig. 4. Parallax in Reading Volumetric Glassware.

A. Eye too high; reading will be less than correct value.
B. Eye level with meniscus; correct reading can be made.
C. Eye too low; reading will be larger than correct value.

## Other Tools

Other incidental utensils such as crucibles, filters, spatulas, etc., whose use requires special directions, will be discussed under topics where their uses are explained.

### Review Questions and Problems

1. Find the zero point of a balance from the following:

   Swings of the empty balance    −2.9      +4.6
                                      −2.7      +4.4
                                      −2.5

2. If the zero point is −0.5 and the rest point is 3.7 when 15.52 g are on the right pan and the rider is set at 8.0 mg, what is the weight to the nearest 0.1 mg of the object if changing the rider to 9.0 mg gives a new rest point of +2? Find the sensibility of the balance first.

3. Calculate the weight of an object from the following data: Zero point, −0.3. Rest point after adding 1 mg to right pan with rider, −3.0. With object on left pan, 13.37 g on right pan, and rider at 4.0 mg, rest point is 3.6.

4. What is the weight *in vacuo* to the nearest 0.1 mg of an amount of water

that weighs 3.0000 g in air with brass weights? Density of water is 0.9971, density of brass weights is 8.4, and density of air is 0.0012 g per ml.

5. What is the true weight of a platinum crucible which weighed 21.7247 g in air using brass weights? Density of platinum is 21.5.

6. A 0.4200 g sample of density 2.7 gave a precipitate of silver chloride of density 5.6 that weighed 1.1216 g. Calculate the weight *in vacuo* of both sample and precipitate if both are weighed with brass weights. Is it worth while making these corrections if a result accurate to 1 part in 1000 is all that is required?

7. A flask weighing 87.629 g empty weighed 336.772 g when filled to the mark with water at 25° C and weighed with brass weights in air. The density of water at 25° C is 0.9971. Calculate the volume of the flask neglecting buoyancy of air; then calculate its true volume.

8. In calibrating a set of weights by the relative method, the following values were found:

$$
\begin{array}{ll}
1 \text{ g} & 1.0019 \\
2 \text{ g} & 2.0051 \\
5 \text{ g} & 5.0101 \\
10 \text{ g} & 10.0192
\end{array}
$$

Redistribute each of the weights, using the 1 g weight as the standard.

# 3

# Samples and Sampling

Samples chosen for analysis should be such that when their analysis is completed they answer a question or in some way provide valuable information.

## Selection

Every effort should be made, in selecting a sample, to obtain one with the same composition as that of the whole mass being sampled.

**Homogeneous Materials.** Sampling homogeneous gases or liquids is easily done by filling a suitable container with some of them.

**Heterogeneous Materials.** If the materials are not homogeneous, containers which can be opened and then closed anywhere within the body of the material being sampled are inserted, filled, and then closed. An apparatus for this sort of sampling is called a thief sampler, and variations of it are used for sampling solids, as well as liquids and gases.

Sampling nonhomogeneous solids may require several steps, if a representative sample is to be obtained. All of the material should be crushed, ground, and mixed until it is relatively homogeneous. Any small amount taken would then be representative of the whole. This is seldom possible, however. More often a small portion of the whole is removed either continuously, as from a conveyor or chute; intermittently, as every hundredth shovelful; or by picking samples at random. The last method is obviously the least reliable. Any one of these methods gives a gross sample which should be at least 500 times as large as the biggest single piece in the sample.

REDUCTION IN PARTICLE SIZE. Big chunks of gross samples must be reduced to a fine powder without any change in composition. Generally the crushing in a jaw crusher, gyratory crusher, or roll mill is followed by further subdivision in a ball mill. The material is

17

then sieved through a fine screen, and any material that does not pass through the screen is returned for more grinding.

REDUCTION IN TOTAL AMOUNT OF SAMPLE. This is done by quartering, which involves dumping the whole sample on a smooth surface, piling it into a cone, cutting the cone into two equal parts, and then cutting these two halves into two equal parts. This gives four piles, each one quarter the size of the original. Two such quarters opposite each other are taken, and the rest is discarded. Quartering is repeated as many times as necessary, usually after each grinding operation is completed. As soon as the gross sample has been reduced to some such quantity as a few grams or a pound or two, or whatever is desired, the selection of the sample is finished.

Sampling alloys and metals is usually done by drilling or turning them on a lathe. For special cases of sampling consult Wilfred W. Scott, *Standard Methods of Chemical Analysis*, D. Van Nostrand, 1939, pp. 1301–1333, and other standard works.

## Storage

The sample must be stored so that the container, air, moisture, light, or heat will not change the composition before it is analyzed. Usually dark glass jars, tightly covered, are satisfactory protection.

## Chemical Changes in Samples

Operations such as grinding, mixing, and sieving may cause changes in composition of some part of the sample. Loss of moisture from crystals, and reactions of metals, oxides, or other materials with oxygen, carbon dioxide, or moisture in the air must be avoided. The high temperatures created locally by vigorous grinding can oxidize ferrous compounds, dehydrate salts, and oxidize some sulfides. Special treatment to avoid chemical changes during the preparation of samples is discussed in publications by the U.S. Bureau of Mines and the American Society for Testing Materials, and in comprehensive texts.

## Treatment of the Sample

Before an analysis is made the sample must be dried, weighed, and made largely soluble in water if it is not already so.

**Drying.** The conditions under which samples are weighed should be as reproducible as possible. Solids and nonvolatile liquids are usually dried at just above 100° C. They are then placed in a desiccator with a standard desiccant until equilibrium is reached, and the sample is cooled. The weighing is then made as quickly as possible.

**Weighing.** Samples are weighed by difference (see p. 11) whenever possible. This reduces the number of weighings, if more than one sample is needed, and consequently reduces possible errors.

**Solution of the Sample.** Wherever possible the first choice of solvents is water. Alloys, ores, and minerals are seldom soluble in water and may require acids, alkalis, or other treatment for their solution. To make them more soluble in water, materials such as silicates, ceramics, some alloys, rocks, and ores require treatment at very high temperatures with melted reagents, called fluxes.

TABLE 1

COMMON AGENTS FOR TREATING SAMPLES

| SAMPLE | TREATMENT |
|---|---|
| Soluble salts | Water |
| Iron ores | HCl with $SnCl_2$ or fusion with $KHSO_4$ |
| Nonferrous ores | Acids or fusions |
| Ferrous alloys | HCl, $HNO_3$, or $HClO_4$ |
| Nonferrous alloys | $HNO_3$ |
| Carbonate rocks | HCl |
| Silicate rocks | $Na_2CO_3$ fusion |
| Tin ore, $SnO_2$ | $Na_2CO_3$—S fusion |
| Titanium ore, $TiO_2$ | $KHSO_4$ fusion |
| Chromium ore | $Na_2CO_3$—$Na_2O_2$ fusion |

HYDROCHLORIC ACID. HCl is a weak reducing acid that converts carbonates, oxides, and some sulfides to chlorides. It reduces $MnO_2$ and other strong oxidizing agents, giving chlorides of metals in a lower valence state. Stannous chloride with hydrochloric acid is a stronger reducing agent. It reduces weak oxidizing agents such as ferric iron to ferrous iron, increasing the rate at which some minerals dissolve.

NITRIC ACID. $HNO_3$ is a strong oxidizing acid which is used to oxidize the sulfur in sulfides to free sulfur and sulfur dioxide, and to convert some metals, as tin and antimony, to insoluble oxides. Treatment with nitric acid converts metals in alloys and metal ions in sulfide minerals to nitrates.

PERCHLORIC ACID. $HClO_4$ is an oxidizing acid which converts metals to perchlorates quickly and dehydrates silica nearly completely. Unless it is dilute and cool, one must use it carefully when working with combustible materials. Mixing nitric acid or sulfuric acid with the perchloric acid reduces danger of explosions.

POTASSIUM BISULFATE. $KHSO_4$, when heated, changes to pyrosulfate, $K_2S_2O_7$, which in the molten state attacks oxides and other minerals that other acids used at lower temperatures will not affect. Metals and metal ions in materials treated with this agent are converted to sulfates.

SODIUM CARBONATE. $Na_2CO_3$ is the commonest alkaline flux. It converts silica and insoluble silicates to soluble sodium silicate, and metal ions to carbonates. Further treatment of these products with acids yields soluble salts of metal ions and silicic acids which are fairly easily washed and dehydrated to $SiO_2$. The silica can be ignited and weighed as $SiO_2$, and the soluble salts can be analyzed for whatever metal ions are present.

The addition of sodium peroxide to sodium carbonate makes a powerful alkaline oxidizing flux. It converts chromium compounds to chromates and is capable of oxidizing many elements to their highest possible valence.

## Review Questions and Problems

1. List three general ways in which samples are taken. Which is the least reliable?

2. Define: (a) quartering; (b) thief sampler; (c) gross sample; (d) flux.

3. Give an example of: (a) acid flux; (b) alkaline flux; (c) alkaline oxidizing flux.

4. What agent would you recommend for attacking: (a) limestone; (b) an iron ore; (c) a manganese ore of $MnO_2$; (d) a piece of granite; (e) a stainless steel alloy; (f) a cast iron?

5. What chemical changes might occur during the vigorous grinding of: (a) $Fe_3O_4$; (b) quicklime, CaO; (c) washing soda, $Na_2CO_3 \cdot 10H_2O$; (d) CuS?

of the accuracy of the results. In analytical chemistry, precision is

# 4

# Precision, Accuracy, and Errors

The subject of precision and accuracy should be studied early in
any course in analytical chemistry but, in order that students can
understand its importance and the meaning of terms used, it is often
deferred until later. Sometimes the subject is divided, so that part
is studied early and part later. The importance of knowing how to
treat numerical data in every phase of an analytical chemistry course
is undisputed.

## Significant Figures

Significant figures are defined as the digits needed to express the
results obtained to whatever degree of accuracy can be expected from
the precision of the measurements used.

**Example 1.** When a buret is read, the volume is reported to the nearest
0.01 ml. Thus, if the buret reading is 34.27, the digit 7, though doubtful
because it might be 6 or 8, is significant and should be included in the
reading. The reading should not be reported as 34.270 because the zero
has no meaning unless the buret could be read to approximately 0.001 ml,
in which case the reading should contain three digits to the right of the
decimal.

**Example 2.** An object weighed on a rough balance is found to weigh
18.2 g. The digit 2 is a bit doubtful because the balance is not reliable for a
more precise measurement. The three digits in 18.2 are all that are significant because they express the weight to the extent of precision of the
instrument. The same object, with a more precise balance, was found to
weigh 18.1732 g. All six figures are significant because they are needed to
express the weight to the degree of precision of the balance.

## Accuracy and Precision

Accuracy is the correctness of a measurement or determination;
precision is the reproducibility of results of measurements. The

closer a result is to its true value, the more accurate it is. The closer several results are to each other, the more precise they are, regardless of the accuracy of the results. In analytical chemistry, precision is often mistaken for accuracy.

The difference between precision and accuracy as applied to an analytical measurement such as a titration is shown in Fig. 5. The

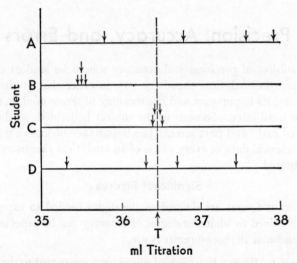

Fig. 5. Precision and Accuracy of Student Results. *A* had poor precision and accuracy, *B* had good precision but poor accuracy, *C* had good precision and accuracy, and *D* had poor precision but good accuracy, merely through chance, not from accurate work.

results of student *D* are not very common, but they occur frequently enough so that the grading of a student's work should be based on factors of precision as well as accuracy.

All measurements are subject to errors. It is well to recognize this and to be prepared to reduce such errors to a minimum. It is also advisable to recognize the limitations, in terms of precision, of the methods of analysis chosen.

**Determinate Errors.** These are errors that occur in one determination after another with about the same magnitude. They are due to some definite inaccuracy in the procedure, such as the high solubility of a precipitate or the color change of an indicator at the wrong pH. Usually two or more different methods of analysis applied to the same determination will tend to minimize determinate errors. A blank titration (a titration made against a solution which contains everything but the reactive material being determined) may reduce a determinate error if it cannot be corrected in any other way.

**Indeterminate Errors.** These are also known as accidental errors. They occur with random quantity and random frequency of error. Small errors occur more frequently than large ones, and errors on the high side occur with the same frequency as those on the low side. If the latter case is untrue, then the error is a determinate error. Mathematically it can be shown that the frequency and magnitude of indeterminate errors fall on a prob-

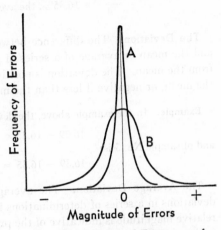

Fig. 6. Magnitude and Frequency of Indeterminate Errors.

ability curve such as is shown in Fig. 6 in which curve *A* shows the probability of frequency and magnitude of errors to be expected for a method of analysis that is more precise than the method associated with curve *B*. Nothing of the accuracy of either method is indicated by such curves.

## Mathematics of Errors

The complete mathematical treatment of errors is left to more extensive works than this, but a simple discussion of the statistical approach to handling results of analyses is necessary here.

**The Average or Mean.** This value is obtained by adding together all the results of different determinations and dividing the sum by the number of determinations.

**Example.** Four different samples of a silver alloy were analyzed for silver with the following results.

| Sample No. | 1 | 2 | 3 | 4 |
|---|---|---|---|---|
| % Ag | 16.37 | 16.29 | 16.39 | 16.35 |

Find the average or mean per cent of silver in the alloy using these values.

Step 1. Add all values together.

$$16.37 + 16.29 + 16.39 + 16.35 = 65.40.$$

Step 2. Divide the sum by the number of values.

$$\frac{65.40}{4} = 16.35\%, \text{ the average or mean.}$$

**The Deviation.** The difference between any result of an analysis and the mean or average of a series of results is called the deviation from the mean. The deviation is positive if the value is greater than the mean, or negative if less than the mean.

**Example.** In the example above, the deviation of sample No. 2 is:

$$16.29 - 16.35 = -0.06,$$

and of sample No. 3 is:

$$16.39 - 16.35 = +0.04.$$

**The Average Deviation.** The average of the absolute values of deviations in a series of determinations is the average deviation. Its relative magnitude is indicative of the precision of a series of determinations. The smaller the average deviation, the greater the precision.

**Example.** In the example above, the average deviation would be found by adding the individual deviations and dividing by 4, the number of deviations concerned.

| Sample No. | 1 | 2 | 3 | 4 |
|---|---|---|---|---|
| Deviation | +0.02 | −0.06 | +0.04 | 0.00 |

Adding the absolute values and dividing by 4:

$$\frac{0.02 + 0.06 + 0.04 + 0.00}{4} = \frac{0.12}{4}$$

$$= 0.03, \text{ the average deviation.}$$

The general formula for finding the average deviation is:

$$d_{\text{average}} = \frac{|d_1| + |d_2| + |d_3| + \cdots + |d_n|}{n}, \qquad (4-1)$$

where $|d_1|$ and so on are the absolute values of the deviations of individual determinations and $n$ is the number of determinations.

**The Standard Deviation.** This differs from the average deviation. The deviations are squared, the squares are added, and the sum is divided by $n - 1$, where $n$ is the number of deviations. The result of this operation is a number whose square root is called the standard deviation. The general formula for its calculation is:

$$d_{standard} = \sqrt{\frac{d_1^2 + d_2^2 + d_3^2 + \cdots + d_n^2}{n - 1}}. \quad (4-2)$$

The standard deviation is a more commonly used measure of deviation than the average deviation because its value can be more reliably estimated from a given number of determinations in any statistical study. For many determinations such as thirty or more, $n$, instead of $n - 1$, may be used as the divisor in Equation (4–2).

**Example.** Find the standard deviation for the results given in the above example by substituting in Equation (4–2) and solving for $d_{standard}$.

$$d_{standard} = \sqrt{\frac{0.0004 + 0.0036 + 0.0016 + 0.00}{3}}$$

$$= \sqrt{\frac{0.0056}{3}}$$

$$= \sqrt{0.0019}$$

$$= 0.0435, \text{ the standard deviation.}$$

From the mathematical derivation of the curves in Fig. 6 it can be shown that for a large number of determinations:

a. The standard deviation is larger than 68% of all single deviations.

b. Two times the standard deviation is larger than 95% of all single deviations.

c. 2.5 times the standard deviation is larger than 99% of all single deviations.

**Relative Error.** The relative error is the magnitude of an error or deviation from the true value as compared to the true value.

$$\text{Relative error} = \frac{\text{error}}{\text{true value}}. \quad (4-3)$$

**Example.** If we assume that 16.35%, the average value in the example above, is the true value, then the error of sample 1 is $\frac{0.02}{16.35}$ or 2 units of error in 1635 units. Since the error is related to the true value, this is the relative error. This can be changed to units of error per 1000 units by dividing 2 by 1635 and multiplying by 1000:

$$\frac{2 \times 1000}{1635} = 1.22 \text{ parts per 1000,}$$

the relative error in parts per thousand. Parts per thousand is a common way of expressing relative error or relative precision. Parts per thousand deviation gives relative deviation, which is important in statistical appraisal of work done.

The relative standard deviation is found as follows:

$$\text{Relative standard deviation} = \frac{d_{\text{standard}}}{\text{average}}, \qquad (4\text{-}4)$$

where the average is the average of several determinations. This value when multiplied by 100 gives the relative standard deviation in parts per 100, and when multiplied by 1000 gives the relative standard deviation in parts per 1000.

**Rejection of a Measured Value.** The question often arises as to whether a result with a large deviation is best discarded. Certain rules apply generally, but they are not necessarily the only possible nor the most reliable ones.

Rule 1. If any cause is known for an error in the result, such as spillage or dirt in a precipitate, the result should be discarded.

Rule 2. If there are only three or fewer results to be considered, none may be discarded safely except by rule 1.

Rule 3. If there are four or more results to be considered with only one large deviation, several courses have been suggested. The commonest procedure is to average all values except the one in question. Then, if the deviation of the one in question is four or more times the average deviation of the other values, the result in question is to be discarded. For a criticism of this rule and a suggestion for a better procedure see W. J. Blaedel, V. W. Meloche, and J. A. Ramsey, "A Comparison of Criteria for the Rejection of Measurements," *J. Chem. Ed.* (1951), XXVIII, 643.

**Example.** In a series of analyses the following values were found for the per cent of Ag in an alloy:

| Sample No. | 1 | 2 | 3 | 4 |
|---|---|---|---|---|
| % Ag | 16.17 | 16.29 | 16.39 | 16.35 |

Should the value for sample No. 1 be kept and averaged with the others to find the most probable result or should it be discarded? Applying rule 3:

Step 1. Find the average of the values for samples 2, 3, and 4.

$$\text{Average} = \frac{16.29 + 16.39 + 16.35}{3}$$
$$= 16.34\% \text{ Ag.}$$

Step 2. Find the deviations for each of all four values.

| Sample No. | 1 | 2 | 3 | 4 |
|---|---|---|---|---|
| Deviation | 0.17 | 0.05 | 0.05 | 0.01 |

Step 3. Find the average deviation for samples 2, 3, and 4.

$$d_{average} = \frac{0.05 + 0.05 + 0.01}{3}$$
$$= \frac{0.11}{3}$$
$$= 0.04.$$

Step 4. Multiply this value, 0.04, by 4. If this product is smaller than the deviation for sample No. 1, the chances are at least 995 out of 1000 that the deviation for sample No. 1 is due to some error in operation, and it should be discarded.

$$0.04 \times 4 = 0.16.$$

This is smaller than the deviation of sample No. 1 so that according to the rule, sample No. 1 should be discarded.

Rule 4. If there are four results to be considered, two close together at one value and two close together at another value, neither pair of results is necessarily better than the other and neither can safely be discarded. More samples should be analyzed in order to pinpoint the most probable result more closely.

## Review Questions and Problems

1. Define: a. Significant figures, b. Accuracy, c. Precision, d. Determinate errors, e. Indeterminate errors, f. Deviation, g. Standard deviation.
2. State four rules for discarding or rejecting results of analyses which have large deviations.
3. Write the general formula for finding the standard deviation in a series of determinations.
4. A series of chloride samples are analyzed and the results are found as follows:

| Sample No. | 1 | 2 | 3 | 4 |
|---|---|---|---|---|
| % Chloride | 23.02 | 23.41 | 23.15 | 23.12 |

Calculate: a. The average.
b. The deviation of each result.
c. The average deviation.
d. The standard deviation.
e. Whether sample No. 2 should be discarded or retained.
f. The relative error in parts per 1000 of each determination if the average of the results for samples 1, 3, and 4 is taken as the true value.

# 5

# Gravimetric Analysis Theory

Gravimetric analysis involves the preparation and weighing of a stable substance of known composition that contains the constituent to be determined. The most common method of doing this is to cause the stable substance to precipitate from a solution, leaving behind materials that might contaminate and alter the composition of the substance. Laws governing such operations can be applied to help understand the principles involved, and such applications are best made quantitatively by using mathematics.

## Stoichiometry

Stoichiometry is the measurement of weight relations between constituents of substances and products of reactions. Its application to quantitative analysis is fundamental and relatively simple.

**Example 1.** In the analysis of a 1.5 gram sample containing chloride, silver nitrate solution is added to the solution of the chloride to form 0.9214 gram of insoluble silver chloride. By the use of both atomic weights and the formula for silver chloride one can calculate the relation of chloride to silver chloride and, subsequently, determine the per cent of chloride in the sample.

The part of AgCl that is chloride is $\dfrac{Cl}{AgCl} \times$ the weight of silver chloride, or in this case:

$$\frac{35.46}{143.34} \times 0.9214 = 0.2282 \text{ g of chloride in the sample.}$$

The per cent of chloride is found by dividing the part of the sample that is chloride by the weight of the whole sample and then multiplying by 100.

$$\frac{0.2282}{1.5000} \times 100 = 15.20\% \text{ chloride.}$$

These steps may be combined thus:

$$\frac{35.46 \times 0.9214 \times 100}{143.34 \times 1.5000} = 15.20\% \text{ chloride.}$$

The gravimetric factor is defined as the ratio of the weight of any substance to the weight of the substance to which it is converted in an analysis. The ratio of chloride to silver chloride in example 1 is the gravimetric factor of chloride to silver chloride.

Gravimetric factors are used to save time in cases where a large number of analyses are run. The chloride to silver chloride factor is calculated:

$$\frac{\text{Cl}}{\text{AgCl}} = \frac{35.46}{143.34} = 0.2472$$

and is used in the calculation in place of the fraction $\frac{35.46}{143.34}$ thus:

$$\frac{0.2472 \times 0.9214 \times 100}{1.5000} = 15.20\% \text{ chloride.}$$

**Example 2.** Using the gravimetric factor, calculate the per cent of sulfur in coal if a 2.000 g sample of coal gave a precipitate of $BaSO_4$ that weighed 0.0840 g.

The gravimetric factor is found by inspecting the reactions sulfur undergoes during the analysis. These need not be completed equations but must be balanced with respect to sulfur. The sulfur is oxidized to sulfate, one atom to one ion of sulfate:

$$S \rightarrow SO_4^{-2}.$$

Sulfate is precipitated by reaction with barium ions in barium chloride:

$$SO_4^{-2} + Ba^{+2} \rightarrow BaSO_4.$$

Therefore one atom of sulfur in coal yields one formula weight of barium sulfate, the final product in the analysis. The gravimetric factor is:

$$\frac{S}{BaSO_4} = \frac{32.066}{233.426} = 0.1374.$$

The weight of barium sulfate found, multiplied by this factor, gives the weight of sulfur in the original sample. The per cent of sulfur in coal is the weight of sulfur divided by the weight of the sample and multiplied by 100. The complete calculation is:

$$\frac{0.1374 \times 0.0840 \times 100}{2.000} = 0.577\% \text{ sulfur.}$$

**Example 3.** (a) What per cent of iron is there in an iron ore containing $Fe_3O_4$ if 0.2824 g of the ore gave 0.0917 g of $Fe_2O_3$ by gravimetric analysis? (b) What per cent of the ore was $Fe_3O_4$?

(a) Step 1.   Find the iron-ferric oxide gravimetric factor.

$$\frac{2Fe}{Fe_2O_3} = \frac{55.85 \times 2}{159.70} = 0.6994.$$

Step 2.   Find the per cent of iron by multiplying the weight of ferric oxide by the gravimetric factor and 100, and dividing the product by the weight of the sample.

$$\frac{0.6994 \times 0.0917 \times 100}{0.2824} = 22.71\% \text{ iron.}$$

(b) Step 1.   Find the $Fe_3O_4/Fe_2O_3$ gravimetric factor.

$$\frac{2Fe_3O_4}{3Fe_2O_3} = \frac{231.55 \times 2}{159.70 \times 3} = 0.9666.$$

The gravimetric factor is thus seen to be obtained from the conversion of $2Fe_3O_4$ to $3Fe_2O_3$.

Step 2.   The per cent of $Fe_3O_4$ is found as in step 2 of (a), above.   Multiply the weight of $Fe_2O_3$ by the gravimetric factor to get the weight of $Fe_3O_4$ in the sample.   This value divided by the weight of the sample and multiplied by 100 gives the per cent of $Fe_3O_4$ in the sample.

$$\frac{0.9666 \times 0.0917 \times 100}{0.2824} = 31.40\% \text{ } Fe_3O_4.$$

# Factors Affecting the Solubility of Precipitates

In order to be able to design conditions so that precipitation reactions occur as completely or as uniformly as possible, the analytical chemist must understand the principles of equilibrium reactions. Precipitation reactions are never quite complete, since every precipitate is at least minutely soluble.   The concern of the analytical chemist is the control of conditions near the point of completion.

**The Law of Mass Action.**   A special case of the principle of Le Chatelier is the law of mass action.   Le Chatelier's principle states that when a stress is applied to a system at equilibrium the system changes to a new equilibrium, the change tending to reduce or relieve the stress applied.   The law of mass action is concerned only with stresses applied to equilibria by changes in mass or quantities of reactants.   Such masses are expressed in terms of molar concentration, that is, moles per liter of the reactants in solutions.   An equilibrium is a situation in which two reactions opposing each other are occurring simultaneously and the two opposing rates are equal.

$$\text{Rate} \rightarrow = \text{Rate} \leftarrow.$$

The law of mass action states that the rates of reactions are proportional to the products of the active concentrations of the reactants, each concentration being taken to a power equal to its coefficient in the balanced equation for the reaction. Thus for the general reaction at equilibrium:

$$aA + bB \cdots \rightleftarrows mM + nN \cdots$$
Rate toward right: $R_1 \propto [A]^a \times [B]^b \cdots$
Rate toward left:  $R_2 \propto [M]^m \times [N]^n \cdots$

Brackets mean gram moles per liter, and the symbol $\propto$ means "is proportional to."

To change the proportions to equations, rate constants $k_1$ and $k_2$ are introduced. These constants represent the effects of the nature of the reactants, catalysts, temperature, and all other factors, except concentrations, that affect speeds of reactions. Then:

$$R_1 = k_1[A]^a[B]^b \cdots$$
$$R_2 = k_2[M]^m[N]^n \cdots$$

Since $R_1$ and $R_2$ are equal at equilibrium and things equal to the same things are equal to each other we can write:

$$k_1[A]^a[B]^b \cdots = k_2[M]^m[N]^n \cdots$$

Collecting all constants on one side and all variables on the other:

$$\frac{k_1}{k_2} = \frac{[M]^m[N]^n \cdots}{[A]^a[B]^b \cdots}$$

A ratio of two constants is a constant, so the ratio $k_1/k_2$ is replaced by $K_e$, giving:

$$K_e = \frac{[M]^m[N]^n \cdots}{[A]^a[B]^b \cdots} \tag{5-1}$$

This is the general form of the equilibrium constant. It can be applied to many kinds of reactions such as those of ionization, decomposition, and precipitation.

**Solubility Products.** An important application of the law of mass action is in precipitation reaction calculations.

The precipitation of silver chloride involves the equilibrium between solid silver chloride and silver and chloride ions:

$$AgCl(\text{Solid}) \rightleftarrows Ag^+ + Cl^-.$$

The equilibrium constant for this reaction is:

$$K_e = \frac{[Ag^+][Cl^-]}{[AgCl](\text{Solid})},$$

but at equilibrium the total quantity of solid present is immaterial as the solubility of the salt controls the concentration of ions completely, regardless of the amount of solid. Therefore, for convenience, the value for the concentration of AgCl solid can be taken as unity, leaving:

$$K_{sp} = [Ag^+][Cl^-], \tag{5-2}$$

where $K_{sp}$ is the solubility product constant for silver chloride.

For a reaction such as $As_2S_3$ in equilibrium with its ions in a saturated solution, the coefficients of the ions are used as exponents exactly as in the determination of the equilibrium constant, thus:

$$K_{sp} = [As^{+3}]^2[S^{-2}]^3.$$

CALCULATING SOLUBILITY PRODUCTS FROM SOLUBILITIES. The numerical values for solubility products are obtained from measurements of the solubility of the salts in water. Solubility values for salts in various solutions can be applied, but since exactly the same methods would be used, solubilities in pure water, except in special cases, will be considered here.

**Example 1.** The solubility of AgCl is 0.0016 g per liter at 20° C. Calculate the solubility product for AgCl.

In a saturated solution, every mole of AgCl dissolved yields one mole each of $Ag^+$ and $Cl^-$ thus:

$$AgCl \rightleftarrows Ag^+ + Cl^-$$

and the molar concentration of AgCl, [AgCl], is equal to the molar concentration of $Cl^-$, $[Cl^-]$, and to the molar concentration of $Ag^+$, $[Ag^+]$. The molar concentration of AgCl is found by dividing the concentration in grams per liter by the formula weight:

$$[AgCl] = \frac{0.0016}{143.34} = 0.000011 = 1.1 \times 10^{-5}.$$

Substituting in the formula for the $K_{sp}$:

$$\begin{aligned}
K_{sp} &= [Ag^+][Cl^-] \\
&= 1.1 \times 10^{-5} \times 1.1 \times 10^{-5} \\
&= 1.2 \times 10^{-10}.
\end{aligned}$$

Values for solubility product constants of various substances are given in the Appendix in Table III.

**Example 2.** In a saturated solution of $Ag_2CrO_4$, 0.022 g of silver chromate is dissolved. Calculate its solubility product constant.

The molar solubility of $Ag_2CrO_4$ is found by dividing the solubility in grams per liter by the formula weight.

$$[Ag_2CrO_4] = \frac{0.022}{331.77} = 6.6 \times 10^{-5}.$$

For each mole of silver chromate dissolved, two silver ions and one chromate ion are produced. Therefore:

$$[CrO_4^{-2}] = 6.6 \times 10^{-5}.$$
$$[Ag^+] = 2 \times 6.6 \times 10^{-5} = 13.2 \times 10^{-5}.$$

Then, substituting in the $K_{sp}$ thus:

$$K_{sp} = [Ag^+]^2[CrO_4^{-2}]$$
$$= (13.2 \times 10^{-5})^2(6.6 \times 10^{-5})$$
$$= 1.15 \times 10^{-12}.$$

CALCULATING SOLUBILITIES FROM SOLUBILITY PRODUCTS. The solubility can be calculated from the solubility product.

**Example 1.** The $K_{sp}$ of AgBr is $7.7 \times 10^{-13}$. Calculate its solubility in grams per 100 ml.

Since the molar concentrations of $Ag^+$ and $Br^-$ are equal and each is equal to the molar solubility of AgBr, then:

$$[Ag^+] = [Br^-] = [AgBr] = \sqrt{7.7 \times 10^{-13}}$$
$$= 8.8 \times 10^{-7} \text{ moles per liter,}$$

the concentration of AgBr in a saturated solution. To change moles to grams, multiply by the formula weight of AgBr, 188:

$$8.8 \times 10^{-7} \times 188 = 0.000165 \text{ g per liter.}$$

Since 100 ml is 0.1 times as large as a liter:

$$1.65 \times 10^{-4} \times 0.1 = 1.65 \times 10^{-5} \text{ g per 100 ml.}$$

**Example 2.** Calculate the solubility in grams per 100 ml of $PbCl_2$. Its solubility product constant is $1 \times 10^{-4}$.

The molar solubility of lead chloride will be the same as the molar concentration of lead ions, $[Pb^{+2}]$, and will be one-half the molar concentration of chloride ions, $[Cl^-]$, since for every mole of $PbCl_2$ dissolved, one $Pb^{+2}$ and two $Cl^-$ are formed. Therefore, if $m$ = molar solubility of $PbCl_2$:

$$2m = [Cl^-].$$
$$m = [Pb^{+2}].$$

The solubility product constant for lead chloride is:

$$[Pb^{+2}][Cl^-]^2 = 1 \times 10^{-4}.$$

Then:

$$m[2m]^2 = 1 \times 10^{-4}.$$
$$4m^3 = 1 \times 10^{-4}.$$
$$m^3 = 0.25 \times 10^{-4}.$$
$$m = \sqrt[3]{25 \times 10^{-6}}.$$
$$\log m = \frac{\log (25 \times 10^{-6})}{3}.$$
$$m = 2.92 \times 10^{-2}$$
$$= 0.0292 \text{ mole of lead chloride per liter in solution.}$$

To find the solubility in grams:

$0.0292 \times 278.12 = 8.13$ g, the solubility of lead chloride per liter. Since 100 ml is 0.1 liter:

$8.13 \times 0.1 = 0.813$ g is the solubility of $PbCl_2$ in grams per 100 ml.

**Example 3.** Using $1.1 \times 10^{-33}$ as the $K_{sp}$ of $As_2S_3$, calculate its solubility in grams per liter.

As in example 2, let $m$ = molar solubility of $As_2S_3$.

Then:

$$2m = [As^{+3}].$$
$$3m = [S^{-2}].$$
$$[2m]^2 \times [3m]^3 = 1.1 \times 10^{-33}.$$
$$108 m^5 = 1.1 \times 10^{-33}.$$
$$m^5 = \frac{1.1 \times 10^{-33}}{108}.$$
$$m^5 = 1.09 \times 10^{-35}.$$
$$\log m = \frac{\log (1.09 \times 10^{-35})}{5}.$$
$$m = 1.02 \times 10^{-7} \text{ moles per liter of } As_2S_3$$
$$\text{in a saturated solution.}$$

To convert to grams per liter, multiply the molar concentration by the formula weight of $As_2S_3$:

$$1.02 \times 10^{-7} \times 246.02 = 269.3 \times 10^{-7}$$
$$= 2.69 \times 10^{-5} \text{ g per liter}$$
$$\text{of } As_2S_3 \text{ in a saturated solution.}$$

THE COMMON ION EFFECT. One can calculate the effect that a small excess of one of the ions of a slightly soluble salt will have on the solubility of that salt.

**Example 1.** The $K_{sp}$ of $Ag_2CrO_4$ is $1.1 \times 10^{-12}$. Calculate the molar concentration of $Ag^+$ in a water solution saturated with $Ag_2CrO_4$ and 0.02 molar in chromate ion.

The solution of this problem requires a simple substitution in the formula for the solubility product constant. In 0.02 M $CrO_4^{-2}$ the $[Ag^+]$ is found as follows:

$$[Ag^+]^2 CrO_4^{-2} = 1.1 \times 10^{-12}.$$
$$[Ag^+]^2 0.02 = 1.1 \times 10^{-12}.$$
$$[Ag^+]^2 = \frac{1.1 \times 10^{-12}}{0.02} = 55 \times 10^{-12}.$$
$$[Ag^+] = \sqrt{55 \times 10^{-12}}.$$
$$\log [Ag^+] = \frac{\log (55 \times 10^{-12})}{2}.$$
$$[Ag^+] = 7.42 \times 10^{-6}.$$

The silver ion concentration in a solution, saturated with silver chromate and without any excess of chromate, is found as follows.

Let $m$ = the molar concentration of the $Ag_2CrO_4$ in the saturated solution. Then:

$$2m = [Ag^+].$$
$$m = [CrO_4^{-2}].$$
$$(2m)^2 m = 1.1 \times 10^{-12}.$$
$$4m^3 = 1.1 \times 10^{-12}.$$
$$m^3 = 0.275 \times 10^{-12}.$$
$$\log m = \frac{\log 275 \times 10^{-15}}{3}.$$
$$m = 6.5 \times 10^{-5}.$$
$$2m = [Ag^+] = 1.3 \times 10^{-4}.$$

Thus, the small excess of chromate ion appreciably decreases the silver ion concentration.

**Example 2.** If the silver ion concentration is 0.02 molar in a solution saturated with silver chromate, what will the molar concentration of the $CrO_4^{-2}$ be? Substituting in the solubility product constant formula:

$$[Ag^+]^2 [CrO_4^{-2}] = 1.1 \times 10^{-12}.$$
$$[0.02]^2 [CrO_4^{-2}] = 1.1 \times 10^{-12}.$$
$$[CrO_4^{-2}] = \frac{1.1 \times 10^{-12}}{0.0004}$$
$$= 0.275 \times 10^{-8}$$
$$= 2.8 \times 10^{-9}.$$

Solubility products and values derived from them are seldom accurate to more than two significant figures. Therefore the $2.75 \times 10^{-9}$ can be rounded off to $2.8 \times 10^{-9}$. However, the third significant figure may be carried along as a doubtful figure, and it frequently is.

ERRORS IN ANALYSIS FROM SOLUBILITY. All salts, even the most insoluble ones, have a certain solubility in solutions from which they precipitate. Errors due to solubility can be calculated by using the solubility product constant.

**Example 1.** In the analysis of a chloride, the AgCl was precipitated from 150 ml of solution 0.002 M in $Ag^+$. (a) Calculate the weight in grams of chloride left in solution, and (b) if the precipitate is washed with 100 ml of 0.05 M nitric acid and the washings are assumed to be saturated with AgCl, what weight of AgCl will be washed away?

(a) Substituting in the solubility product constant equation:

$$[0.002][Cl^-] = 1.1 \times 10^{-12}.$$

$$[Cl^-] = \frac{1.1 \times 10^{-12}}{0.002}$$

$$= 55 \times 10^{-11} \text{ moles per liter of } Cl^- \text{ in solution.}$$

To convert moles per liter to grams, multiply by the atomic weight of chloride:

$55 \times 10^{-11} \times 35.46 = 1.95 \times 10^{-8}$ g of chloride per liter left in solution after precipitation. The amount in 150 ml would be 0.15 of this:

$1.95 \times 10^{-8} \times 0.15 = 2.9 \times 10^{-9}$ g per 150 ml. This amount is obviously negligible.

(b) Moles per liter of AgCl washed away are found first by letting $m$ = molar concentration of AgCl. This will be equal to the $[Ag^+]$ and also to $[Cl^-]$ since one of each of these ions is produced from each mole of AgCl. Substituting $m$ for each $[Ag^+]$ and $[Cl^-]$ we get:

$$m^2 = 1.1 \times 10^{-12}.$$

$$m = \sqrt{1.1 \times 10^{-12}}$$

$$= 1.05 \times 10^{-6} \text{ moles of AgCl washed away}$$

by each liter of wash solution.

Grams of AgCl washed away are found by multiplying moles by the formula weight:

$$1.05 \times 10^{-6} \times 143.34 = 1.5 \times 10^{-4} \text{ or } 0.00014 \text{ g per liter.}$$

One hundred ml of wash solution will dissolve only 0.1 of this or $1.5 \times 10^{-5}$ g of AgCl.

Such calculations show that excessive washings may cause loss of precipitates, especially of the more soluble ones. However, wash solutions seldom dissolve enough precipitate to become saturated, so that such calculations may be misleading. They indicate the possible, not necessarily the actual, magnitude of errors. If solubility of a precipitate is appreciable, it is customary to use a wash solution saturated with the precipitate.

**Activities.** Calculations involving the equilibrium constant and solubility product constant are reasonably correct only in solutions of low ionic concentration. In ionic concentrations up to $10^{-4}$ molar, experimental and calculated results show no appreciable deviation. In ionic concentrations up to 0.01 molar, deviations are of only a few per cent. In concentrations above 0.01 molar, either interionic attraction or the formation of complex ions, or both effects, cause large deviations between measured and calculated values. The ions are no longer effective in acting as discrete units, and their effective concentration is therefore different from their actual concentration.

DEFINITION. The effective concentration of a substance is known as its activity. The concentration and activity are related to each other by the expression:

$a = cf$, where

$a$ is the activity or effective concentration;

$c$ is the concentration, moles per liter in solution;

$f$ is the activity coefficient. It is the factor by which a concentration must be multiplied in order to give the activity of an ion or molecule in the solution being considered.

THE DEBYE-HÜCKEL LIMITING LAW. The value of $f$, the activity coefficient, is dependent upon the charge on the ion and the surrounding atmosphere of ions and solvent molecules. It can be calculated with reasonable accuracy for ions in solutions of $\mu$ (ionic strength, defined below) up to 0.01 from a simplified form of the Debye-Hückel equation, commonly called the Debye-Hückel limiting law:

$$\log f_{\pm} = -0.506 z_{+} z_{-} \sqrt{\mu}, \qquad (5\text{--}3)$$

where:

$f_{\pm}$ is the mean activity coefficient for the positive and negative ions;

0.506 is a constant for water as solvent at 25° C;

$z_{+}$ and $z_{-}$ are the charges on the ions considered;

$\mu$ is the ionic strength of the solution.

THE IONIC STRENGTH. The ionic strength, $\mu$, is dependent on the charges on the ions and the number of ions in a given volume of solution. It is defined by:

$$\mu = \frac{\Sigma c z^2}{2}. \qquad (5\text{--}4)$$

This equation, stated in words, says that the ionic strength equals one-half the summation of the separate products of the molar concentrations, $c$, of each ion species, multiplied by the square of the charge, $z$, on the ions without regard to sign of the charge.

**Example.** Calculate the ionic strength, $\mu$, for:

(a) 0.02 molar sodium chloride;

(b) 0.02 molar sodium sulfate;

(c) 0.02 molar magnesium sulfate;

(d) 0.2 molar nitric acid and 0.5 molar barium nitrate together in one solution.

(a) $\mu = \dfrac{0.02 \times 1^2 + 0.02 \times 1^2}{2} = 0.02.$

(b) $\mu = \dfrac{0.04 \times 1^2 + 0.02 \times 2^2}{2} = 0.06.$

(c) $\mu = \dfrac{0.02 \times 2^2 + 0.02 \times 2^2}{2} = 0.08.$

(d) $\mu = \dfrac{0.2 \times 1^2 + 0.5 \times 2^2 + 1.2 \times 1^2}{2} = 1.7.$

Thus $\mu$, the ionic strength, is much greater for divalent ions and still greater for trivalent ions. It is obvious from the equation by which activities are calculated that the greater the value of $\mu$ the smaller the activity.

*Note.* Using the complete Debye-Hückel equation rather than the limiting law, one finds that activities decrease as $\mu$ increases up to values of $\mu$ of about 0.5. Then activities begin to decrease less and in some cases to increase again so that, in strong solutions, monovalent compounds often have activities greater than their concentrations. This may be due to hydration of ions removing solvent water from the solution.

ACTIVITIES AND SOLUBILITY PRODUCTS. Calculations and experimentation involving activities, showing the effects of ions not common to the precipitate, indicate that the solubility of a slightly soluble salt may be increased as much as threefold in 0.1 molar salt solutions of the monovalent type, and as much as tenfold by 0.1 molar salts of the divalent type. Usual analytical procedures are adjusted to provide a safety factor that is much larger than this. Consequently, errors due to activity effects are negligible except in calculating the end point error for a precipitation titration or in calculating whether a proposed method of analysis can be relied upon to give the precision desired. The following example illustrates the method of applying activity coefficients in solubility product problems.

**Example.** The $K_{sp}$ of $Ag_2CrO_4$ is $1.1 \times 10^{-12}$. Calculate the molar concentration of $Ag^+$ in a water solution saturated with $Ag_2CrO_4$ and 0.02

molar in $K_2CrO_4$, applying activity coefficients. This is the same as example 1, p. 34, except for considering activities.

Step 1. Calculate the ionic strength, $\mu$. It is obvious that the concentrations of $CrO_4^{-2}$ and $Ag^+$ from the solubility of $Ag_2CrO_4$ are negligibly small as compared to the concentrations of $K^+$ and $CrO_4^{-2}$ from the $K_2CrO_4$. Therefore:

$$\mu = \frac{0.04 \times 1^2 + 0.02 \times 2^2}{2} = 0.06,$$ the ionic strength based solely on

the concentration of the $K^+$ and $CrO_4^{-2}$ ions from the $K_2CrO_4$. If the concentrations of the other ions were larger in proportion, they would need to be considered.

Step 2. Using the limiting law equation, calculate the mean activity coefficient of the $Ag^+$ and $CrO_4^{-2}$ ions.

$$\begin{aligned}
\log f_\pm &= -0.506 \times 1 \times 2\sqrt{0.06} \\
&= -1.012 \times 0.245 \\
&= -0.248. \\
f_\pm &= 0.565.
\end{aligned}$$

Step 3. Using $f$ as 0.565 for each ion, the mean value for the two, calculate the concentration of $Ag^+$ in a saturated solution of $Ag_2CrO_4$ employing the solubility product constant equation where $[CrO_4^{-2}] = 0.02$ and the $K_{sp}$ is $1.1 \times 10^{-12}$.

$$[0.565Ag^+]^2[0.565 \times 0.02] = 1.1 \times 10^{-12}.$$
$$[Ag^+]^2 0.319 \times 0.01130 = 1.1 \times 10^{-12}.$$
$$[Ag^+]^2 = \frac{1.1 \times 10^{-12}}{0.00361}.$$
$$[Ag^+] = \sqrt{305 \times 10^{-12}}.$$

$[Ag^+] = 1.75 \times 10^{-5}$, as compared to $7.42 \times 10^{-6}$ as calculated without activities being considered. See p. 35. The $[Ag^+]$ must be more than twice as great, to saturate the solution with $Ag_2CrO_4$, as one would estimate if activities were not considered.

**Complex Ion Formation.** Appreciable errors can occur in analytical work if ions from the precipitate combine with ions or molecules in the solution to form complexes of moderate stability. Cyanides and thiosulfates form highly stable complexes with silver ion such as $AgS_2O_3^-$ and $Ag(CN)_2^-$. These and other obvious reactions are known and well provided for by analysts. Formation of other less well-known associations is more apt to cause solubility errors. For example, oxalates with magnesium make magnesium ammonium phosphate more soluble with small amounts of oxalate, by forming $Mg(C_2O_4)_2^{-2}$, and acetate ions in solution make lead sulfate much more soluble than in water alone. Silver chloride is much more soluble in 0.1 N sodium chloride or 0.1 N sodium nitrate than in water because of the formation of $AgCl_2^-$ in sodium chloride solution, and $Ag_2Cl^+$ and $Ag_2NO_3^+$ in silver nitrate solution. It is obvious, then, that high concentrations of any salts should be avoided while precipitating substances unless their effects on the ions or molecules being precipitated are studied thoroughly. Almost all metal ions other than those of the alkalis readily form complexes of varying stability. Complex ion formation and its applications are discussed more fully in Chapter 13.

**pH.** The pH is an important factor in dealing with slightly soluble salts of such relatively weak acids as phosphates, sulfates, carbonates, and oxalates.

For example, consider the effect of acid on the solubility of barium sulfate. The second ionization constant for sulfuric acid, a relatively strong acid, is:

$$\frac{[H^+][SO_4^{-2}]}{[HSO_4^-]} = 1 \times 10^{-2}. \qquad (5\text{–}5)$$

**Example.** Calculate the solubility of barium sulfate in a solution of pH 0, $[H^+] = 1$. Neglecting activities, from Equation (5–5):

$$\frac{[SO_4^{-2}]}{[HSO_4^-]} = \frac{1 \times 10^{-2}}{1} = 0.01. \qquad (5\text{–}6)$$

If there is no sulfate or bisulfate except from barium sulfate dissolving, then:

$$[Ba^{+2}] = [HSO_4^-] + [SO_4^{-2}].$$

But, according to Equation (5–6), sulfate ions are outnumbered, one to a hundred, by bisulfate ions. Therefore:

$$[Ba^{+2}] \cong [HSO_4^-],$$

where $\cong$ means "approximately equal to." By similar reasoning:

$$[SO_4^{-2}] = 0.01[HSO_4^-] \cong 0.01[Ba^{+2}].$$

Substituting in the solubility product constant equation for barium sulfate, letting $0.01[Ba^{+2}]$ replace $[SO_4^{-2}]$, then, where $1 \times 10^{-10}$ is the solubility product constant for $BaSO_4$:

$$0.01[Ba^{+2}][Ba^{+2}] \cong 1 \times 10^{-10}.$$
$$0.01[Ba^{+2}]^2 \cong 1 \times 10^{-10}.$$
$$[Ba^{+2}]^2 \cong 1 \times 10^{-8}.$$
$$[Ba^{+2}] \cong 1 \times 10^{-4}.$$

Thus the barium sulfate is ten times as soluble in 1 N acid as in water only, where its solubility is $1 \times 10^{-5}$ molar. Using activity coefficients for the calculations, the solubility is found to be considerably greater. The effect of pH on solubility is of more importance in dealing with more soluble salts than barium sulfate, but this example will serve to show how such calculations are made.

For barium sulfate the increase in solubility with acid is not undesirable, since an excess of sulfate ions decreases the solubility far more than acid increases it. Therefore, a little acid has been found to be beneficial because it increases the solubility of phosphates, carbonates, and other possible contaminants, and improves crystal growth by raising slightly the solubility of barium sulfate. Large crystals are more easily made from solutions of high rather than low solubility.

**Temperature.** Solubilities of slightly soluble salts generally increase with rising temperature. Solubility products change accordingly. Table 2 shows that changes in solubility with an increase in temperature are different for different salts.

TABLE 2
SOLUBILITY PRODUCT AND TEMPERATURE

| Temp. °C | SILVER CHLORIDE | | BARIUM SULFATE | |
|---|---|---|---|---|
| | Solubility mg per liter | $K_{sp}$ | Solubility mg per liter | $K_{sp}$ |
| 10 | 0.89 | $0.38 \times 10^{-10}$ | 2.2 | $0.89 \times 10^{-10}$ |
| 25 | 1.7 | $1.4 \times 10^{-10}$ | 2.4 | $1.1 \times 10^{-10}$ |
| 50 | 5.2 | $13.2 \times 10^{-10}$ | 3.4 | $2.1 \times 10^{-10}$ |
| 100 | 21.1 | $216 \times 10^{-10}$ | 3.9 | $2.66 \times 10^{-10}$ |

The commonly accepted value of the solubility product constant of silver chloride at 25° C is $1.2 \times 10^{-10}$, yet the table above gives the value $1.4 \times 10^{-10}$. Such variations are found by different analysts because of the difficulty of measuring very small solubilities.

**Solvent.** Organic solvents such as methyl, ethyl, and amyl alcohols, acetone, and ether reduce the solubility of inorganic ionic salts. Application of this fact is made in precipitating strontium chromate, potassium perchlorate, and lead sulfate in ethyl alcohol-water solutions. Lithium chloride is extracted from water solutions by using amyl alcohol as solvent. Care must be used when adding organic solvents to water solutions. Adding too much solvent may precipitate salts other than the one desired.

**Particle Size.** Besides affecting the actual solubility of a substance, the particle size of precipitates is of extreme importance when separation by filtration is required.

PARTICLE SIZE AND SPEED OF PRECIPITATION. Rapid precipitation does not allow time for ions or molecules to build up on existing surfaces. They therefore start new crystals, with many fine crystals resulting. Slower precipitation yields larger, purer, more perfect crystals because time permits growth on existing surfaces.

The more the solubility of a substance is exceeded by the concentration, the faster crystallization occurs. A qualitative rule developed by Von Weimarn covers this:

$$\text{Speed of precipitation} \propto \frac{Q-S}{S}, \qquad (5\text{-}7)$$

where:     $Q$ = concentration of supersaturated solution,
               $S$ = solubility of precipitate.

No precipitate will form unless its solubility is exceeded. The more it is exceeded, the faster precipitation occurs. A certain minimum of supersaturation is required before any precipitation can occur. Barium sulfate will not begin to precipitate until the concentration of the ions exceeds the solubility product constant by a factor of 400. Silver and chloride ions must exceed the solubility product of silver chloride by a factor of at least 6.

Von Weimarn's rule makes it clear that to make large crystals one should mix dilute solutions and, for very insoluble substances, increase solubility by heating, or adding acid, as in precipitating barium sulfate. This will reduce the rate of precipitation, and the crystals will be fewer and larger. The precipitation of calcium oxalate is an example. The ions of the precipitate are mixed in acid; then ammonia is added slowly to gradually decrease the solubility of calcium oxalate. This produces pure, easily-filtered crystals.

PARTICLE SIZE AND SURFACE ENERGY. If a solid is digested (heated in contact with the solution from which it has been precipitated) the crystals grow with the smallest ones disappearing almost entirely.

The reason for this is that surface energy on crystals, as on a drop of water, tends to pull the crystals into forms with less surface. Solids can decrease their surfaces by:

1. Growing larger.
2. Aggregation, small crystals joining others.
3. Precipitation on surfaces by ions.
4. Perfection of irregularities in a crystal.

It has been shown that for crystals below 1 to 2 microns diameter, and for a hard crystal (one with high surface energy), solubility increases as size decreases. Much of the benefit of "Ostwald ripening" from digestion is from a decrease in surface of crystals by perfecting irregularities in them. Thus, growth in hollows, reduction in area by filling in feathery crystals, and even diffusion of atoms or ions all tend to improve the quality of crystals during digestion. Those crystals that do not benefit by digestion are thought to have not enough surface energy or too great a charge on the particles to permit aggregation.

## Coprecipitation

The separation of a solid from a liquid from which it is precipitated is never complete. Some of the soluble materials contaminate the precipitate and, if they cannot be removed by washing, are said to be coprecipitated.

**Solid Solutions.** Certain substances when precipitated carry with them, as an integral part of the crystal, other ions that would normally be soluble. Thus barium chromate will coprecipitate with barium sulfate; potassium, by replacing some ammonium ions, will coprecipitate with magnesium ammonium phosphate; and chloride, by replacing bromide ions, will coprecipitate with silver bromide. Certain conditions must be met for this to occur:

1. The coprecipitated material must have the same crystal structure as (be isomorphous with) the host crystal.

2. The coprecipitated ions must have an ionic radius not more than 10% different from that of the replaced ions.

3. The coprecipitated ions must not be very soluble since less soluble salts coprecipitate, by forming solid solutions, to a greater extent than the more soluble ones.

Prevention of solid solution coprecipitation can be achieved by converting the contaminating material into some other form. Thus, chromates, as contaminants of barium sulfate, can be prevented by converting the chromate to chromic ion. Contamination due to solid solution is reduced only slightly by digestion or reprecipitation.

**Adsorption.** Rapidly formed, imperfect, or very small crystals have very large surface areas in relation to their mass. The large areas leave many ions exposed to the solution which attract ions of opposite charge, causing coprecipitation by adsorption.

Ions common to the precipitate are adsorbed most strongly. If barium sulfate is precipitated from a solution with an excess of barium ions, the barium ions will be strongly adsorbed and will give a positive charge to the particles. The positive charge will draw negative ions from the solution and, if the crystals grow very rapidly, some of these adsorbed ions may be trapped inside the crystal. Similarly, if barium sulfate is precipitated from a solution containing an excess of sulfate ions, the sulfate ions will be adsorbed strongly, giving the particles of precipitate a negative charge.

On barium sulfate, barium ions are adsorbed more strongly than sulfate ions. This is indicated by the fact that if barium sulfate is shaken up in water, sulfate ions will dissolve to a greater extent than barium ions and the particles of barium sulfate become positively charged because of loss of negative sulfate ions to the solution. To change the charge on the particles to negative, the sulfate ion concentration in the solution must be increased to $10^{-3}$ molar. Thus, many more sulfate than barium ions must be present in solution for both ions to be adsorbed equally.

**Reprecipitation.** Adsorption is reduced by precipitation from dilute solutions, and by reprecipitation. Reprecipitation is not as efficient as might be expected.

The Freundlich isotherm equation gives the relation between the amount of adsorbed material per given weight of precipitate and the concentration of impurity in solution:

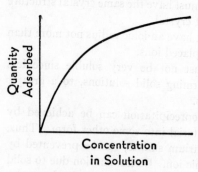

$x = kc^n$, where

$x$ = amount of impurity adsorbed by a given weight of precipitate;

$k$ and $n$ are constants ($n$ is less than 1, usually about 0.5 for most cases);

$c$ = concentration of impurity in solution that is in equilibrium with adsorbed impurity.

A typical isotherm is graphically shown in Fig. 7.

Fig. 7. Adsorption Isotherm.

**Example.** If the concentration of an impurity in the original solution is such that a given precipitate adsorbs one-tenth of it, what portion would be adsorbed if the precipitate is dissolved, diluted to the same volume as the original solution, and then reprecipitated? Let $n = 0.5$.

In the equation, $x = kc^n$, $c$ is one-tenth what it was before the first precipitation; $x$ was one-tenth in the first precipitation but in the second will be proportional to $c^{0.5}$:

$$x_2 = k \frac{1}{\sqrt{10}}.$$

In words, $x_2$, the amount adsorbed by the precipitate during the second precipitation, is $\frac{1}{3.2}$ (nearly one-third) of the impurity in the solution. A third reprecipitation would adsorb an even larger fraction of the impurity remaining in the solution after the second precipitation. Thus it is clear that more than one or two reprecipitations require a great deal of work that yields small returns in the purifying of a precipitate.

**Washing Precipitates.** Dissolved impurities in the solution from which the precipitate forms must be removed from the surfaces of the precipitate before it is weighed. This is done as completely as possible by washing or rinsing with a solvent or solution that removes everything nonvolatile from the crystals. Several washings with small portions are more effective than one washing with a large portion, just as in extractions with solvents (see p. 182) several extractions are more effective than one.

CRYSTALLINE PRECIPITATES. These are easily washed with water or some other solvent. If the precipitate is somewhat soluble, a saturated solution of the precipitate may be used. If the precipitate can be dried at a low temperature, it may be washed with some organic solvent, like alcohol, which dries easily.

CURDY PRECIPITATES. It would seem that curdy precipitates, with more surface than crystalline ones, would adsorb strongly. But, because the crystals are loosely held together in porous curds, they are easily purified by washing. For this purpose a solution of a strong electrolyte such as dilute nitric acid is used. The ions of the electrolyte replace adsorbed ions by ion exchange (see p. 183) and at the same time prevent peptization (a dispersal of a solid into a colloidal suspension) of the precipitate. The electrolyte chosen should be volatile so that it will be removed during the drying or ignition of the precipitate.

GELATINOUS PRECIPITATES. These are made up of such very small crystals that their surfaces are huge. The charges on the particles are controlled by the pH of the solution. Thus, hydrous ferric oxide below pH 10 preferentially adsorbs nitrate and other negative ions. Above pH 10 it preferentially adsorbs positive ions. Hydrous oxides are usually washed with an electrolyte solution such as ammonium nitrate. This prevents peptization of the material, and the ions adsorbed are largely replaced by the volatile ions of ammonium nitrate.

**Occlusion.** Occlusion is the trapping of ionic impurities within crystals. This occurs when the crystals grow so rapidly that the ions of the precipitate do not have time to replace all the adsorbed impurities before the crystal grows around them. This produces distortion in the crystal and changes its composition. The same rule holds for occlusion as for adsorption. Less soluble ions are occluded most. Thus, nitrate is occluded on barium sulfate more strongly than is chloride, since barium nitrate is less soluble than barium chloride.

Occlusion is controlled largely by decreasing the rate of precipitation and by digestion after precipitation. Digestion has only limited value because ions trapped inside of crystals are not removed and because the contaminating ion may form a compound with the precipitate, as ammonium ions do with hydrous ferric oxide.

**Postprecipitation.** If a precipitate forms after, and on the surface of, the primary precipitate, postprecipitation is said to have occurred. This form of contamination:

1. Increases with time.
2. Increases at higher temperatures.
3. Occurs whether contaminant is added to liquid after or before the precipitate forms.

Danger of contamination by postprecipitation occurs when calcium is separated from magnesium or when metal sulfides are precipitated for the purpose of separating some metal ions from others. The postprecipitated material is supersaturated in the solution from which it separates. The precipitate on which it forms acts as a nucleus upon which the postprecipitation can occur. In most cases, if the pH is adjusted before precipitation takes place, and if the filtering is performed reasonably quickly, this sort of contamination can be controlled.

## Precipitation from Homogeneous Solutions

In order to avoid local high concentration of a precipitating agent, the agent can be liberated in solution as it is needed. The hydrolysis of dimethyl sulfate:

$$(CH_3)_2SO_4 + 2H_2O \rightarrow 2CH_3OH + H_2SO_4$$

yields sulfate ions and increases the acidity of the solution. The reaction of urea:

$$CO(NH_2)_2 + H_2O \rightarrow CO_2 + 2NH_3$$

yields ammonia, which slowly raises the pH of the solution. These and other slow reactions can be used for controlling conditions so that crystals that form are large, pure, and easily filtered. Thus calcium can be precipitated as the oxalate (free of magnesium) by adding oxalate in acid solution and allowing urea to slowly raise the pH. Barium sulfate can be precipitated free of iron or calcium by using dimethyl sulfate, and such gelatinous precipitates as hydrated ferric and aluminum oxides are more easily filtered and washed if brought down by homogeneous precipitation. A possible disadvantage is that most homogeneous precipitations are slow.

## Drying and Ignition of Precipitates

A precipitate that is to be weighed must be dry and have definite composition. Heating helps to bring about both of these conditions.

**Drying Precipitates.** Adherent water can be removed by washing with a volatile solvent like alcohol or by warming in air.

The removal of water adsorbed on the surface of crystals, due to the attraction of ions of the crystal lattice for the poles of water molecules, may require heating to high temperatures. Hydrated aluminum oxide and silicon dioxide require strong heating. The latter must be heated to about 1100° C before the last traces of water are removed.

Occluded water (water trapped inside rapidly growing crystals) may require fusion of the salt. This is true of silver chloride if the very last traces of water are to be removed. Barium sulfate often requires heating up to 1000° C for removal of last traces of occluded water. For any but the most exacting analyses, such as atomic weight determinations, the last traces of moisture of this sort are usually negligible.

Water of hydration of crystals can be driven off by heat. Heating hydrates to constant weight is seldom satisfactory. It is generally better to dehydrate precipitates completely before weighing.

**Ignition of Precipitates.** Before the thermobalance gave insight into reactions occurring during ignition of substances, chemists could only surmise what changes occurred and at what temperatures the changes took place.

The thermobalance (Fig. 8) is constructed with a crucible $C$ held inside an electric furnace $E$ by a quartz rod $R$ which is supported

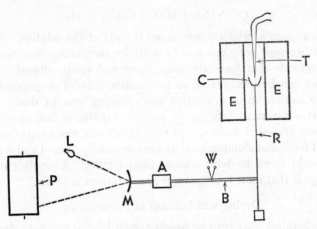

Fig. 8. The Thermobalance.

at one end of the balance beam $B$. The beam is supported by a pair of wires $W$ acting as the fulcrum. The counterweight $A$ balances the crucible end of the beam, and a mirror $M$ reflects a beam from a tiny light $L$ onto a photographic paper on the roll $P$, which turns slowly. A thermocouple $T$ measures the temperature. The roll of photographic paper is calibrated so as to record the temperature and the weight. The resulting curves are shown in Fig. 9. These are called pyrolysis curves.

Curve 1, Fig. 9, is for calcium oxalate precipitated from water solution as $CaC_2O_4H_2O$. This is stable up to 100° C and can be weighed as such if dried. From 226° to 398° C $CaC_2O_4$ is stable, but at 420° C it loses CO, giving $CaCO_3$, which is stable enough to be weighed between 420° and 660° C. Above 840–850° C $CaCO_3$ is decomposed and CaO is stable and can be weighed as such.

Curves 2 and 3, Fig. 9, are for hydrous aluminum oxide, often called aluminum hydroxide. Curve 2 is for hydrous aluminum oxide obtained by adding a water solution of ammonia to an aluminum ion solution. This precipitate shows a loss in weight up to 1031° C. Curve 3 is for hydrous aluminum oxide obtained by bubbling air, containing ammonia, through an aluminum ion solution (homogeneous precipitation). This curve shows that aluminum oxide is dehydrated and stable enough to weigh above 475° C if it is precipitated slowly.

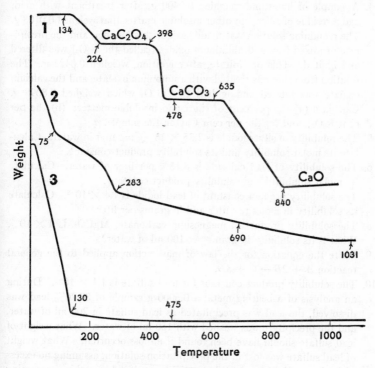

Fig. 9. Pyrolysis Curves.

From Clement Duval, *Inorganic Thermogravimetric Analysis*, Elsevier Press, 1953.

## Review Questions and Problems

1. What is the per cent of sulfur in a mineral if 0.6114 g of it, upon proper treatment, produced 0.0971 g of barium sulfate? What is the sulfur—barium sulfate gravimetric factor?
2. On treatment of 0.4800 g of brass with nitric acid, the precipitated stannic oxide formed was filtered, ignited, and found to weigh 0.0299 g.

What per cent of the brass was tin and what is the tin—tin oxide gravimetric factor?

3. Exactly one g of phosphate rock was dissolved, and the phosphate was precipitated as magnesium ammonium phosphate. This was filtered off, ignited, and weighed as 0.6240 g of $Mg_2P_2O_7$. Calculate the per cent of phosphorus in the sample. Calculate the per cent of $Ca_3(PO_4)_2$ in the rock, assuming all phosphorus is in that form. Use gravimetric factors.

4. A sample of limestone weighing 0.9400 g, after treatment with acid, had a residue of silica and other insoluble matter that weighed 0.0108 g. The remaining solution was made basic with ammonia, and the precipitate of mixed iron and aluminum oxides (called the $R_2O_3$) was filtered and ignited. This precipitate, after ignition, weighed 0.0422 g. The solution from this was treated with ammonium oxalate, and the calcium oxalate was filtered and ignited to $CaCO_3$ which weighed 0.8098 g. Calculate (a) the per cent of silica and insoluble matter; (b) the per cent $R_2O_3$; and (c) the per cent CaO in the sample.

5. The solubility of silver iodide is $2.35 \times 10^{-6}$ g per liter in water. Calculate its molar solubility and its solubility product constant.

6. The solubility of lead chloride is 8.15 g per liter of water. Calculate its molar solubility and solubility product constant.

7. The solubility product constant of lead iodide is $1.4 \times 10^{-8}$. Calculate its solubility in moles per liter and in grams per liter.

8. The solubility product of magnesium carbonate, $MgCO_3$, is $4 \times 10^{-5}$. What is its solubility in grams per 100 ml of water?

9. Write the equation for the law of mass action applied to the general reaction $A + 2B \rightarrow C + 3D$.

10. The solubility product constant for lead sulfate is $1.1 \times 10^{-8}$. During an analysis of a bearing metal a 0.5000 g sample of 80.20% lead was dissolved, the lead was precipitated as lead sulfate in 200 ml of water, and the precipitate was washed with 150 ml of water. What weight of lead sulfate should have been found if no loss occurred? What weight of lead sulfate was lost in the precipitation solution, assuming no excess of lead or sulfate ions? What weight was lost by washing, assuming the wash water was saturated? What per cent of lead would be reported as being in the sample after the losses from solubility?

11. Calculate the grams of calcium ion in 100 ml of solution saturated with $CaC_2O_4$. Calculate the grams of calcium ion in the same solution which has been made 0.01 molar in oxalate ion by adding excess oxalate. Make the same calculations for $MgC_2O_4$ in a saturated solution. Solubility products: $CaC_2O_4$, $2.6 \times 10^{-9}$; $MgC_2O_4$, $8.7 \times 10^{-5}$.

12. What is the ionic strength of a solution which is 0.04 molar in hydrogen ions, 0.03 molar in sulfate ions, $3 \times 10^{-5}$ molar in barium ions, and 0.02 molar in chloride ions?

13. Calculate the solubility of calcium oxalate (concentration of $Ca^{+2}$) in a solution of pH = 2, $H^+$ = 0.01. The solubility product of calcium oxalate is $2.6 \times 10^{-9}$ and ionization constants for oxalic acid are first, $5 \times 10^{-2}$, and second, $3 \times 10^{-5}$. Compare the solubility in acid and water.

14. Why are some substances precipitated from hot solution and then cooled before filtering?

15. What advantage is there in adding a precipitating agent slowly?

16. What are three conditions necessary for a substance if it is to coprecipitate by forming a solid solution?

17. In general, what ions are adsorbed most strongly by the ions on the surface of a precipitate?

18. Describe what can be done to prevent coprecipitation by:
    a. Solid solution.
    b. Adsorption.
    c. Postprecipitation.
    d. Occlusion.

19. Give two reasons why a precipitate should be washed with a solution containing a volatile electrolyte.

20. What is meant by homogeneous precipitation, and what advantage does this method offer?

21. What are two ways to remove water adhering to a precipitate?

22. How can adsorbed water be removed? Occluded water? Water of hydration?

23. What do pyrolysis curves show about weighing calcium oxalate after heating it at different temperatures?

# 6

# Typical Gravimetric Analyses

Certain analyses used for some elements and ions have become standards because they are applied frequently and illustrate the principles of many other analyses.

## Analysis of a Chloride

The following list of operations are those necessary for precipitating a fairly insoluble, curdy precipitate which is easily washed free of impurities. The precipitate must not be exposed to direct light for more than a few minutes and must be dried without contacting any reducing agent, such as paper.

**Procedure.**

1. Dry sample for one hour at about 105° C.
2. Weigh samples of about 0.5 g (enough to give 0.1 g or more of AgCl precipitate) into 250 ml beakers.
3. Add 100 ml distilled water.
4. Make acid with nitric acid, using methyl orange as an indicator.
5. While stirring, add 5% silver nitrate solution, drop by drop. Assume the unknown to be NaCl, unless it is known to be something else. Calculate volume of silver nitrate solution needed, and add an excess of 10%.

**Example.** If a sample containing chloride weighs 0.5164 g, what volume of 5% silver nitrate solution will be needed to precipitate the chloride, assuming the sample to be pure NaCl? What total volume will be required to provide an excess of 10%?

From the equation:

$$NaCl + AgNO_3 \rightarrow AgCl + NaNO_3$$

it is clear that one formula weight of $AgNO_3$, 169.89 g, reacts with one formula weight of NaCl, 58.45 g.

52

Step 1. Compute the weight of $AgNO_3$ that will react with 0.5164 g of NaCl by using a proportion:

$$\frac{169.89}{58.45} = \frac{x}{0.5164}.$$

$$58.45x = 169.89 \times 0.5164.$$

$$x = \frac{169.89 \times 0.5164}{58.45} = 1.501 \text{ g of } AgNO_3 \text{ needed.}$$

Step 2. Calculate the volume of 5% silver nitrate solution that contains 1.501 g of $AgNO_3$. Remember that a 5% solution contains 5 g per 100 g of solution. If we assume each ml of the solution weighs 1 g, then there is 5 g of $AgNO_3$ in 100 ml of solution. Again a proportion can be used to determine the volume sought.

$$\frac{5 \text{ g}}{100 \text{ ml}} = \frac{1.501 \text{ g}}{x \text{ ml}}.$$

$$5x = 100 \times 1.501.$$

$$x = \frac{100 \times 1.501}{5} = 30 \text{ ml of solution needed.}$$

Step 3. To calculate the total volume needed if 10% in excess is required, take 10% of 30, which is 3, and add it to the 30, giving 33 ml as the volume of 5% $AgNO_3$ to be used in precipitating the sample. This volume need not be measured with great exactness.

6. Heat nearly to boiling in dim light or dark for one hour. This process is called digestion (see p. 42).

7. Cool and test for completeness of precipitation by adding a drop of silver nitrate solution. (If a precipitate forms, add more silver nitrate and repeat steps 6 and 7.)

8. Set in the dark for at least one hour.

9. Prepare either a Gooch or filter crucible. See note 1 and Fig. 10 on p. 54.

10. Filter through the crucible, using suction.

11. Wash the precipitate with 0.01 M $HNO_3$ solution until washings give only a faint test with dilute HCl solution.

12. Dry crucible and precipitate to constant weight in a beaker at about 105° C. When crucible and precipitate show no more than 0.2 mg change in weight between two successive heatings, followed by cooling and weighing, the weight is considered constant.

13. Calculate the per cent of chloride in the sample.

**Example.** A sample containing chloride and weighing 0.5508 g was dissolved, nitric acid and silver nitrate were added, and the precipitate formed was found to weigh 0.8220 g. Calculate the per cent of chloride in the sample.

Step 1. Calculate the chloride—silver chloride gravimetric factor.

$$\frac{Cl^-}{AgCl} = \frac{35.46}{143.34} = 0.2474.$$

Step 2. Multiplying the weight of the precipitate by the gravimetric factor gives the weight of chloride in the precipitate. This value multiplied by 100 and divided by the weight of the sample gives the per cent of chloride in the sample. These operations can be combined into one step.

$$\frac{0.8220 \times 0.2474 \times 100}{0.5508} = 36.93\% \text{ chloride.}$$

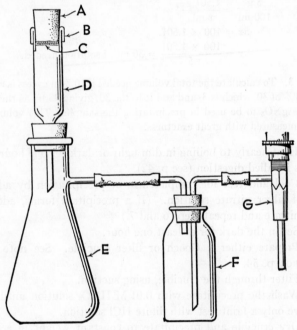

Fig. 10. Filtering by Suction.

*Note 1.* Preparation of a Gooch or filter crucible. An arrangement illustrated by Fig. 10 is used for filtering by suction. $A$ is a Gooch crucible, $B$ a Gooch rubber washer, $C$ the filter pad of asbestos or other material, $D$ a Gooch funnel. An ordinary filter funnel will do in place of the Gooch funnel if it is supplied with a rubber ring washer. $E$ is the suction flask and $F$ a trap to prevent water from the aspirator $G$ entering $E$. The asbestos pad is made from a soup of asbestos and water and should be thick enough to retain all of the precipitate but should filter rapidly. Instead of an asbestos pad, many glass, platinum, quartz, and porcelain crucibles have porous bottoms for filtering by suction. These filter rapidly and can be heated to constant weight more readily than asbestos filters.

**Errors in the Method.** With careful work, errors due to adsorption, occlusion, and solubility (see Chap. 5) of the precipitate are negligible.

EFFECT OF LIGHT. Silver chloride is decomposed by light in amounts directly proportional to the amount of light.

$$2AgCl \xrightarrow{\text{light}} 2Ag + Cl_2.$$

Thus, if chloride is being determined, an excess of silver ions will be added to the solution, and liberated chlorine will make more silver chloride. The precipitate will be heavier because of the free silver and, consequently, results will be high. If silver is being determined, the liberated chlorine escapes and the results are low.

ADSORPTION. Adsorption of everything but water can be overcome by washing. Last traces of water can be removed by fusing at 455° C. Only the most precise work such as atomic weight determinations requires this treatment.

PEPTIZATION. (See p. 45.) Peptization of the precipitate while washing must be prevented by the use of weak nitric acid instead of water. This electrolyte solution furnishes ions for the precipitate to adsorb, so that no large amount of charge can be developed on the extremely small crystals of AgCl. Thus, formation of a colloidal dispersion that would go through the filter is prevented.

INTERFERENCES. Bromides, iodides, cyanides, and thiocyanates also give insoluble silver salts under similar conditions and must be absent when chloride is determined this way.

## Analysis of a Soluble Sulfate

This analysis illustrates procedures used for precipitating and washing an almost insoluble precipitate of very small crystals, only slightly more soluble in acid solution at high temperature than in water at room temperature. The precipitate adsorbs many substances strongly but is not peptized by being washed with water. Sulfur in most sulfur-containing compounds can usually be converted to sulfate and determined by this method.

**Procedure.**

1. Heat porcelain crucibles to constant weight at 800° C (Bunsen burner flame).

2. Dry sample at 105° to 110° C for one hour.

3. Weigh samples of about 0.5 g into 600 ml beakers.

4. Dissolve in 200 ml water.

5. Add about 1 ml hydrochloric acid.

6. Heat to boiling.

7. Add 5% (approximately 0.25 M) barium chloride solution drop by drop while stirring vigorously. Assuming that the sample is sodium sulfate, unless it is known to be otherwise, calculate the volume of barium chloride solution needed, and add an excess of 10%.

**Example.** What volume of 5% $BaCl_2$ solution is to be used for precipitation of a sample of sulfate weighing 0.4880 g if the sample is assumed to be $Na_2SO_4$ and an excess of 10% is added?

Step 1. Calculate the weight of $BaCl_2$ that will react with 0.4880 g of $Na_2SO_4$ according to the equation:

$$Na_2SO_4 + BaCl_2 \rightarrow BaSO_4 + 2NaCl.$$

The equation indicates that 142.05 g of $Na_2SO_4$ reacts with 208.27 g of $BaCl_2$. By proportion then:

$$\frac{142.05}{208.27} = \frac{0.4880}{x}$$

$$x = \frac{0.4880 \times 208.27}{142.05} = 0.7155 \text{ g of } BaCl_2 \text{ will react with 0.4880 g of}$$

$Na_2SO_4$ if no excess is added.

Step 2. Assume the density of 5% $BaCl_2$ solution is one. Then each 100 ml of solution will contain 5 g of $BaCl_2$. By proportion, calculate the volume of solution needed to precipitate the sulfate.

$$\frac{5}{100} = \frac{0.7155}{x}.$$

$$5x = 100 \times 0.7155.$$

$$x = \frac{100 \times 0.7155}{5} = 14.31 \text{ ml of 5\% } BaCl_2 \text{ solution required if no}$$

excess is added.

Step 3. Calculate the volume needed if 10% in excess is to be measured out. This is done by calculating 10% of 14.31, which is 1.431, and adding to 14.31.

14.31 + 1.431 = 15.74 ml, the total volume to be added, including 10% in excess.

8. Digest at just under boiling for at least one hour. Two hours or more is preferable. See pp. 42-43.

9. Filter through a fine-pored, ashless filter paper. This precipitate tends to run or creep up the sides of vessels. Fill filter paper only about three-fourths full while filtering.

10. Wash the precipitate about 10 times with hot water.

11. Fold filter paper, precipitate down, into the tared (weighed to constant weight) crucibles.

12. Dry, char the paper, and burn off the char with a low flame. Be careful not to envelop the crucibles in flame or the $BaSO_4$ is reduced by unburned gas and carbon in the char to $BaS$.

13. Ignite at 800° C to constant weight.

14. Calculate the per cent of sulfate, sulfur, or other sulfur-containing material in the original sample.

**Example 1.** What per cent of a mixture of salts is $SO_3$ if 0.4880 g gives a precipitate of $BaSO_4$ which weighs 0.3009 g?

Step 1. Find the gravimetric factor for $SO_3/BaSO_4$.

$$\frac{SO_3}{BaSO_4} = \frac{80.07}{233.43} = 0.3431.$$

Step 2. Multiplying the weight of $BaSO_4$ by the gravimetric factor gives the weight of $SO_3$. This divided by the weight of the sample and multiplied by 100 gives the per cent of $SO_3$. These operations combined in one step are as follows:

$$\frac{0.3009 \times 0.3431 \times 100}{0.4880} = 21.15\% \; SO_3.$$

**Example 2.** If a precipitate of $BaSO_4$ weighing 0.1131 g is obtained from a solution containing sodium sulfate made by dissolving 0.4180 g of an unknown mixture, what per cent of the mixture is $Na_2SO_4$?

Step 1. Find the sodium sulfate—barium sulfate gravimetric factor.

$$\frac{Na_2SO_4}{BaSO_4} = \frac{142.06}{233.43} = 0.6087.$$

Step 2. Multiplying the weight of $BaSO_4$ by the gravimetric factor gives the weight of $Na_2SO_4$. This divided by the weight of the sample and multiplied by 100 gives the per cent of $Na_2SO_4$. These operations in one step are:

$$\frac{0.1131 \times 0.6087 \times 100}{0.4180} = 16.47\% \; \text{sodium sulfate.}$$

*Note 2.* Crucibles, with or without precipitates, should be heated about 20 minutes or more, cooled, and then weighed. The time of cooling and weighing should be as nearly the same for each weighing as possible. Crucibles gain weight while cooling; therefore, before the crucible is weighed, exactly the same time to gain weight should be allowed after each heating.

**Errors in the Method.** Many factors cause errors in this analysis. Because it is an important analysis it has been studied thoroughly, and the errors are well known.

ADSORPTION. The worst difficulty with $BaSO_4$ as a precipitate is that it tenaciously adsorbs almost all ions. Less soluble salts are adsorbed more strongly. Precipitation in very dilute solutions and digestion reduce this effect. Reprecipitation is impossible because of the slight solubility of $BaSO_4$ in almost all reagents.

OCCLUSION. If crystals of $BaSO_4$ are allowed to grow too rapidly, there are small amounts of soluble substances trapped within the crystals. Precipitation in very dilute solutions and slow addition of the precipitating agent help reduce this effect.

SOLUBILITY. The precipitated $BaSO_4$ is soluble in acids to an appreciable extent. This is overcome by adding an excess of precipitating agent. The solubility product indicates that the excess of barium ions added reduces the solubility of $BaSO_4$ more than the acid increases it.

SOLID SOLUTIONS. Barium sulfate crystals often retain foreign ions if the ions are of about the same ionic radius as those in the crystal lattice. Chromate ions thus form solid solutions in $BaSO_4$ by replacing sulfate ions. Since metallic ions can replace barium ions, any metallic ions present should be removed before precipitation if their relative concentration is not extremely small.

REDUCTION OF THE SULFATE. If unburned gases from a flame surround the crucible containing $BaSO_4$, part of the latter may be reduced to BaS:

$$BaSO_4 + 4H_2 \rightarrow BaS + 4H_2O.$$

The formula weight of BaS is less than that for $BaSO_4$ so that the per cent of sulfur as calculated will be too low, if any BaS is formed. Burning the paper off seldom reduces much $BaSO_4$, though this process should be done at as low a temperature as possible and with free access of air. Treatment of the ignited precipitate with sulfuric acid and then reheating is not very satisfactory but is sometimes done to convert BaS back to $BaSO_4$ quickly.

SUPERSATURATION. If insufficient time is allowed for all of the $BaSO_4$ to crystallize out, the solution may remain supersaturated with respect to barium and sulfate ions. This gives low results and is more troublesome where small amounts of sulfate are being determined.

CREEP. Even after digestion, $BaSO_4$ crystals are so small they creep up the sides of funnels and beakers. Loss due to creep can be appreciable. Care in policing (rubbing down the beaker walls with a rubber-tipped stirring rod) and not overfilling funnels help reduce this loss. Wiping the lip and the inside of the beaker and around the funnel with filter paper picks up all the stray material of importance.

## Analysis of a Ferric Ion Solution

This analysis is seldom made on iron ores or alloys of iron because volumetric methods are faster. On cements, limestones, and other minerals this gravimetric method is used to determine the collective content, in these materials, of aluminum, iron, and sometimes titanium. The mixed oxides are called the $R_2O_3$. The method illustrates precipitation of a gelatinous, very insoluble, highly adsorbent material.

### Procedure.

1. Prepare crucibles by cleaning them and heating them to constant weight at 1000° C in a furnace or on Meker burners to the highest temperature the burners will yield.

2. Weigh out samples of such size as will give about 0.3 g of ignited oxide. If samples are solutions, measure out the samples.

3. In 400 ml beakers, dissolve solid samples in 10–15 ml of 1:1 HCl solution and dilute to 250 ml. A liquid sample should be diluted to 250 ml.

4. Heat to boiling.

5. Add dilute (1:2) ammonia solution slowly, while stirring, until the odor of ammonia can be detected rising from the solution.

6. Boil about three or four minutes.

7. Let stand until precipitate settles.

8. Decant (pour off clear liquid, leaving the precipitate behind) through a coarse-pored, ashless filter paper.

9. Add 40 ml of 1% ammonium nitrate solution to the precipitate, heat, and decant again.

10. Transfer the precipitate to the filter paper.

11. Immediately wash the precipitate four or five times with 1% ammonium nitrate solution.

12. Remove filter paper and precipitate from funnel; place it in beaker from which it came.

13. Add 30–35 ml of 3 N (1:3) hydrochloric acid solution.

14. Warm and stir to dissolve all the precipitate.

15. Dilute to about 150 ml.

16. Repeat steps 4 through 9, washing about eight times before the precipitate dries out.

17. Fold paper, precipitate down, into the prepared crucible.

18. Dry and burn off the paper slowly, being careful not to envelop the crucible with flame or to overheat it.

19. After all carbon is burned out, heat the residue in an oxidizing atmosphere to constant weight at 1000° C.

20. Calculate the per cent of $Fe_2O_3$ in the sample.

**Example.**   A sample weighing 1.1090 g and containing ferric ions was dissolved.   The ferric ions were precipitated as hydrous oxide, which was ignited to $Fe_2O_3$ and found to weigh 0.2742 g.   Calculate the per cent of $Fe_2O_3$ in the sample, assuming that all of the iron was present in that form. Also calculate the per cent of iron in the sample.

Calculate the per cent of $Fe_2O_3$ by dividing the weight of $Fe_2O_3$ found by the weight of the sample, and multiplying by 100.

$$\frac{0.2742 \times 100}{1.1090} = 24.72\% \ Fe_2O_3.$$

Calculating the per cent of iron can be done in two steps.

Step 1.   Find the $Fe/Fe_2O_3$ gravimetric factor:

$$\frac{Fe}{Fe_2O_3} = \frac{55.84}{159.68} = 0.3497.$$

Step 2.   Multiplying the weight of $Fe_2O_3$ by the gravimetric factor gives the weight of Fe in the sample.   This weight divided by the weight of the sample and multiplied by 100 gives the per cent of iron.

$$\frac{0.3497 \times 0.2742 \times 100}{1.1090} = 8.65\% \ Fe.$$

**Errors in the Method.**   This type of precipitate has so much surface that errors are largely due to adsorption.   The solubility of iron and aluminum oxides is extremely small, which accounts for the extreme minuteness of their crystals.

ADSORPTION. Because of the gelatinous nature of hydrous oxides they have enormous surfaces and adsorb strongly. The primary ion adsorbed, such as the hydroxide ion in basic solutions, attracts and holds secondary ions of opposite charge. Ammonium nitrate in the wash solution furnishes both positive and negative ions for such adsorption. These ions replace other adsorbed ions by ion exchange (see Chap. 12) and are volatile when heated so that they are easily removed. Reprecipitation is a means of reducing the concentration of adsorbable ions, thus reducing errors from this source.

Removal of adsorbed moisture from hydrous ferric oxide is complete at 1000° C, and removal from hydrous aluminum oxide is complete at about 1050° C.

REDUCTION. Iron oxide, but not aluminum oxide, is easily reduced to $Fe_3O_4$ by either unburned gases or carbon. An oxidizing atmosphere is necessary during the burning off of paper and ignition to constant weight, if iron is present in the sample.

## Analysis of a Soluble Phosphate

Analysis for phosphate is a very important determination because of the use of phosphorus compounds in fertilizers and cleaning agents. The precipitation of a crystalline material, with a composition that may vary with the pH of the solution from which it originates, is illustrated by this analysis.

**Procedure.**

1. Prepare Gooch crucibles (see Fig. 10) for as many samples as will be run, by making pads, washing them, and heating with the Gooch crucible set inside another crucible to constant weight at 1000° C (Meker burner). See note 3, p. 63.

2. Weigh out samples, dried at 105° C for about one hour, of such size as to contain 100 to 200 mg of $P_2O_5$.

3. Dissolve samples in 100 ml water in 250 ml beakers.

4. Add 15 ml of magnesia mixture, made by dissolving in water 50 g of $MgCl_2 \cdot 6H_2O$, 100 g of $NH_4Cl$, and 5 ml of 3 N HCl and diluting to one liter.

5. Add a few drops of methyl red indicator, cool in ice water, and while stirring, add ammonia solution until the indicator changes to yellow. Then add an excess of 5 ml ammonia solution.

6. Cool at least four hours in ice water.

7. Filter through a fine-pored paper.

8. Wash three or four times using cold 1 N ammonia solution.

9. Dissolve the precipitate by pouring 50 ml of hot 1 N HCl solution through the paper in the funnel. Catch the solution in the beaker where the precipitate was formed.

10. Wash the paper, using hot water.

11. Dilute solution of the phosphate to 100 ml.

12. Add at least 4 ml of magnesia mixture. If the precipitate seemed large, add more magnesia.

13. Repeat steps 5 and 6.

14. Filter through the weighed Gooch crucible, and wash with 1 N ammonia solution until free of chloride. Use silver nitrate solution to test for chloride.

15. Dry precipitate and crucible at about 105° C.

16. Ignite to constant weight in exactly the same way the empty crucibles were ignited.

17. Calculate the per cent of $P_2O_5$ in the sample. The ignited precipitate is $Mg_2P_2O_7$.

**Example.** A chemist dissolved 0.8050 g of a cleaning agent in water and obtained 0.3122 g of $Mg_2P_2O_7$ by ignition of the precipitated magnesium ammonium phosphate. Calculate (a) the per cent of $P_2O_5$ in the cleaning agent and (b) the per cent of $Na_3PO_4$; assuming this to be the form in which the phosphate occurred in the sample.

(a) Step 1. Find the $P_2O_5/Mg_2P_2O_7$ gravimetric factor.

$$\frac{P_2O_5}{Mg_2P_2O_7} = \frac{141.95}{222.6} = 0.6374.$$

Step 2. Multiplying the weight of $Mg_2P_2O_7$ by the gravimetric factor gives the weight of $P_2O_5$ in the sample. This weight divided by the sample weight and multiplied by 100 gives the per cent of $P_2O_5$ in the sample.

$$\frac{0.6374 \times 0.3122 \times 100}{0.8050} = 24.72\% \; P_2O_5.$$

(b) Step 1. Find the $Na_3PO_4/Mg_2P_2O_7$ gravimetric factor.

Two formula weights of $Na_3PO_4$ are required to produce one formula weight of $Mg_2P_2O_7$.

$$\frac{2(Na_3PO_4)}{Mg_2P_2O_7} = \frac{328}{222.6} = 1.4734.$$

Step 2. Multiplying the weight of $Mg_2P_2O_7$ by the gravimetric factor gives the weight of $Na_3PO_4$. This weight divided by the sample weight and multiplied by 100 gives the per cent of $Na_3PO_4$.

$$\frac{1.4734 \times 0.3122 \times 100}{0.8050} = 57.14\% \; Na_3PO_4.$$

*Note 3.* Ignition to constant weight of crucibles and precipitates could be done at lower temperatures except that asbestos does not reach constant weight unless heated to at least 880° C. The $Mg_2P_2O_7$ reaches constant weight at slightly over 400° C so that if glass or porcelain filter crucibles were used 450° C would be hot enough for ignition. Glass crucibles melt at something over 500° C and must be used with caution.

**Errors in the Method.** Inaccuracies in analyses by this method can result from several causes.

SOLUBILITY. Magnesium ammonium phosphate is slightly soluble in water and much more soluble in acid solutions. Phosphate ion, $PO_4^{-3}$, is a base. With acids it forms $HPO_4^{-2}$ and $H_2PO_4^-$, which reduces the $PO_4^{-3}$ concentration of a solution. $NH_4^+$ ions are strongly enough acid to reduce the phosphate ion concentration and dissolve the $MgNH_4PO_4 \cdot 6H_2O$, even though the ammonium ions are needed as part of the precipitate. Therefore, an excess of ammonia must be added to increase the phosphate ion concentration. This raises the pH, which furnishes a sufficiently high concentration of all ions needed to yield complete precipitation. Cooling the solution during and after precipitation aids in reducing the solubility of the precipitate.

IMPROPER pH. If the pH is too high the hydroxide ion concentration may be great enough to precipitate some $Mg(OH)_2$ or even $Mg_3(PO_4)_2$. Large amounts of ammonium ion reduce the pH to below the point where either of these can form. If the pH is too low, $MgHPO_4 \cdot 6H_2O$ may precipitate along with the desired $MgNH_4PO_4 \cdot 6H_2O$. This in itself causes no error since both precipitates, upon ignition, yield $Mg_2P_2O_7$. But, in a solution so acid, the solubility of both compounds is almost certain to be too great for good results to be achieved.

CONTAMINATION. Calcium, or any other metallic ions present, will contaminate the precipitate if the phosphates of the ions are insoluble in water. All metallic ions except alkali and ammonium ions must be removed before the precipitation. Silica, if present, will be separated when the precipitate is dissolved and washed through the filter paper in operation 9, p. 62. Reprecipitation tends to reduce the concentration of adsorbable ions while the second precipitation is being made, thus reducing the amount of contamination.

SUPERSATURATION. The $MgNH_4PO_4 \cdot 6H_2O$ tends to form highly supersaturated solutions. Stirring and allowing to stand for a long time at low temperatures reduces this effect.

## Review Questions and Problems

1. Outline the principal steps in the analysis of a chloride.
2. What other ions may be determined by the same procedure as is used for chloride?
3. Why cannot silver salts be filtered and ignited on quantitative filter paper?
4. Why is the precipitated silver chloride washed with nitric acid solution rather than with water?
5. Why must cyanides, iodides, and certain other ions be absent when chloride is determined gravimetrically?
6. Why is the sulfate determination important to so many commercial firms?
7. Why should barium sulfate be digested for at least two hours before filtering?
8. What chemical reaction may cause an error in the sulfate analysis if a flame envelops the crucible while ignition or burning off of paper is in progress?
9. Why should exactly the same amount of time for cooling crucibles in a desiccator be allowed before the crucibles are weighed?
10. List some causes of possible errors in the sulfate analysis.
11. What can be done to prevent or reduce each of the errors you listed for question 10?
12. In determining $Fe_2O_3$ or $R_2O_3$ why is the precipitate dissolved in acid and then reprecipitated?
13. Why is the $R_2O_3$ precipitate washed with ammonium nitrate solution rather than with water?
14. If hydrous aluminum oxide is present in an $R_2O_3$ precipitate, what small error will occur if ignition of the precipitate is made at 900° C?
15. Why is magnesium ammonium phosphate soluble in a solution of an ammonium salt in water in spite of the fact that ammonium ions are needed in forming the precipitate?
16. What elements commonly occur with phosphorus and magnesium in nature that could interfere with the analysis of phosphate?
17. Why must the phosphate precipitate in a Gooch crucible be ignited to constant weight at such a high temperature as 1000° C?
18. Why is the precipitate of phosphate, made with magnesia mixture, cooled in contact with the solution from which it is precipitated?
19. What errors can occur in the phosphate analysis if the solution is either too acid or too basic?
20. How is possible contamination by silica, $SiO_2$, avoided in precipitating magnesium ammonium phosphate?
21. The analysis of a sample containing $FeS_2$ which weighed 0.2000 g

produced 0.6000 g of $BaSO_4$. Calculate the per cent of sulfur in the sample.

22. A 1.5444 g sample of soluble chloride produced, upon analysis, a precipitate of AgCl which weighed 1.3201 g. Calculate the per cent of chloride and, assuming all chloride was $CaCl_2$, the per cent of calcium chloride in the sample.

23. A soluble sulfate sample weighing 0.4201 g was analyzed. The $BaSO_4$ produced after the first ignition was found to weigh 0.5988 g but gained weight on further heating, due to oxidation of BaS to $BaSO_4$, until a weight of 0.6010 g of $BaSO_4$ was found. Calculate the per cent of $SO_3$ in the sample and, assuming the sample is $ZnSO_4$, the per cent of that in the sample. Also calculate the values that would have been obtained had the first weight of the precipitate been taken.

24. What volume of 5% barium chloride solution is needed for precipitation of a sample of $Na_2SO_4$ weighing 0.3008 g? What volume would be needed if 10% excess is added to assure complete precipitation? Assume that one ml of barium chloride solution weighs one g.

25. A sample of steel weighing 4.8110 g was dissolved in nitric acid, and sulfur was precipitated and weighed as barium sulfate. The barium sulfate weighed 0.0121 g. Calculate the per cent of sulfur in the steel.

26. A sample of steel was analyzed for phosphorus. The final product after ignition was $Mg_2P_2O_7$. The sample weighed 2.8416 g and the $Mg_2P_2O_7$ weighed 0.0108 g. Calculate the per cent of phosphorus in the steel.

27. A sample of limestone weighing 1.0000 g was found to yield 0.0989 g of $R_2O_3$. Calculate the per cent of $R_2O_3$ in the sample. If all of the $R_2O_3$ was ferric oxide, calculate the per cent of Fe in the sample.

28. What weight of $Al_2O_3$ can be obtained from a 2.4088 g sample of alum which is 95% $KAlSO_4 \cdot 12H_2O$ and 5% impurities which contain nothing that will form a precipitate with ammonia?

29. If a sample of soluble chloride is known to be 22.84% chloride, what weight of AgCl can be expected to be found when 0.2000 g of the sample is analyzed for chloride?

30. A superphosphate fertilizer was analyzed for phosphorus. Upon analysis, a 0.5414 g sample was found to give 0.1277 g of $Mg_2P_2O_7$. What was the per cent of $P_2O_5$ in the fertilizer?

# 7

# Volumetric Analysis Theory

Far more rapid than separating and weighing a precipitate is analyzing by volumetric methods. These methods depend on measurements of volumes of solutions. A solution of known concentration, called a *standard solution*, is mixed with a solution of unknown concentration until chemically equivalent quantities of the two have been brought together. Then the volume of standard solution used is employed to calculate the quantity of a material in the unknown solution. The process of adding a measured volume of one solution to another is called *titration* (see p. 11). The analyst depends on some physical change to inform him when chemically equivalent quantities have been mixed. Usually this physical change is the color change of a material called an *indicator*. The indicator is a substance chosen to give a color change at or very near to the equivalence point. The point at which the indicator changes is called the *end point*. It is as close to the equivalence point (called the *stoichiometric end point*) as the analyst can come.

## Standard Solutions

A standard solution is one of known concentration. An analysis can be no more reliable than the value accepted for the concentration of the standard solution used. As the name implies, a standard solution is one against which comparisons of the strengths of other solutions are made.

**Expression of Concentration.** There are many ways in which concentrations may be expressed. Those found most useful to the analyst are mentioned here.

MOLAR. A molar solution, represented by M, is one which contains one gram-molecular weight or one gram-formula weight of a substance dissolved in one liter of solution. A solution may have the same molarity as normality (see p. 68) if the equivalent and molecular weights are equal.

**Example 1.** Calculate the weight of $KCl$ needed to make one liter of 0.1 M solution.

Step 1. Find the formula weight of $KCl$. This is the sum of the atomic weights.

$$39.1 + 35.46 = 74.56.$$

Step 2. Find one-tenth of this for a tenth molar solution.

$$74.56 \times 0.1 = 7.456 \text{ g of } KCl,$$

which must be dissolved and diluted to one liter to make a liter of 0.1 M $KCl$ solution.

**Example 2.** What weight of $CaBr_2$ is needed to make 500 ml of 0.2 M solution?

Step 1. Calculate the formula weight of the $CaBr_2$.

$$40.08 + (79.12 \times 2) = 198.32.$$

Step 2. Find the weight needed for one liter of 0.2 M solution.

$$198.32 \times 0.2 = 39.664 \text{ g.}$$

Step 3. Find the weight needed for half a liter.

$$39.664 \times 0.5 = 19.832 \text{ g.}$$

FORMAL. When one gram-formula weight of a substance is contained in one liter of solution, the solution can be said to be *one formal*. The substance in solution may be in several ionic forms or species. Thus a 0.1 formal solution of sulfate ions may be partly bisulfate ions and even partly sulfuric acid, but the solution is still said to be 0.1 formal with respect to the sulfate. The term *formal* is applied to ionic substances. *Molar* refers to either ionic or molecular substances.

Advocates of the use of *formal* in the above sense also advocate use of the term *molal* for expressing concentrations of ions or molecules as they exist in solution, not necessarily as they were added. Thus if sulfate ions are added to a solution and some of them were to form bisulfate, only that part which remains as sulfate would be expressed as molality of sulfate ions.

MOLAL. Most chemists consider a molal solution, represented by m, as one where one gram-molecular weight or one gram-formula weight of solute is dissolved in 1000 g of solvent. This is quite different from the definition of *molal* given above, but it is the better known of the two definitions.

NORMAL. A normal solution, represented by N, contains one gram-equivalent weight of material per liter of solution. An *equivalent weight* is an amount of material that will react with one atomic weight of hydrogen or its chemical equivalent. If the equivalent weight and the formula weight are the same, the solution may have the same normality and molarity (see p. 67). See the example on p. 75 for calculations involving normality during a titration.

**Example 1.**  What weight of iodine is needed to make one liter of a 0.2 N solution?

Step 1.   Find the equivalent weight of iodine.  One atomic weight of iodine is equivalent to one atomic weight of hydrogen in forming HI, hydrogen iodide.  Therefore the atomic weight of iodine is its equivalent weight.  This is 126.92 g.

Step 2.   Find 0.2 of the equivalent weight.

$$126.92 \times 0.2 = 25.384 \text{ g of iodine needed.}$$

**Example 2.**  What weight of $Na_2SO_4$ must be dissolved in 500 ml to make a 0.5 N solution?

Step 1.   Find the equivalent weight of sodium sulfate.  Each formula weight of sodium sulfate contains two sodium ions, each equivalent to one hydrogen atom.  Therefore one-half the formula weight is the equivalent weight.

$$\frac{142.06}{2} = 71.03 \text{ g, the equivalent weight.}$$

Step 2.   Find 0.5 of the equivalent weight.

$71.03 \times 0.5 = 35.515$ g of $Na_2SO_4$ needed to make one liter of 0.5 N solution.

Step 3.   Find 0.5 of the weight needed for one liter.

$35.515 \times 0.5 = 17.7575$ g needed for one-half of a liter of 0.5 N solution.

**Example 3.**  What volume of concentrated (98%) sulfuric acid, sp. g. 1.84, is needed to make 500 ml of 0.2 N sulfuric acid?

Step 1.   Find the equivalent weight of $H_2SO_4$.

If each molecular weight contains two hydrogen atoms, then the equivalent weight is half the molecular weight.

$$\frac{98.076}{2} = 49.04 \text{ g, the equivalent weight of sulfuric acid.}$$

Step 2.   Find the weight of acid needed for one-half liter of 0.2 N solution. This is the same as is needed for one liter of 0.1 N solution.

$49.04 \times 0.1 = 4.9039$ g of sulfuric acid needed for one liter of 0.1 N or for 500 ml of 0.2 N sulfuric acid.

Step 3. Find the volume that this weight of sulfuric acid would occupy if it were 100% pure.

$$\frac{4.904}{1.84} = 2.67 \text{ ml.}$$

Since this is only 98% sulfuric acid, step 4 is needed.

Step 4. Find the volume of 98% sulfuric acid.

$$\frac{2.67}{0.98} = 2.72 \text{ ml of } 98\% \text{ sulfuric acid needed to make 500 ml of 0.2 N } H_2SO_4.$$

PER CENT BY WEIGHT. Per cent means parts per 100 parts. A solution which has its concentration expressed in per cent is read per cent by weight, unless otherwise stated.

PER CENT BY VOLUME. The strengths of a few solutions are expressed as per cent by volume. Whenever this is so the analyst should state that the concentration is in per cent by volume to avoid confusion.

TITER. The titer of a solution is the weight of a substance equivalent to one ml of the standard solution. Thus the milligrams of chloride equivalent to one ml of a silver nitrate solution would be called the chloride titer of the silver nitrate solution. When stated, the titer should include the units of weight per unit of volume. An example is shown later, under Volumetric Calculations, p. 79.

**Preparation of Standard Solutions.** (See also Chap. 10.) There are two ways of preparing solutions of known concentration. Both methods depend upon the use of a primary standard.

FROM A PRIMARY STANDARD. A primary standard is a substance of high purity, with the purity known within very close limits. It can be dried and weighed on a balance, and it will react stoichiometrically. To react stoichiometrically means to react exactly as an equation indicates. To prepare a solution using a primary standard material, dry and weigh out the quantity desired, put the accurately weighed material in a volumetric flask, dissolve it, and dilute to the mark on the flask. The flask size is determined by the volume of solution needed.

The resulting solution's concentration is known because the weight of reagent added to a given volume is measured accurately on a balance. This method makes use of a relatively large amount of expensive primary standard material.

**Example.** To prepare 500 ml of 0.1 N solution of benzoic acid:

1. Dry the primary standard benzoic acid at about 105° C.

2. Weigh out exactly 6.1060 g ($\frac{1}{20}$ of an equivalent weight) of benzoic acid into a 500 ml volumetric flask.

3. Dissolve the benzoic acid in alcohol.

4. Dilute to the 500 ml mark with a water solution strong enough in alcohol to retain the benzoic acid in solution.

The quantity, $\frac{1}{20}$ of an equivalent weight of benzoic acid, is needed because $\frac{1}{10}$ of an equivalent weight would make a liter of 0.1 N solution. Since 500 ml is required, only half as much is used.

BY STANDARDIZATION AGAINST A PRIMARY STANDARD. To prepare a standard solution by this method the reagent is roughly weighed out and dissolved. The concentration is then found by titrating, with the prepared solution, an accurately weighed quantity of dried primary standard reagent.

**Example.** To prepare one liter of a 0.1 N solution of sodium hydroxide:

1. Dilute to one liter about 6 ml of a saturated, carbonate free, sodium hydroxide solution with freshly boiled, $CO_2$ free water, cooled to room temperature.

2. Weigh out about 0.5000 g of potassium acid phthalate, weighed accurately to 0.1 mg. This material must be of known purity. It is the primary standard.

3. Dissolve the primary standard in about 75 ml of $CO_2$ free water.

4. Titrate the primary standard with the sodium hydroxide solution, using phenolphthalein as the indicator. The end point is recognized by the slightest pink color appearing, for 30 seconds, throughout the solution.

5. Calculate the exact normality of the NaOH solution using the equivalent weight of potassium acid phthalate ($KHC_8H_4O_4$) as 204.22. Thus if it required 24.00 ml of the NaOH solution to titrate the 0.5000 g of the primary standard, then the normality of the NaOH solution is found as follows:

$$\text{Normality of NaOH} = \frac{0.5000}{0.20422 \times 24.00}$$

$$= \frac{2.448}{24.00} = 0.1020 \text{ N.}$$

Dividing the weight of the primary standard by 0.20422 (the grammilliequivalent weight of the primary standard; see p. 76) gives the number of milliliters of 1 N solution equivalent to the weight of primary standard used. Thus:

$$\frac{0.5000}{0.20422} = 2.448.$$

This is also the number of ml of 1 N solution equivalent to 0.5000 g of potassium acid phthalate. This number divided by the ml of solution needed to titrate the primary standard gives the normality of the solution.

The general equation for calculating the normality of a solution after titrating a primary standard is:

$$N = \frac{\text{weight of primary standard}}{\text{gme of primary standard} \times \text{volume of titration}}. \quad (7\text{-}1)$$

**Types of Primary Standards.** There are types of primary standards for every purpose. All must be of the highest degree of purity, and their compositions must be known accurately. All must be capable of:

1. Being dried at 100° to 110° C.
2. Being cooled in weighing bottles inside desiccators.
3. Being weighed with no more than ordinary care.
4. Reacting stoichiometrically. That is, they must follow exactly the course of a chemical equation.

PRIMARY STANDARD ACIDS. A solid acid is used for standardizing a solution of a base.

The commonest is potassium acid phthalate, $KHC_8H_4O_4$, which has the advantages of having a high equivalent weight and of being nonhygroscopic. But it is a weak acid, useful only for standardization of solutions of strong bases, using phenolphthalein as the indicator.

Benzoic acid, $C_6H_5COOH$, is another commonly used primary standard acid. It has a high equivalent weight but has the disadvantage of being insoluble in water. It must be dissolved in water-alcohol solutions.

Sulfamic acid, $HNH_2SO_3$, is rapidly becoming a popular primary standard acid. It has a sufficiently high equivalent weight and is soluble in water.

Oxalic acid, $H_2C_2O_4 \cdot 2H_2O$, is a satisfactory primary standard that is often used in special cases.

PRIMARY STANDARD BASES. A solid base is required for standardizing solutions of acids.

Sodium carbonate, $Na_2CO_3$, is the commonest primary standard base. It is stable and fills all requirements of a good primary standard. One disadvantage is that it may pick up $CO_2$ from the air. To decompose bicarbonate thus formed may require heating to 270° C. Since the carbonate ion is a weak base and bicarbonate is still weaker, sodium carbonate can be used only for standardizing solutions of strong acids, such as HCl and $HNO_3$. Methyl orange or methyl purple are suitable indicators. The equivalent weight of sodium carbonate is one-half its formula weight, as seen in the following equation:

$$2H_3O^+ + CO_3^{-2} \rightarrow CO_2 + 3H_2O.$$

Calcium carbonate, $CaCO_3$, may be used in place of sodium carbonate as the reaction of both substances is identical.

Borax, $Na_2B_4O_7 \cdot 10H_2O$, recrystallized from a water solution and equilibrated (allowed to come to equilibrium) with sodium bromide in a desiccator, can be used as a primary standard. The difficulty of preparing it, however, prevents its use except in rare cases where nothing else is available or satisfactory. The equivalent weight of borax is one-half its formula weight.

PRIMARY STANDARD OXIDIZING AGENTS. Although several are known, only one primary standard oxidizing agent is in common use.

Potassium dichromate, $K_2Cr_2O_7$, is easily purified and easily dried at over 140° C. It is stable and inexpensive enough to use for making up solutions by weighing directly. Its equivalent weight is one-sixth its formula weight.

PRIMARY STANDARD REDUCING AGENTS. Several good primary standard reducing agents are available.

Sodium oxalate, $Na_2C_2O_4$, is useful in standardizing permanganate and cerate solutions. Though it can be safely dried at 105° C it must not be heated in strong acid solutions to near boiling, as it decomposes because of the formation of oxalic acid in the sulfuric acid solution. The decomposition is as follows:

$$C_2O_4^{-2} + 2H_3O^+ \rightarrow H_2C_2O_4 + 2H_2O.$$

Its subsequent decomposition is:

$$H_2C_2O_4 \rightarrow CO + CO_2 + H_2O.$$

This disadvantage is somewhat compensated for by its availability in very pure form and its stability while dry.

Arsenic trioxide, $As_2O_3$, is used to standardize iodine, permanganate, and cerate solutions. It is difficult to dissolve unless a pellet of sodium hydroxide with a little water is used. Then sodium bicarbonate is added in large excess to buffer the solution during titration. Its equivalent weight is one-fourth its formula weight.

Electrolytic iron, Fe, is available in a high degree of purity. It can be used to standardize dichromate, permanganate, and cerate solutions. The Fe is dissolved in hydrochloric acid, any ferric iron is reduced to the ferrous state with stannous chloride or zinc, and the titration is carried out in an acid solution containing phosphate. The phosphate is added to form a stable, colorless compound with the ferric ions formed during the titration. The ferric ion color does not then interfere with the color change at the end point.

OTHER PRIMARY STANDARDS. There are many other primary standards used for various purposes.

Calcium carbonate, $CaCO_3$, is often used to make up standard solutions of $Ca^{+2}$ for standardizing versene solutions which are used, in turn, to titrate hardness in water.

Sodium chloride, NaCl, is used to standardize silver nitrate solutions that are employed in titrating chloride ions in samples where the chloride content is important.

Constant-boiling hydrochloric acid solution is sometimes considered a primary standard. It is easily prepared in large quantities for making standard solutions. There are tables in handbooks with the concentration, specific gravity, and other properties of constant-boiling solutions of HCl and water.

**Choice of Concentration.** Most standard solutions range in strength between 0.05 N and 0.2 N, although 0.1 N is probably used most frequently. Stronger solutions give sharper end points with indicators but require smaller volumes for titration. If a buret reading is accurate to 0.03 ml, the possible error from reading a 25 ml titration would be $\frac{0.03}{25}$ or one part in 833. If the volume were only 10 ml, the possible reading error would be $\frac{0.03}{10}$ or one part in 333, far too large an error to be permissible in most analytical work. It is clear that if inaccuracies resulting from errors in reading the buret are to be kept small, standard solutions must be as dilute as will still be satisfactory. However, there is a limit to the dilution of a standard solution because errors due to lack of sharpness in the end point eventually become larger than errors from reading the buret.

It is often desirable to have the concentration of the standard solution chosen so that the volume in milliliters, as read on the buret, is the per cent of the desired constituent. To do this the concentration of the standard solution is adjusted so that one ml of the standard is equivalent to 0.01 of the weight of the sample, assuming that the sample is 100% pure constituent analyzed.

**Example.** How many grams of potassium dichromate must be dissolved in one liter of solution so that, when a 0.3000 g sample of iron ore is titrated, the per cent of iron in the sample will be equal to the ml of dichromate solution delivered by the buret?

Step 1.   Find the weight of dichromate chemically equivalent to one-hundredth the weight of the sample.   Assume that the sample is pure iron.

$$0.3000 \times 0.01 = 0.003 \text{ g of iron.}$$

This is the amount of iron to which each ml of the dichromate must be chemically equivalent, so that a pure iron sample would require 100 ml for titration.

Step 2.   With the equivalent weight of potassium dichromate equal to 49.04 and that of iron equal to 55.85, calculate the weight of potassium dichromate equivalent to 0.003 g of iron.

$$\frac{49.04}{55.85} = \frac{x}{0.003}$$

$$x = \frac{49.04 \times 0.003}{55.85} = 0.002634 \text{ g.}$$

This many grams of potassium dichromate must be in one ml of the standard solution.

Step 3.   Find the weight of dichromate needed in one liter.

$$1000 \times 0.002634 = 2.634 \text{ g of } K_2Cr_2O_7 \text{ needed.}$$

**Storage of Standard Solutions.**   Solutions differ in storage requirements.   Most standard solutions are safely kept in glass-stoppered bottles to prevent evaporation.

Sodium and potassium hydroxide, as well as other strong hydroxides, should be stored in plastic bottles or in glass bottles waxed inside to prevent action of the solution on the glass.   In addition, caution should be exercised to prevent absorption of carbon dioxide from the air, usually by filtering all air allowed to enter the storage bottle through soda lime or some other carbon dioxide absorbent.

Silver nitrate is stored in brown bottles in the dark to prevent light from decomposing the silver salt.

Because of possible contamination, any solution once removed from the storage bottle should never be returned.

## Volumetric Calculations

In volumetric analysis it is necessary to make calculations involving both dilutions and titrations of solutions.

**Dilution Problems.**   It is frequently necessary to make up a definite volume of a standard solution of a definite strength.   If the strength does not have to be any fixed value exactly, the solution is made up of the approximate normality and standardized against a primary standard. If the strength must be an exact value, the following procedure is suggested.

1. Dissolve the reagent in the desired volume, making sure that the concentration of reagent is slightly higher than will be needed.

2. Determine the strength of this solution by titration against a primary standard.

3. Measure out accurately with a pipet or buret the exact volume of this standardized solution needed to make up the desired volume of solution with the necessary concentration. Place the measured solution in a volumetric flask.

4. Dilute the measured volume to the mark on the flask.

5. Standardize this solution against a primary standard to insure that its concentration is as intended.

**Example.** A liter of a solution of acid was made up intentionally over 0.1 N. On titrating it with sodium carbonate it was found to be 0.1202 N. What volume of this should be taken and diluted to one liter (1000 ml) in order to make the solution exactly 0.1000 N?

To solve dilution problems one needs to remember that the volume of a solution taken, multiplied by its normality, is equal to the volume of 1 N solution equivalent chemically to the volume taken; thus:

$$V_1 \times N_1 = \text{volume of 1 N solution chemically equivalent to } V_1. \quad (7–2)$$

Therefore:

$$V_1 \times 0.1202 = 1000 \times 0.1000.$$

The volume $V_1$ times its normality, 0.1202, equals a certain number of milliliters of 1 N solution. The volume 1000 ml times its normality, 0.1000, equals the same number of milliliters of 1 N solution, which enables them to be set equal to each other. The two volumes in the equation are chemically equivalent to each other because they both will have the same amount of acid content. $V_1$ will be diluted to 1000 ml.

Solving for $V_1$:

$$V_1 = \frac{1000 \times 0.1000}{0.1202} = 832 \text{ ml of 0.1202 N solution,}$$

which must be measured out to make one liter of exactly 0.1000 N solution of acid.

No matter what volume a quantity of solution is changed to by dilution, if the reagent in the solution is not increased or decreased, the product of the first volume, $V_1$, and first normality, $N_1$, will always equal the product of the final volume, $V_2$, and the final normality, $N_2$.

The general dilution formula then is:

$$V_1 \times N_1 = V_2 \times N_2. \tag{7-3}$$

This can also be said to be the general formula for titration problems.

**Titration Problems.** The basic principle involved in solving these is the same as that for solving dilution problems. Instead of one volume being chemically equivalent to another because they contain the same quantity of reagent, two solutions of different volume may be found chemically equivalent to each other by titration of one against the other.

Example. If 50 ml of a solution of unknown concentration is titrated to an end point with 38.27 ml of a standard reagent that is 0.0990 N, calculate the normality of the unknown solution.

Substituting in Equation (7–3) we have:

$$38.27 \times 0.0990 = 50 \times N_2.$$
$$N_2 = \frac{38.27 \times 0.0990}{50} = 0.0758 \text{ N}.$$

Such calculations apply to acid-base, precipitation, oxidation-reduction, or any other type of titration reaction.

THE GRAM-MILLIEQUIVALENT. When a reactant, either an unknown or a primary standard, is weighed, dissolved, and titrated, calculations are best made by using the gram-milliequivalent weight (gme). This value is the gram-equivalent weight of the reactant divided by 1000.

$$\text{gme} = \frac{\text{gram-equivalent weight}}{1000}. \tag{7-4}$$

The important thing about the gme is that 1 ml of 1 N solution contains 1 gme of reactant. Since the volume times normality of any solution always equals milliliters of 1 N solution equivalent to the volume, the number of gme (a weight value) and the number of ml of 1 N solution (a volume value) are always equal to each other. Thus the gme is a value common to both weights and volumes.

Example 1. To standardize a silver nitrate solution, 0.2400 g of very pure sodium chloride was weighed out, dissolved in water, and titrated to the end point with 31.19 ml of the silver nitrate solution. Calculate the normality of the silver nitrate.

Step 1. Calculate the gme of sodium chloride. The equivalent weight of sodium chloride is the same as its formula weight, 58.45 g. The gme is one-thousandth of this, or 0.05845 g.

Step 2. Find the number of gme in the sample weighed.

$$\frac{0.2400}{0.05845} = 4.106 \text{ gme of sodium chloride.}$$

This is the number of ml of 1 N solution chemically equivalent to the 31.19 ml used in titrating the primary standard sodium chloride.

Step 3. Calculate the normality of the solution by substituting in Equation (7-2).

$$31.19 \times N = 4.106.$$

$$N = \frac{4.106}{31.19} = 0.1316 \text{ N.}$$

Steps 2 and 3 can be combined thus, as in Equation (7-1):

$$N = \frac{0.2400}{0.05845 \times 31.19} = 0.1316 \text{ N.}$$

**Example 2.** To standardize a ceric sulfate solution, 0.1900 g of primary standard $As_2O_3$, purity 99.81%, was weighed out and dissolved. Using 1,10 phenanthroline ferrous sulfate as indicator and a trace of osmium oxide as a catalyst, the $As_2O_3$ was titrated to an end point with 38.24 ml of the ceric sulfate solution. Calculate the normality of the ceric solution.

The equation for the reaction:

$$As^{+3} + 2Ce^{+4} \rightarrow As^{+5} + 2Ce^{+3}$$

indicates that one-half of an atomic weight of arsenic is an equivalent weight. In $As_2O_3$ there are two atomic weights of arsenic. Therefore the equivalent weight of $As_2O_3$ is one-fourth its formula weight.

Step 1. Calculate the gme of $As_2O_3$.

$$\frac{197.82}{4} = 49.45.$$

$$\frac{49.45}{1000} = 0.04945 \text{ g, the gme of } As_2O_3.$$

Step 2. Find the number of gme weighed out. Since the primary standard arsenous oxide is only 99.81% pure, its weight must be multiplied by 0.9981 to obtain the weight of pure arsenous oxide weighed out. This value divided by the gme will give the number of gme.

$$\frac{0.1900 \times 0.9981}{0.04945} = 3.835 \text{ gme.}$$

The weighed-out arsenous oxide and the ml of ceric sulfate are thus both chemically equivalent to 3.835 ml of 1 N solution.

Step 3. Calculate the normality of the solution. Substituting in Equation (7–2):

$$38.24 \times N = 3.835.$$
$$N = \frac{3.835}{38.24} = 0.1003 \text{ N}.$$

PER CENT OF A CONSTITUENT. The use of the gme for calculating the per cent of a constituent in a sample requires application of the same principles as are used in finding the normality of a solution.

**Example 1.** A 0.4112 g sample containing chloride was titrated to an end point with 40.01 ml of 0.1019 N silver nitrate. Calculate the per cent of chloride in the sample.

Step 1. Calculate the number of gme of chloride.

$40.01 \times 0.1019 = 4.077$, the number of gme of chloride. This is also the number of ml of 1 N solution equivalent to 40.01 ml of 0.1019 N solution.

Step 2. Find the weight of chloride in the sample.

$$4.077 \times 0.03546 = 0.1446 \text{ g chloride in the sample.}$$

The gme of chloride is 0.03546 g. If there are 4.077 gme, then the product of these two gives the weight of the chloride in the sample.

Step 3. Find the per cent of chloride in the sample.

$$\frac{0.1446 \times 100}{0.4112} = 35.16\% \text{ chloride in the sample.}$$

The 0.1446 is the part of the sample that is chloride. The 100 changes the decimal to per cent. The 0.4112 is the weight of the sample.

These steps may be combined, giving:

$$\frac{40.01 \times 0.1019 \times 0.03546 \times 100}{0.4112} = 35.16\% \text{ chloride.}$$

The general formula for such a calculation is:

$$\frac{V \times N \times \text{gme} \times 100}{\text{weight of sample}} = \begin{array}{l} \text{per cent of the constituent of the} \\ \text{sample for which the gme is intro-} \\ \text{duced into the equation.} \end{array} \quad (7\text{--}5)$$

The gme of chloride was introduced in the example; therefore, the answer was in per cent of chloride. $V$ is the volume of solution used in titrating the constituent in the sample, and N is the normality of the solution.

**Example 2.** A sample of iron ore containing $Fe_2O_3$ and weighing 0.2471 g was dissolved in a mixture of hydrochloric acid and stannous chloride. The solution was poured into a mercuric chloride solution, diluted, and titrated with 22.95 ml of 0.1120 N dichromate, using diphenylamine sulfonate as indicator. Calculate the per cent of iron in the ore and also the per cent of $Fe_2O_3$.

Step 1. Calculate the number of gme of the titrated Fe and $Fe_2O_3$.

$$22.95 \times 0.1120 = 2.570 \text{ gme of constituents.}$$

Step 2. Find the weight of each constituent.

$$2.570 \times 0.05585 = 0.1436 \text{ g Fe in the sample.}$$

0.05585 is the gme of Fe.

$$2.570 \times 0.07985 = 0.2052 \text{ g of } Fe_2O_3.$$

The formula weight of $Fe_2O_3$, 159.7, divided by 2000 is 0.07985, the gme of $Fe_2O_3$. Half the formula weight is the equivalent weight of $Fe_2O_3$ since there are two atoms of Fe, each with a valence change of one during the titration of one.

Step 3. Calculate the per cent of each constituent.

$$\frac{0.1436 \times 100}{0.2471} = 58.10\% \text{ Fe.}$$

$$\frac{0.2052 \times 100}{0.2471} = 83.06\% \text{ } Fe_2O_3.$$

All the steps may be combined by using Equation (7–5). For per cent of Fe:

$$\frac{22.95 \times 0.1120 \times 0.05585 \times 100}{0.2471} = 58.10\% \text{ Fe.}$$

For per cent of $Fe_2O_3$:

$$\frac{22.95 \times 0.1120 \times 0.07985 \times 100}{0.2471} = 83.06\% \text{ } Fe_2O_3.$$

Note that the only difference between the two calculations is the value substituted for the gme.

TITER OF SOLUTIONS. A quick method of calculating results from routine titrations makes use of the titer. The titer is the weight of any constituent in a substance chemically equivalent to one ml of the solution used for titrating the constituent. It is numerically equal to the normality of the solution times the gme of the constituent sought. It reduces the number of factors in Equation (7–5).

Example 1. If a 0.2771 g sample of primary standard sodium carbonate, 99.88% pure, required 42.07 ml of HCl solution for titration to a methyl orange end point, what is the HCl titer, the NaOH titer, and the $Ba(OH)_2$ titer of the HCl solution?

Step 1. Calculate the normality of the solution using 0.053 as the weight of one gme of sodium carbonate. The normality can be determined in several steps: (a) Multiply the weight of sample (0.2771) by the purity factor (0.9988) to find the weight of pure sodium carbonate in the sample. (b) Divide the weight of pure sodium carbonate thus found by the weight of one gme (0.053) to get the number of gme of sodium carbonate in the sample. (c) Divide the number of gme in the sample by the volume of titration (42.07) to obtain the normality. Combining these steps into one as in equation (7–1):

$$N = \frac{0.2771 \times 0.9988}{0.053 \times 42.07} = 0.1241.$$

This is the normality of the HCl solution.

Step 2. Find the titer of the solution for each substance by multiplying the normality of the solution by the gme of each substance.

$$HCl \text{ titer} = 0.1241 \times 0.03646 = 0.004527.$$

Thus each ml of the solution contains 0.004527 g of HCl.

$$NaOH \text{ titer} = 0.1241 \times 0.040 = 0.004965.$$

Thus each ml of the HCl solution is chemically equivalent to 0.004965 g of NaOH.

$$Ba(OH)_2 \text{ titer} = 0.1241 \times \frac{171.4}{2000}$$
$$= 0.1241 \times 0.0857$$
$$= 0.01064.$$

Thus each ml of the HCl solution is chemically equivalent to 0.01064 g of $Ba(OH)_2$. 171.4 is the formula weight, and 0.0857 is the gme of $Ba(OH)_2$.

**Example 2.** Calculate the HCl and $CH_3COOH$ (acetic acid) titer of a sodium hydroxide solution if 30.08 ml of it was used to titrate 0.8202 g of pure potassium acid phthalate. Using the titer value, calculate the per cent of acetic acid in a vinegar solution, 10 ml of which is just neutralized by 47.22 ml of the above NaOH solution. The gme of potassium acid phthalate is 0.2042.

Step 1. Calculate the normality of the NaOH solution.

$\frac{0.8202}{0.2042} = 4.016$ gme of NaOH and potassium acid phthalate involved in the titration.

$$N = \frac{4.016}{30.08}$$
$$= 0.1335.$$

This is the normality of the NaOH solution.

Step 2. Calculate the titers of the solution for the acids.

$$HCl \text{ titer} = 0.1335 \times 0.03646$$
$$= 0.004868.$$

This is the weight of HCl that will react with one ml of the NaOH solution.

$$CH_3COOH \text{ titer} = 0.1335 \times 0.06005$$
$$= 0.008018.$$

This is the weight of acetic acid that will react with one ml of the NaOH solution.

To calculate the per cent of acetic acid, assuming the solution of it to have a specific gravity of one, use the formula:

$$\text{Titer} \times \text{volume of titration} = \text{grams of constituent.} \qquad (7\text{--}6)$$

$0.008018 \times 47.22 = 0.3786$ g of acetic acid in the 10 ml of vinegar titrated. If this volume weighs 10 g, then:

$$\frac{0.3786 \times 100}{10} = 3.79\% \text{ acetic acid in the vinegar.}$$

Combining these two steps we get:

$$\frac{0.008018 \times 47.22 \times 100}{10} = 3.79\% \text{ acetic acid.}$$

The general formula for calculating per cent of a constituent from the titer of a solution is a slight modification of Equation (7–5).

$$\frac{\text{Titer} \times V \times 100}{\text{weight of sample}} = \% \text{ of constituent.} \qquad (7\text{--}7)$$

$V$ is the volume of solution delivered during the titration. Examples of the use of titers are given on pp. 152 and 155 of Chap. 10.

## Detecting End Points

It is necessary for the analyst to find the point at which equivalent quantities of reacting materials have been mixed. This is called the equivalence point or stoichiometric end point. Some observable change in a property of the solution is chosen so that the change in property coincides as nearly as possible with the stoichiometric end point. Such a change in property is called the end point of the titration whether it corresponds exactly to the equivalence point or not.

**Change in Color.** Most frequently a change in the color of the solution is employed to indicate that the end point is reached.

COLORED SOLUTIONS. The color strength of one of the reacting materials is rarely sufficient for the material to be used as an indicator. Permanganate ion is the only common example of a reagent acting as its own indicator, though $I_3^-$ and $Cu(NH_3)_4^{+2}$ have been employed as both indicators and reagents.

INDICATORS. (See pp. 94 and 116.) Substances added to solutions to give a color change at the end point are called indicators. They are usually very highly colored dyes that undergo a striking change in color when going from a solution in which one reactant is in excess to one where the other reactant is in excess. Somewhere in between an excess of either reactant is the end point. By the proper choice of an indicator for each titration the analyst can determine the end point quite accurately. Color changes may be from one color to another, from colored to colorless, or from colorless to colored. Sometimes a change in turbidity occurs simultaneously with the change in color.

**Turbidity.** Some change in turbidity may indicate the end point.

1. The appearance of a precipitate may indicate the end point in a titration such as that of a cyanide ion titrated with silver ion. Excess cyanide forms a soluble complex ion with silver until the excess is gone. Then a precipitate forms.

2. Addition of a reagent until no further precipitation occurs can be used to indicate the end point. This is obviously a very tedious operation.

3. The disappearance of a precipitate may be used to indicate the end point as in the titration of $Ni(NH_3)_4^{+2}$ with cyanide.

**Other Methods.** During a titration certain properties of solutions change in a way that is useful for detecting end points. These will be discussed in later chapters. Some of them are:

1. Conductivity (pp. 208–211).

2. Single electrode potentials (p. 84 for theory and p. 134 for application of a typical electrode potential method, using a glass electrode).

3. Fluorescence effects due to radiation of light of one wave length, by particles suspended in a liquid, when light of a different wave length impinges upon them (p. 207).

### Review Questions and Problems

1. What weight of the following would be contained in 100 ml of a 0.1 N solution?

   a. NaCl         d. $AgNO_3$
   b. $Ba(OH)_2$     e. $H_3PO_4$
   c. $CaCl_2$       f. $HNO_3$

2. Define:

   a. Primary standard.

b. Gram milliequivalent (gme).

c. Indicator.

d. Stoichiometric end point.

3. If 38.22 ml of a solution of HCl exactly titrated 0.2808 g of pure primary standard sodium carbonate, what is the normality of the solution, and what volume of it would be needed to make one liter of exactly 0.1000 N HCl solution?

4. What is the normality of a solution of NaOH of which 27.22 ml was needed to titrate 0.4047 g of pure potassium acid phthalate?

5. What volume of 0.1000 N $KMnO_4$ solution would be needed to titrate 0.1980 g of 99.89% pure sodium oxalate?

6. What is the normality of a ceric ion solution (ceric sulfate) if 33.72 ml of it titrates 0.3419 g of 99.78% pure $As_2O_3$?

7. Calculate the normality of a potassium dichromate solution if 40.08 ml of it is needed to titrate the ferrous iron obtained by dissolving 0.2214 g of 99.94% pure iron in hydrochloric acid.

8. What is the normality of a nitric acid solution if 26.49 ml of it is needed to neutralize 25.00 ml of 0.1029 N sodium hydroxide solution?

9. What is the NaOH titer of a solution of HCl if 27.00 ml of the HCl solution is needed to titrate 0.1994 g of sodium carbonate?   What are the KOH and the $Na_2CO_3$ titers of the solution?

10. What is the per cent of iron in a sample if 30.07 ml of 0.0991 N potassium dichromate solution is needed to titrate the reduced iron in 0.4129 g of iron ore?

11. What is the percent of $As_2O_3$ in a sample of impure $As_2O_3$ if 0.2071 g of the sample required 26.11 ml of 0.0889 N ceric ion for titration?

12. If a 3.0000 gram sample of a silver alloy was found by titration to be equivalent to 25.17 ml of 0.1009 N sodium chloride, what is the per cent of silver in the alloy?

13. What is the normality of a potassium thiocyanate (KCNS) solution if it takes 28.32 ml of the solution to titrate 0.3214 g of pure silver that has been dissolved in nitric acid?

14. What weight of pure primary standard $CaCO_3$ must be weighed out to give one liter of a solution which will contain 35 ppm (parts per million) of $Ca^{+2}$?

# 8

# Oxidation-Reduction Theory

Reactions in which electrons are lost and gained are called oxidation-reduction or redox reactions. Analyses in which such reactions are employed are so numerous and useful that the theory which is the basis for their operations must be studied in some detail.

## The Oxidation Potential

The tendency for an element, either in ionic, atomic, or molecular form, to act as an oxidizing or reducing agent can be measured as a voltage or electric potential. The greater the voltage required to remove an electron from an element and the greater the element's affinity for electrons of other elements, the stronger the element is as an oxidizing agent. The easier it is for electrons to be removed from an element and the less tendency an element has to acquire electrons, the stronger the element is as a reducing agent. These properties of elements vary from compound to compound. An element may act as a reducing agent in one compound or ion and as an oxidizing agent in another. There is confusion as to sign, positive or negative, of oxidation potentials. The + and − sign conventions used in this book are those adopted by the International Union of Pure and Applied Chemistry at a meeting in Stockholm, 1953.

**Energy for Redox Reactions.** The energy for redox (reduction-oxidation) reactions comes from atoms acquiring electrons. When an atom acquires electrons, energy is released. Energy is used when electrons are removed from atoms. If, in a reaction, more energy is released than absorbed, the exchange of electrons (the reaction) will occur. The more energy released in the over-all reaction, the greater the vigor of the reaction.

**Single Electrode Potentials.** The tendency to gain or lose electrons is actually measured as an oxidation potential. This is done by using a single electrode of the substance to be measured and a reference electrode. The standard reference electrode is the hydrogen electrode (*A* in Fig. 11). This is a platinized platinum metal plate which is constantly washed with pure hydrogen gas and dips into a solution that is 1 M in activity of hydrogen ions. The other electrode is an inert, bright metal plate, usually platinum (*B* in Fig. 11), which dips into the solution containing the ions or molecules being studied.

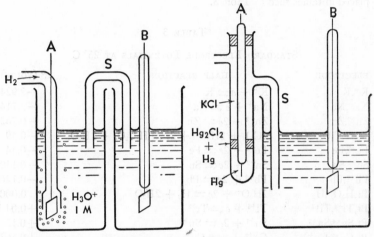

Fig. 11. An arrangement for measuring electrode potentials, with the hydrogen half cell connected to the unknown half cell by a salt bridge *S*.

Fig. 12. An arrangement for measuring electrode potentials with the calomel half cell unit containing the salt bridge *S*.

The two solutions are connected by a salt bridge, usually a tube packed with asbestos saturated with a KCl solution. The salt bridge connects the two half cells electrically without making an appreciable contribution to the cell potential.

Very often the inconvenient hydrogen electrode is replaced by a much more conveniently used calomel reference electrode (*A* in Fig. 12). This electrode has a potential of $+0.242$ volt, if the electrolyte in the half cell is saturated with KCl, which can be subtracted from all potentials measured to give the potential with respect to the hydrogen electrode. Other reference electrodes may also be used.

**Example.** For the $Fe^{+3}, Fe^{+2}$ system, a solution is prepared that has an activity (see p. 37) of one with respect to both $Fe^{+3}$ and $Fe^{+2}$. The bright platinum and the saturated calomel electrodes are dipped into the solution, and the potential between the two is measured by means of a potentiometer. The potential will be found to be about 1.003 volts. Subtracting the 0.242 volt due to the calomel electrode gives 0.761 volt. This is the $E^0$ or standard electrode potential for the $Fe^{+3}, Fe^{+2}$ equilibrium. $E^0$ values are defined as the potentials of half cells in which all of the ions involved are at unit activity; that is, the concentrations of the ions are such that they form a solution of one molar activity. $E^0$ values for many systems are placed in tables such as Table 3.

## TABLE 3

### STANDARD ELECTRODE POTENTIALS AT 25° C

| ELECTRODE | HALF REACTION | $E^0$ (VOLTS) |
|---|---|---|
| $K^+, K$ | $K^+ + e \rightleftharpoons K$ | −2.924 |
| $Na^+, Na$ | $Na^+ + e \rightleftharpoons Na$ | −2.714 |
| $Zn^{+2}, Zn$ | $Zn^{+2} + 2e \rightleftharpoons Zn$ | −0.762 |
| $Pt, H_2C_2O_4, CO_2$ | $2CO_2 + 2H_3O^+ + 2e \rightleftharpoons H_2C_2O_4 + 2H_2O$ | −0.49 |
| $Fe^{+2}, Fe$ | $Fe^{+2} + 2e \rightleftharpoons Fe$ | −0.44 |
| $Sn^{+2}, Sn$ | $Sn^{+2} + 2e \rightleftharpoons Sn$ | −0.140 |
| $Pb^{+2}, Pb$ | $Pb^{+2} + 2e \rightleftharpoons Pb$ | −0.126 |
| $Pt, H_3O^+, H_2$ | $2H_3O^+ + 2e \rightleftharpoons H_2 + 2H_2O$ | 0.000 |
| $Pt, Ti^{+4}, Ti^{+3}$ | $Ti^{+4} + e \rightleftharpoons Ti^{+3}$ | +0.04 |
| $Pt, Sn^{+4}, Sn^{+2}$ | $Sn^{+4} + 2e \rightleftharpoons Sn^{+2}$ | +0.15 |
| $Pt, Cu^{+2}, Cu^+$ | $Cu^{+2} + e \rightleftharpoons Cu^+$ | +0.167 |
| Saturated calomel electrode | $\frac{1}{2}Hg_2Cl_2 + e \rightleftharpoons Hg + Cl^-$ | +0.242 |
| Normal calomel electrode | $\frac{1}{2}Hg_2Cl_2 + e \rightleftharpoons Hg + Cl^-$ | +0.280 |
| $Cu^{+2}, Cu$ | $Cu^{+2} + 2e \rightleftharpoons Cu$ | +0.34 |
| $Pt, I_2, I^-$ | $I_2 + 2e \rightleftharpoons 2I^-$ | +0.536 |
| $Pt, Fe^{+3}, Fe^{+2}$ | $Fe^{+3} + e \rightleftharpoons Fe^{+2}$ | +0.771 |
| $Ag^+, Ag$ | $Ag^+ + e \rightleftharpoons Ag$ | +0.799 |
| $Hg^{+2}, Hg$ | $Hg_2^{+2} + 2e \rightleftharpoons 2Hg$ | +0.799 |
| $Pt, Br_2, Br^-$ | $Br_2 + 2e \rightleftharpoons 2Br^-$ | +1.066 |
| $Pt, Cr_2O_7^{-2}, Cr^{+3}$ | $Cr_2O_7^{-2} + 14H_3O^+ + 6e \rightleftharpoons 2Cr^{+3} + 21H_2O$ | +1.34 |
| $Pt, Cl_2, Cl^-$ | $Cl_2 + 2e \rightleftharpoons 2Cl^-$ | +1.36 |
| $Pt, MnO_4^-, Mn^{+2}$ | $MnO_4^- + 8H_3O^+ + 5e \rightleftharpoons Mn^{+2} + 12H_2O$ | +1.51 |
| $Pt, Ce^{+4}, Ce^{+3}$ | $Ce^{+4} + e \rightleftharpoons Ce^{+3}$ | +1.61 |

$K^+, K$ represents a potassium metal electrode in contact with a one molar solution of potassium ions.

$Pt, H_3O^+, H_2$ represents a platinum electrode dipping into a solution one molar in hydronium ions, the electrode simultaneously in contact with hydrogen gas which has saturated the solution with hydrogen at one atmosphere of pressure.

**The Nernst Equation.** The oxidation potential $E$ for any combination of concentrations of ions in a half reaction system can be calculated if the standard electrode potential $E^0$ and the respective concentrations of the oxidized and reduced forms of the substance are known. The calculation is made by applying the Nernst equation.

FORMS OF THE EQUATION. The original form of the Nernst equation is of little practical value in analytical chemistry. It has the following form.

$$E = E^0 + \frac{RT}{nF} \ln Q, \qquad (8\text{-}1)$$

where:

$E$ is the potential one would expect to find if an inert (bright platinum) electrode and a hydrogen electrode make up a cell. The inert electrode would dip into a solution of known concentration of both oxidized and reduced form of some reagent.

$E^0$ is the potential at unit activity of both the oxidized and reduced forms.

$R$ is the gas constant, 8.314 joules per degree-mole.

$T$ is the absolute temperature.

$n$ is the number of electrons involved in the equilibrium.

$F$ is the faraday, 96,500 coulombs.

$Q$ is the equilibrium constant for the reaction.

Under ordinary conditions, at 25° C, with constants combined and the base 10 used, this can be reduced to:

$$E = E^0 + \frac{0.059}{n} \log Q. \qquad (8\text{-}2)$$

For half reactions such as $Zn^{+2} \rightleftharpoons Zn$ or $Fe^{+3} \rightleftharpoons Fe^{+2}$, the $Q$ becomes a ratio and the general equation for such cases is:

$$E = E^0 + \frac{0.059}{n} \log \frac{[Ox]}{[Red]}, \qquad (8\text{-}3)$$

where:

[Ox] is the molar concentration (activity) of the oxidized form and [Red] is the molar concentration (activity) of the reduced form of the reagent.

Equation (8-3) is the useful form of the Nernst equation for analytical chemists.

**Example 1.** Write the Nernst equation for the half reaction

$$Zn^{+2} + 2e \rightleftharpoons Zn.$$

$$E = -0.762 + \frac{0.059}{2} \log \frac{[Zn^{+2}]}{[Zn]}.$$

**Example 2.** Write the Nernst equation for the half reaction

$$MnO_4^- + 8H_3O^+ + 5e \rightleftharpoons Mn^{+2} + 12H_2O.$$

$$E = 1.51 + \frac{0.059}{5} \log \frac{[MnO_4^-][H_3O^+]^8}{[Mn^{+2}]}.$$

Note that the hydronium ion, $H_3O^+$, is included in the equation because it is an integral part of the reaction. From this it can be seen that the pH is of importance in permanganate reactions.

APPLICATIONS OF THE NERNST EQUATION. Applying Equation (8–3) it is possible to:

1. Calculate oxidation potentials through a wide range of concentrations of ions without the time-consuming necessity of measuring them individually.

2. Calculate ratios of oxidized to reduced forms of reagents for any given or measured oxidation potential in a solution. Such values give the extent to which a reaction can be expected to go to completion.

3. Calculate the potential at the equivalence point of a titration, which in turn suggests possible indicators that would be suitable for a titration.

4. Calculate the equilibrium constant values for reactions.

VARIATIONS IN $E$ WITH VARIATIONS IN CONCENTRATION. The values of $E$ can be calculated for all variations in the ratio of the oxidized form to the reduced form of any reagent. These values, with concentration plotted against $E$, give characteristic curves. See Fig. 13.

**Example.** Calculate the values of $E$ for the half reaction

$$Fe^{+3} + e \rightleftharpoons Fe^{+2},$$

for the following concentrations of ions. (Brackets indicate molar concentrations of inclosed ions.)

(a) $[Fe^{+3}] = 10^{-5}$, $[Fe^{+2}] = 10^{-1}$.
(b) $[Fe^{+3}] = 10^{-4}$, $[Fe^{+2}] = 10^{-2}$.
(c) $[Fe^{+3}] = 10^{-3}$, $[Fe^{+2}] = 10^{-3}$.

(d) $[Fe^{+3}] = 10^{-2}$, $[Fe^{+2}] = 10^{-4}$.

(e) $[Fe^{+3}] = 10^{-1}$, $[Fe^{+2}] = 10^{-5}$.

Step 1. From a table, the $E^0$ value for the $Fe^{+3}, Fe^{+2}$ system is seen to be 0.771 volt measured against the hydrogen electrode.

Step 2. Substitute the values in Equation (8–3) and solve for $E$ thus:

(a) $E = 0.771 + \dfrac{0.059}{1} \log \dfrac{10^{-5}}{10^{-1}} = 0.771 + 0.059 \log 10^{-4}$

$= 0.771 - 0.236 = 0.535$ volt.

(b) $E = 0.771 + 0.059 \log \dfrac{10^{-4}}{10^{-2}} = 0.771 - 0.118 = 0.653$ volt.

(c) $E = 0.771 + 0.059 \log \dfrac{10^{-3}}{10^{-3}} = 0.771 - 0 = 0.771$ volt.

$$\left( \log \dfrac{10^{-3}}{10^{-3}} = \log 1 = 0. \right)$$

(d) $E = 0.771 + 0.059 \log \dfrac{10^{-2}}{10^{-4}} = 0.771 + 0.118 = 0.889$ volt.

(e) $E = 0.771 + 0.059 \log \dfrac{10^{-1}}{10^{-5}} = 0.771 + 0.236 = 1.007$ volt.

If a large number of such variations in concentration are used in calculating values of $E$ and these values are plotted against different ratios of $Fe^{+3}$ to $Fe^{+2}$, a curve is obtained as in Fig. 13.

Note that in Equation (c) above where $[Fe^{+3}] = [Fe^{+2}]$ the potential is equal to $E^0$ for the reaction.

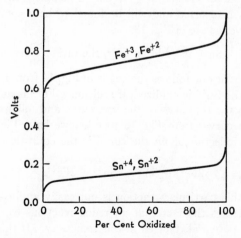

Fig. 13. Typical curves of $E$ plotted against the per cent of ions in the oxidized form.

In an exactly similar manner $E$ can be calculated and plotted for solutions of the $Sn^{+4}$,$Sn^{+2}$ system with a large number of variations in concentration. Such a curve is shown in Fig. 13 along with the curve for the $Fe^{+3}$,$Fe^{+2}$ system. The curves for both the tin and iron systems have the same form except that where $E = E^0$ the slope for the tin curve is less steep. The more electrons involved in a half reaction, the more nearly horizontal this slope becomes.

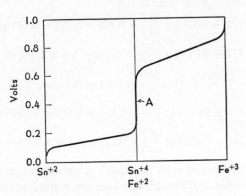

Fig. 14. A Redox Titration Curve. An actual titration, starting at $Sn^{+2}$, would proceed only to $A$ or very slightly past $A$.

CALCULATION OF TITRATION CURVES. A complete titration curve (Fig. 14) can be plotted and will be found to be a combination of two such curves as are in Fig. 13.

Starting with $Sn^{+2}$ and adding $Fe^{+3}$, the ratio $\dfrac{[Sn^{+4}]}{[Sn^{+2}]}$ grows larger, and $E$ changes as one follows the curve in Fig. 14 from left to right. After all of the $Sn^{+2}$ is oxidized, if still more $Fe^{+3}$ is added, the $E$ changes from the tin curve to the iron curve and follows the latter. Putting both curves from Fig. 13 together we have Fig. 14, where the point of inflection $A$ on the curve is the equivalence point for the reaction:

$$2Fe^{+3} + Sn^{+2} \rightarrow Sn^{+4} + 2Fe^{+2}.$$

Although this particular reaction is not easily applied to a titration, it illustrates the fact that all redox reactions can have their half reaction potentials plotted in this same way. If the reaction is suitable for analytical work, a curve such as the combined one above indicates the voltage one could read on an instrument at the equivalence point during a titration. Thus, colored indicators of end points are not absolutely essential if a potentiometer is available. However, color changes are more quickly observable than potentiometric readings, and indicators have been found that are suitable for most redox reactions.

EXTENT OF A REACTION. If during a titration involving redox reactions the $E$ (oxidation potential) is measured, the extent of the reaction at that point can be calculated.

**Example 1.** A potential of $+1.00$ volt is reached in titrating a solution of ferrous iron with ceric ions. What is the ratio of $[Fe^{+3}]$ to $[Fe^{+2}]$ at that point?

Step 1. Substitute the values $+1.00$ volt from the problem and 0.771 volt for $E^0$ from Table 3 into the Nernst equation for $Fe^{+3}, Fe^{+2}$. This is Equation (8–3).

$$1.00 = 0.771 + 0.059 \log \frac{[Fe^{+3}]}{[Fe^{+2}]}.$$

Step 2. Solve for the value of the ratio of $[Fe^{+3}]$ to $[Fe^{+2}]$.

$$\log \frac{[Fe^{+3}]}{[Fe^{+2}]} = \frac{0.229}{0.059} = 3.88.$$

Thus:
$$\frac{[Fe^{+3}]}{[Fe^{+2}]} = \frac{7586}{1} = \frac{7.6 \times 10^3}{1}.$$

Therefore the oxidation of the ferrous iron is practically complete at an $E$ of $+1.00$ volt.

**Example 2.** Calculate the ratio of $[Ce^{+4}]$ to $[Ce^{+3}]$ at the same potential.

Step 1. Substitute in the Nernst equation as in example 1.

$$1.00 = 1.61 + 0.059 \log \frac{[Ce^{+4}]}{[Ce^{+3}]}.$$

Step 2. Solve for the value of the ratio $\frac{[Ce^{+4}]}{[Ce^{+3}]}$.

$$\log \frac{[Ce^{+4}]}{[Ce^{+3}]} = \frac{-0.61}{0.059} = -10.34 = -11 + 0.66.$$

Thus:
$$\frac{[Ce^{+4}]}{[Ce^{+3}]} = \frac{4.57 \times 10^{-11}}{1} = \frac{1}{2.2 \times 10^{10}}.$$

$[Ce^{+3}]$ is therefore $2.2 \times 10^{10}$ times as large as $[Ce^{+4}]$ so that in this reaction practically all $Ce^{+4}$ has been reduced by the $Fe^{+2}$.

CALCULATION OF $E$ AT THE EQUIVALENCE POINT. For any pair of half reactions constituting a whole reaction, the oxidation potential,

$E$, can be calculated for the point at which equivalent quantities of both reactants have been brought together.

**Example 1.** For a simple case where equal numbers of electrons are given and taken by the reducing and oxidizing agent respectively, the $E$ at the equivalence point is the average of the two $E^0$ values. Thus for:

$$Ce^{+4} + Fe^{+2} \to Ce^{+3} + Fe^{+3}$$

the number of electrons taken by each $Ce^{+4}$ is the same as that given by each $Fe^{+2}$, and:

$$E_{equivalence} = \frac{E^0_{Ce^{+4},Ce^{+3}} + E^0_{Fe^{+3},Fe^{+2}}}{2}$$

$$= \frac{1.61 + 0.771}{2} = \frac{2.381}{2} = 1.19 \text{ volts.}$$

Where more than one electron is involved in a half reaction, the $E^0$ must be taken as many times as there are electrons involved. There are two half reactions in each reaction, so that the products thus obtained for both are added together. This sum is divided by the sum of the number of electrons involved in both half reactions to give the $E$ at the equivalence point.

**Example 2.** Calculate the $E$ at the equivalence point for the reaction:

$$MnO_4^- + 5Fe^{+2} + 8H_3O^+ \to Mn^{+2} + 5Fe^{+3} + 24H_2O.$$

The $MnO_4^-$ gains 5 electrons. Its $E^0$ must be taken 5 times. The $Fe^{+2}$ loses one electron. Its $E^0$ must be taken once. The sum of these values is divided by 6, the total number of electrons involved in both half reactions, to give $E$ at the equivalence point.

$$E = \frac{0.771 + (5 \times 1.51)}{6} = 1.39 \text{ volts.}$$

If permanganate were not so highly colored as it is, an indicator would be needed for this reaction that would change color at about 1.39 volts oxidation potential.

EQUILIBRIUM CONSTANTS FOR REDOX REACTIONS. A redox reaction is a combination of two half reactions. One can obtain values for equilibrium constants for redox reactions by setting the two Nernst equations for each of the two half reactions equal to each other, and solving for the equilibrium constant. The solution of the general equation gives either the equilibrium constant or its reciprocal. It is obvious that the number of electrons to be gained must be equal to the number lost in both half reactions in order that the equation will balance and that the solution of the value for the equilibrium constant will be correct.

**Example 1.** Calculate the equilibrium constant for the reaction:

$$Sn^{+2} + 2Fe^{+3} \rightarrow Sn^{+4} + 2Fe^{+2}.$$

The half reactions, balanced for electrons exchanged, are:

$$Sn^{+4} + 2e \rightleftharpoons Sn^{+2}, \text{ with } E^0 \text{ of } 0.15 \text{ v.}$$
$$2Fe^{+3} + 2e \rightleftharpoons 2Fe^{+2}, \text{ with } E^0 \text{ of } 0.771 \text{ v.}$$

The Nernst equations are:

$$E = 0.15 + \frac{0.059}{2} \log \frac{[Sn^{+4}]}{[Sn^{+2}]}$$

and:

$$E = 0.771 + \frac{0.059}{2} \log \frac{[Fe^{+3}]^2}{[Fe^{+2}]^2}.$$

The $n$, under the 0.059, must be 2 in both equations just as it is in the balanced equation for the whole reaction, and the $Fe^{+3}$ and $Fe^{+2}$ in the balanced equation have 2 as coefficients which must be used as exponents of their concentrations, as in any equilibrium constant. (See p. 31 for the use of coefficients as exponents in equilibrium constant equations.)

*Note.* Squaring both $[Fe^{+3}]$ and $[Fe^{+2}]$ and then dividing 0.059 by 2 leaves the value of the Nernst equation for iron unchanged; yet it satisfies the rule of coefficients being used as exponents as applied to the balanced equation.

At equilibrium between these two half reactions, since equilibrium will occur in a single vessel, $E$ for one equation is identical to $E$ for the other equation. Therefore:

$$0.771 + \frac{0.059}{2} \log \frac{[Fe^{+3}]^2}{[Fe^{+2}]^2} = 0.15 + \frac{0.059}{2} \log \frac{[Sn^{+4}]}{[Sn^{+2}]}.$$

Collecting like terms:

$$\frac{(0.771 - 0.15)2}{0.059} = \log \frac{[Sn^{+4}][Fe^{+2}]^2}{[Fe^{+3}]^2[Sn^{+2}]}.$$
$$21 = \log K.$$
$$10^{21} = K.$$

**Example 2.** Calculate the equilibrium constant for the reaction:

$$Cr_2O_7^{-2} + 14H_3O^+ + 6Fe^{+2} \rightarrow 2Cr^{+3} + 6Fe^{+3} + 21H_2O.$$

The half reactions are:

$$Cr_2O_7^{-2} + 14H_3O^+ + 6e \rightleftharpoons 2Cr^{+3} + 21H_2O$$

and:

$$6Fe^{+3} + 6e \rightleftharpoons 6Fe^{+2}.$$

Note that there are equal numbers of electrons in the two half reactions.

The Nernst equations, the $E$'s of which are equal to each other, are:

$$E = 1.34 + \frac{0.059}{6} \log \frac{[Cr_2O_7^{-2}][H_3O^+]^{14}}{[Cr^{+3}]^2}$$

and:

$$E = 0.771 + \frac{0.059}{6} \log \frac{[Fe^{+3}]^6}{[Fe^{+2}]^6}.$$

Equating:

$$1.34 + \frac{0.059}{6} \log \frac{[Cr_2O_7^{-2}][H_3O^+]^{14}}{[Cr^{+3}]^2} = 0.771 + \frac{0.059}{6} \log \frac{[Fe^{+3}]^6}{[Fe^{+2}]^6}.$$

Collecting terms:

$$\frac{(1.34 - 0.771)6}{0.059} = \log \frac{[Fe^{+3}]^6[Cr^{+3}]^2}{[Cr_2O_7^{-2}][Fe^{+2}]^6[H_3O^+]^{14}}.$$

$$57.86 = \log K.$$

$$10^{58} = K.$$

For $K$ the exponent is rounded off to the nearest whole number. The accuracy of the value does not deserve a more accurately stated number.

### Theory of Redox Indicators

Certain substances change color with a change in the oxidation potential ($E$) of a solution. Of these substances, permanganate is able to change color and act as an oxidizing agent by itself. A very slight excess of permanganate gives a color that indicates when an end point is reached during a titration. Other substances have been found that also change color with a change of $E$ through a fairly narrow range of $E$. Some of these are useful redox indicators.

**Nernst Equation and Redox Indicators.** Each redox indicator substance can undergo oxidation and reduction in the same way as ferric and ferrous ions. Therefore, a half reaction equation for a redox indicator can be written thus:

$$\text{Oxidized form} + n\text{e} \rightleftharpoons \text{reduced form}$$

where the oxidized form has one color and the reduced form has another. For any half reaction a Nernst equation can be written:

$$E = E^0 + \frac{0.059}{n} \log \frac{[Ox]}{[Red]},$$

where:

$E^0$ is the standard electrode potential of the indicator at activity of one;

[Ox] is the molar concentration of the oxidized form;

[Red] is the molar concentration of the reduced form;

$n$ is the number of electrons involved.

**Color Change Range.** It can be shown that for most indicators the whole range of color from all oxidized form to all reduced form covers about 0.059 volt on each side of the $E^0$ for the indicator. Very intensely colored indicators require only a slight change in proportions of oxidized to reduced form to give a visible color change. Therefore, indicators should be chosen on the basis of having an $E^0$ somewhere near the $E$ at the end point of the reaction for which the indicator is to be used.

A few selected redox indicators, with the corresponding $E^0$ for each, are listed in Table 4.

## TABLE 4

| | COLOR | | |
|---|---|---|---|
| INDICATOR | REDUCED FORM | OXIDIZED FORM | $E^0$ |
| Methylene blue | Blue | Colorless | 0.53 v |
| Barium diphenylamine sulfonate | Colorless | Purple | 0.85 v |
| 1,10-phenanthroline ferrous sulfate (ferroin) | Red | Faint blue | 1.06 v |
| 5 nitro-1,10-phenanthroline ferrous sulfate (nitro ferroin) | Red | Faint blue | 1.25 v |

## Review Questions and Problems

1. What is the difference between $E$ and $E^0$ in redox reactions?
2. Upon what does the magnitude of the $E^0$ of a half reaction depend?
3. Calculate the $E$ values for the following concentrations of ions, both ions of each pair being in the same solution.
   a. $[Ce^{+4}] = 10^{-1}$, $[Ce^{+3}] = 10^{-4}$.
   b. $[Ce^{+4}] = 10^{-2}$, $[Ce^{+3}] = 10^{-3}$.
   c. $[Ce^{+4}] = 10^{-4}$, $[Ce^{+3}] = 10^{-2}$.
   d. $[MnO_4^-] = 10^{-2}$, $[Mn^{+2}] = 10^{-4}$.   (In acid, $E^0 = 1.51$ v.)
4. What is $E$ at the equivalence point for the following reactions?
   a. $2Ti^{+3} + I_2 \rightarrow 2Ti^{+4} + 2I^-$.
   b. $Sn^{+2} + 2Ce^{+4} \rightarrow Sn^{+4} + 2Ce^{+3}$.
   c. $MnO_4^- + 5Fe^{+2} + 8H_3O^+ \rightarrow Mn^{+2} + 5Fe^{+3} + 12H_2O$.
   d. $Cr_2O_7^{-2} + 6Fe^{+2} + 14H_3O^+ \rightarrow 2Cr^{+3} + 6Fe^{+3} + 21H_2O$.
5. Calculate the values for $\dfrac{[Ox]}{[Red]}$ of substances oxidized in the reactions

given in question 4, at the point where equivalent quantities of oxidizing agent and reducing agent have been brought together.

6. Find the equilibrium constant for the first three reactions in question 4.

7. From the calculations of $E$ values for various $\dfrac{[Ce^{+4}]}{[Ce^{+3}]}$ ratios in question 3, and from values of $E$ in the text of Chap. 8 for ratios of $\dfrac{[Fe^{+3}]}{[Fe^{+2}]}$, plot two curves as in Fig. 14, showing where $E$ occurs at the equivalence point.

8. From values calculated in question 4 select, from Table 4, a satisfactory indicator for the reactions $b$, $c$, and $d$. (Reaction $a$ involves iodine, for which starch solution is generally used as indicator.)

# 9

# Neutralization Theory

The study of neutralization reactions has resulted in several theories as to what acids and bases are and how they react. In addition, many laws have been discovered which can be expressed mathematically. The application of these laws to neutralization reactions in quantitative analysis is a large part of neutralization theory.

### Definitions

Two modern concepts express our ideas of acids and bases. The more general Lewis concept is seldom used in discussions of acid-base phenomena. The Brønsted and Lowry definitions are a modification of older concepts and are easily applicable to neutralization problems.

**The Lewis Electron Pair Concept.** The Lewis theory is generally regarded as the most widely applicable of the reasonable ideas about acids, bases, and neutralization. Its definitions are:

ACID. An acid is a substance which can share an unshared electron pair on an atom in another molecule or ion. The hydrogen ion, $H^+$, and the sulfur trioxide molecule, $SO_3$, can be considered acids since either can share a pair of electrons furnished by another atom.

BASE. A base is a substance which contains an atom having an electron pair which is capable of being shared by an atom in another molecule or ion. The hydroxide ion, $OH^-$, and the oxide ion, $O^{-2}$, are both bases because each has a pair of electrons available for sharing. The ammonia molecule is also a base.

NEUTRALIZATION. Neutralization is the formation of a co-ordinate covalent bond between an acid and a base, thus:

$$\text{Acid} \quad \text{Base}$$
$$H^+ + :\overset{..}{\underset{..}{O}}:H^- \rightarrow H:\overset{..}{\underset{..}{O}}:H \qquad (9\text{--}1)$$

97

$$\underset{\substack{\displaystyle \cdot\cdot \\ :\!\!\overset{\cdot\cdot}{O}\!\!: \\ \cdot\cdot}}{\overset{\substack{:\!\!\overset{\cdot\cdot}{O}\!\!: \\ }}{S\!:\!O\!:}} + :\overset{\cdot\cdot}{\underset{\cdot\cdot}{O}}:^{-2} \rightarrow \;\; :\overset{\cdot\cdot}{\underset{\cdot\cdot}{O}}:\underset{\substack{:\overset{\cdot\cdot}{\underset{\cdot\cdot}{O}}:}}{\overset{\substack{:\overset{\cdot\cdot}{O}\!\!: }}{S}}\!:\overset{\cdot\cdot}{\underset{\cdot\cdot}{O}}:^{-2} \qquad (9\text{--}2)$$

$$H^+ + :\underset{\overset{\displaystyle H}{}}{\overset{\overset{\displaystyle H}{\cdot\cdot}}{N}}:H \rightarrow H:\underset{\overset{\displaystyle H}{}}{\overset{\overset{\displaystyle H}{}}{N}}:H^+ \qquad (9\text{--}3)$$

When a proton reacts with either a hydroxide ion or an ammonia molecule, a co-ordinate covalent bond is formed in making a water molecule or an ammonium ion. When an oxide ion unites with sulfur trioxide to form a sulfate ion, the oxide forms a co-ordinate covalent bond by sharing a pair of unshared electrons with the sulfur in the sulfur trioxide.

IMPORTANCE. The Lewis theory is valuable in explaining neutralization reactions that:

1. Do not involve hydrogen.
2. Occur in nonaqueous solutions.

The Brønsted-Lowry Concept. This theory is less general than the Lewis theory since it requires that an acid be a hydrogen-containing substance. No such restriction on composition is placed on a base.

ACID. An acid is a substance capable of donating protons. (It must therefore contain hydrogen.)

BASE. A base is a substance capable of accepting protons.

NEUTRALIZATION. Neutralization is the process of transferring a proton from an acid to a base. During such transfer a new acid is produced and the substance which lost the proton becomes a base, thus:

$$\underset{\text{Acid}_1}{HCl} + \underset{\text{Base}_1}{NH_3} \rightarrow \underset{\text{Acid}_2}{NH_4^+} + \underset{\text{Base}_2}{Cl^-}. \qquad (9\text{--}4)$$

The acid, HCl, donates a proton to the base, $NH_3$, producing a new acid, $NH_4^+$, and a new base, $Cl^-$.

CONJUGATE PAIRS. The substance left behind after an acid donates a proton is the conjugate base of the acid. The base that acquires a proton becomes the conjugate acid of the original base. Thus in Equation (9–4) the $Cl^-$ is the conjugate base of HCl, $NH_4^+$ is the conjugate acid of $NH_3$, $NH_3$ is the conjugate base of $NH_4^+$, and HCl is the conjugate acid of $Cl^-$.

## Strong Acids and Bases

A strong acid or base is strong because it ionizes completely in solution. In water solutions acids form hydrated protons called hydronium ions, $H_3O^+$, and bases form hydroxide ions, $OH^-$. We will deal with water solutions only, where neutralization always involves the formation of water, thus:

$$H_3O^+ + OH^- \rightleftharpoons 2H_2O. \qquad (9\text{--}5)$$

**Ion Product Constant for Water, $K_w$.** In water there is some dissociation into $H_3O^+$ and $OH^-$, as is indicated by the double arrow in Equation (9–5). From the law of mass action (see p. 30) it can be shown that at any temperature the product of the molar concentrations of $H_3O^+$ and $OH^-$ is a constant, thus:

$$[H_3O^+][OH^-] = K_w, \qquad (9\text{--}6)$$

where brackets indicate molar concentrations, and $K_w$ is the ion product constant for water.

TEMPERATURE AND $K_w$. $K_w$ varies with the temperature. Thus at 25° C $K_w$ is $1.04 \times 10^{-14}$ but at 100° C it is $58.2 \times 10^{-14}$. This substantiates the generality that stabilities of substances decrease with increasing temperature.

THE pH SYSTEM. A convenient system of indicating the acidity of a solution is based upon $K_w$. This is the pH system, in which the pH is defined as the logarithm of the reciprocal of the hydronium ion concentration of the solution.

$$pH = \log \frac{1}{[H_3O^+]} = -\log [H_3O^+]. \qquad (9\text{--}7)$$

In exactly the same way the hydroxide ion concentration can be expressed in terms of pOH.

$$pOH = \log \frac{1}{[OH^-]} = -\log [OH^-]. \qquad (9\text{--}8)$$

In water, but only at 25° C:

$$pH = 14 - pOH \qquad (9\text{--}9)$$

and:

$$pOH = 14 - pH. \qquad (9\text{--}10)$$

Table 5 shows the relation of hydronium ion concentration to pH and pOH in water solutions at 25° C. A neutral solution has both a pH and a pOH of 7 at 25° C.

TABLE 5

| ACID SOLUTIONS | | | | BASIC SOLUTIONS | | | |
|---|---|---|---|---|---|---|---|
| $[H_3O^+]$ | pH | $[OH^-]$ | pOH | $[H_3O^+]$ | pH | $[OH^-]$ | pOH |
| $1 = 10^0$ | 0 | $10^{-14}$ | 14 | $10^{-14}$ | 14 | $10^0$ | 0 |
| $0.1 = 10^{-1}$ | 1 | $10^{-13}$ | 13 | $10^{-13}$ | 13 | $10^{-1}$ | 1 |
| $0.01 = 10^{-2}$ | 2 | $10^{-12}$ | 12 | $10^{-12}$ | 12 | $10^{-2}$ | 2 |
| $0.001 = 10^{-3}$ | 3 | $10^{-11}$ | 11 | $10^{-11}$ | 11 | $10^{-3}$ | 3 |
| $0.0001 = 10^{-4}$ | 4 | $10^{-10}$ | 10 | $10^{-10}$ | 10 | $10^{-4}$ | 4 |
| $0.00001 = 10^{-5}$ | 5 | $10^{-9}$ | 9 | $10^{-9}$ | 9 | $10^{-5}$ | 5 |
| $0.000001 = 10^{-6}$ | 6 | $10^{-8}$ | 8 | $10^{-8}$ | 8 | $10^{-6}$ | 6 |

At neutral: $[H_3O^+] = 10^{-7}$, pH = 7; $[OH^-] = 10^{-7}$, pOH = 7.

**pH of Solutions of Strong Acids and Strong Bases.** For strong acids and bases, if the solutions are dilute, the hydronium ion concentration can be considered equal to the normality of the acid, and the hydroxide ion concentration can be considered equal to the normality of the base. Thus a 0.01 N sodium hydroxide solution can be considered as having a hydroxide ion concentration of 0.01 molar.

**Example 1.** Calculate the pH of a 0.001 molar HCl solution.

Step 1. Find the $[H_3O^+]$.

If the HCl is completely dissociated, then the $[H_3O^+]$ is the same as the molar concentration of the acid, which is 0.001 M or $10^{-3}$ M.

Step 2. Calculate the pH. This is done by substituting in Equation (9–7).

$$pH = \log \frac{1}{10^{-3}} = \log 10^3 = 3.$$

**Example 2.** What is the pH of a 0.01 N solution of NaOH?

Step 1. Calculate the $[H_3O^+]$. This is done by substitution in Equation (9–6).

$$[H_3O^+][OH^-] = 10^{-14}.$$
$$[H_3O^+]\, 0.01 = 10^{-14}.$$
$$[H_3O^+] = \frac{10^{-14}}{10^{-2}} = 10^{-12}.$$

Step 2. Calculate the pH, using Equation (9–7).

$$pH = \log \frac{1}{10^{-12}} = \log 10^{12} = 12.$$

An alternate method is:

Step 1. Calculate the $[OH^-]$. This is the same as the concentration of NaOH or 0.01 M or $10^{-2}$ M.

Step 2. Find the pOH, using Equation (9–8).

$$pOH = \log \frac{1}{10^{-2}} = \log 10^2 = 2.$$

Step 3. Calculate the pH, using Equation (9–9).

$$pH = 14 - 2 = 12.$$

**Example 3.** What is the pH of a 0.003 M HCl solution?
Step 1. Find the hydronium ion concentration.
The $[H_3O^+]$ is the same as the molar concentration of the HCl, which is 0.003 M = $3 \times 10^{-3}$ M.
Step 2. Calculate the pH.

$$pH = \log \frac{1}{3 \times 10^{-3}} = \log 0.33 \times 10^3 = \log 3.3 \times 10^2 = 2.52.$$

To find the logarithm of $3.3 \times 10^2$, remember that the exponent of 10 is 2, and 2 is the logarithm of the number $10^2$. The log of 3.3 is 0.52. To multiply, add the logarithms. Therefore, $2 + 0.52 = 2.52$.

**Calculation of pH during a Titration.** The calculation of the pH of a solution during an acid-base titration gives results that can be plotted on a curve such as that in Fig. 15, with the pH plotted along one axis and the volume of base added to acid plotted along the other. The curve shown is a titration curve for a strong acid against a

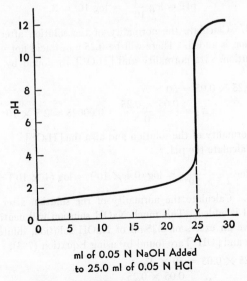

ml of 0.05 N NaOH Added
to 25.0 ml of 0.05 N HCl

Fig. 15. Acid-Base Titration Curve.

strong base. $A$ is the equivalence point. The curve shows a striking resemblance to the titration curve for an oxidation-reduction reaction (see Fig. 14, p. 90).

**Example.** During the titration of 25 ml of a 0.05 N HCl solution with 0.05 N NaOH solution, calculate (a) the pH after 24.00 ml of NaOH solution has been added, (b) the pH after 24.75 ml of NaOH has been added, and (c) the pH after 25.25 ml of NaOH has been added. Assume the total volume to be 50.00 ml after each addition.

(a) Step 1. Find the normality of the solution after the NaOH is added. Since the normalities are equal, 24 ml of NaOH will neutralize 24 ml of the original 25 ml of HCl solution. This leaves 1 ml of 0.05 N HCl not neutralized. Assuming the volume of the solution is 50 ml after the addition (it is really 49 ml) we calculate the normality from Equation (7–3) in Chap. 7.

$$V_1 \times N_1 = V_2 \times N_2.$$
$$1 \times 0.05 = 50 \times N_2.$$

Solving for $N_2$:

$$N_2 = \frac{0.05}{50} = 0.001 = 10^{-3}.$$

This is the normality of the solution with respect to HCl. It is also the molar concentration of $H_3O^+$ in the solution.

Step 2. Calculate the pH.

$$pH = \log \frac{1}{10^{-3}} = \log 10^3 = 3.$$

(b) Step 1. Calculate the normality of the solution after 24.75 ml of NaOH solution is added. There will be 0.25 ml of acid not neutralized in 50 ml of solution. Its normality and $[H_3O^+]$ are found by using Equation (7–3).

$$0.25 \times 0.05 = 50 \times N_2.$$
$$N_2 = \frac{0.05 \times 0.25}{50} = 0.00025 = 2.5 \times 10^{-4}.$$

This is the normality of the solution and also the $[H_3O^+]$.

Step 2. Calculate the pH.

$$pH = \log \frac{1}{2.5 \times 10^{-4}} = \log (0.4 \times 10^4) = \log (4 \times 10^3) = 3.60.$$

(c) Step 1. Calculate the normality of the solution after 25.25 ml of 0.05 N NaOH is added. This much NaOH solution will neutralize all the acid and leave an excess of 0.25 ml of NaOH solution, diluted to 50 ml. Its normality and $[OH^-]$ are found by using Equation (7–3).

$$0.25 \times 0.05 = 50 \times N_2.$$
$$N_2 = \frac{0.05 \times 0.25}{50} = 0.00025 = 2.5 \times 10^{-4}.$$

Step 2.   Calculate the pOH.

$$pOH = \log\left(\frac{1}{2.5 \times 10^{-4}}\right) = \log\,(0.4 \times 10^4) = \log\,(4 \times 10^3) = 3.60.$$

Step 3.   Calculate the pH, using Equation (9–9).

$$pH = 14 - 3.60 = 10.40.$$

## Weak Acids and Bases

Whereas strong acids and bases are considered, when in solution, as existing in a completely ionized state, solutions of weak acids and bases contain not only positive and negative ions but molecules of the undissociated acids and bases.   The relative amounts of ions and molecules are dependent upon the strength of the acid or base; the stronger the acid or base the larger the number of ions, relative to undissociated molecules; the weaker the acid or base the fewer the ions, relative to undissociated molecules.   There is an equilibrium between ions and molecules.

An equilibrium constant is given by applying the law of mass action (see p. 30) to the reaction of ionization of a weak acid or base. Using acetic acid as an example, the reaction of ionization is:

$$HC_2H_3O_2 + H_2O \rightleftharpoons H_3O^+ + C_2H_3O_2^-.$$

The equilibrium constant for this reaction is:

$$K_E = \frac{[H_3O^+][C_2H_3O_2^-]}{[H_2O][HC_2H_3O_2]}. \qquad (9\text{–}11)$$

But this equation contains $[H_2O]$, which in water solutions amounts to about $\frac{1000}{18} = 55.5$ moles per liter.   This does not change appreciably from solution to solution, and its use merely complicates calculations.   Since it never varies much another equation can be set up, in terms of a new constant, which leaves out $[H_2O]$.   This is the same as multiplying both sides of Equation (9–11) by 55.5. $K_E \times 55.5$ is called the ionization constant and is designated $K_A$ for acids and $K_B$ for bases.   For acetic acid:

$$K_A = \frac{[H_3O^+][C_2H_3O_2^-]}{[HC_2H_3O_2]} = 1.8 \times 10^{-5}. \qquad (9\text{–}12)$$

For the weak base, $NH_4OH$, a corresponding ionization constant is:

$$K_B = \frac{[NH_4^+][OH^-]}{[NH_4OH]} = 1.8 \times 10^{-5}. \qquad (9\text{–}13)$$

It is purely coincidental that the ionization constants for $NH_4OH$ and for $HC_2H_3O_2$ are numerically equal. Values of $K_A$ and $K_B$ for several acids and bases are given in the table in Appendix IV.

**Calculation of pH from Ionization Constants.** By the use of ionization constants the pH of solutions of acids and bases, of their salts, or of mixtures of acids or bases with their salts, can be calculated.

**Example 1.** Calculate the pH of a 0.10 N solution of acetic acid.

Step 1. Substitute all known values into the equation for the ionization constant for acetic acid, Equation (9–12). The chemical equation for the ionization of acetic acid shows that for every molecule of acid ionized, one acetate ion and one hydronium ion are produced. Therefore, in such a solution $[H_3O^+] = [C_2H_3O_2^-]$ and, as a result of this equality, in Equation (9–12), $[H_3O^+][C_2H_3O_2^-]$ is the same value as $[H_3O^+]^2$.

Substituting $[H_3O^+]^2$ for $[H_3O^+][C_2H_3O_2^-]$ in Equation (9–12) we get:

$$1.8 \times 10^{-5} = \frac{[H_3O^+]^2}{[HC_2H_3O_2]}.$$

Step 2. The acetic acid concentration is less than 0.10 N because of the fact that some acetic acid molecules are used up in forming ions. For $[HC_2H_3O_2]$ substitute $0.10 - [H_3O^+]$ to get a quadratic equation. It can be shown that the value obtained by solving this quadratic equation is very nearly the same as the one obtained by ignoring the decrease in $[HC_2H_3O_2]$ and solving Equation (9–12) with 0.10 substituted for the $[HC_2H_3O_2]$, thus:

$$1.8 \times 10^{-5} = \frac{[H_3O^+]^2}{0.10}.$$

The results are so similar because such a small portion of the acetic acid molecules, relative to the total number, is used in forming ions. Similar approximations are generally made throughout analytical chemical calculations.

Step 3. Solve for the molar concentration of hydronium ions.

$$[H_3O^+]^2 = 1.8 \times 10^{-5} \times 0.10.$$
$$[H_3O^+] = \sqrt{1.8 \times 10^{-6}} = 1.34 \times 10^{-3}.$$

Step 4. Calculate the pH, using Equation (9–7).

$$pH = \log \left[ \frac{1}{1.34 \times 10^{-3}} \right] = \log [0.747 \times 10^3]$$
$$= \log [7.47 \times 10^2] = 2.87.$$

**Example 2.** Calculate the pH of a solution which is 0.10 N in $HC_2H_3O_2$ and 0.20 N in $NaC_2H_3O_2$.

Step 1. Substitute all known values in the equilibrium constant Equation (9–12).

$$1.8 \times 10^{-5} = \frac{[H_3O^+] \times 0.20}{0.10}.$$

*Note.* The 0.20 N NaC$_2$H$_3$O$_2$ yields a solution 0.20 M in C$_2$H$_3$O$_2$$^-$ by complete ionization. The [C$_2$H$_3$O$_2$$^-$] is therefore taken as 0.20, although a minute amount of acetate ion is produced by ionization of acetic acid (HC$_2$H$_3$O$_2$). The 0.10 N HC$_2$H$_3$O$_2$ is thus assumed to remain entirely in the molecular form as 0.10 M acetic acid although a trace of it is ionized, yielding an increase in acetate ion concentration equal to the increase in hydronium ions. The values thus used for the calculation are therefore very close approximations, rather than exact quantities.

Step 2. Solve for the [H$_3$O$^+$].

$$[H_3O^+] = \frac{1.8 \times 10^{-5} \times 0.10}{0.20} = 0.90 \times 10^{-5} = 9 \times 10^{-6}.$$

Step 3. Calculate the pH.

$$pH = \log\left[\frac{1}{9 \times 10^{-6}}\right] = \log\left[0.111 \times 10^6\right] = \log\left[1.11 \times 10^5\right] = 5.05.$$

The situation described in example 2 may be created either by adding acetic acid and sodium acetate to water or by starting with acetic acid and neutralizing part of it with sodium hydroxide to produce some sodium acetate, but leaving some acid not neutralized. (For special properties of this type of solution see Buffer Solutions, p. 107.) If we calculate the pH at different points during this neutralization process, starting with acid only plus water, and plot the pH against the volume of base added, a curve is obtained such as is shown in Fig. 16, p. 106. This is a titration curve for a weak acid with a strong base. *A* is the equivalence point.

**Example 3.** Calculate the pH of a solution which is 0.20 M in NH$_4$OH and 0.70 M in NH$_4$Cl.

Step 1. Substitute all known values in the ionization constant Equation (9–13) for ammonium hydroxide, making the same type of approximations as in example 2.

$$1.8 \times 10^{-5} = \frac{0.70 \times [OH^-]}{0.20}.$$

Step 2. Solve for the OH$^-$.

$$[OH^-] = \frac{1.8 \times 10^{-5} \times 0.20}{0.70} = 0.514 \times 10^{-5} = 5.14 \times 10^{-6}.$$

Step 3. Solve for the pOH, using Equation (9–8).

$$pOH = \log\left(\frac{1}{5.14 \times 10^{-6}}\right) = \log\left(0.1944 \times 10^6\right)$$
$$= \log\left(1.944 \times 10^5\right) = 5.29.$$

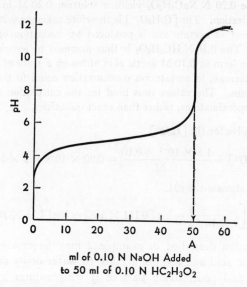

Fig. 16. Titration Curve: Weak Acid — Strong Base.

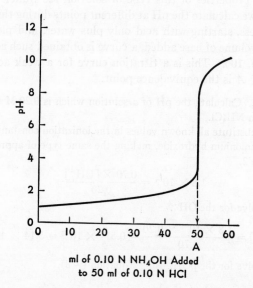

Fig. 17. Titration Curve: Strong Acid — Weak Base.

Step 4. Find the pH, using Equation (9–9).

$$\text{pH} = 14 - 5.29 = 8.71$$

Example 3 is a case where part of a weak base has been neutralized by a strong acid, hydrochloric acid. If we calculate the pH at different points during the neutralization process and plot pH against the volume of acid added, a curve such as is shown in Fig. 17 is obtained. This is a titration curve for a weak base with a strong acid. $A$ is the equivalence point. Actual measurements with a pH meter (an instrument which measures pH directly) would be nearly identical with calculated values.

**Buffer Solutions.** Buffer solutions contain either a weak acid and some salt of the acid or a weak base and some salt of the base. It is possible to add considerable quantities of a strong acid or a strong base to a buffer solution with only a small change in the pH resulting.

Assuming we have a buffer solution containing acetic acid and sodium acetate, how does it maintain a nearly fixed pH? If a strong base such as NaOH solution is added to the buffer, resulting in additional hydroxide ions, the acetic acid molecules react thus:

$$HC_2H_3O_2 + OH^- \rightarrow H_2O + C_2H_3O_2^-.$$

If not all of the acetic acid is used up, the acetate ion concentration is increased exactly as much as the acetic acid concentration is decreased.

If a strong acid such as HCl is added, more hydronium ions enter the solution. These hydronium ions react with the acetate ions to form acetic acid molecules, thus:

$$C_2H_3O_2^- + H_3O^+ \rightarrow HC_2H_3O_2 + H_2O.$$

If not all of the acetate ions are used up, the acetic acid concentration is increased as much as the acetate ion concentration is decreased.

Such changes as are described above are changes in the ratio $\dfrac{[C_2H_3O_2^-]}{[HC_2H_3O_2]}$ which appears in the ionization constant equation, usually resulting in small changes in pH. This can be shown easily by a sample calculation.

**Example.** If 2 ml of 1.0 N solution of HCl is added to 100 ml of a solution that is 0.2 N in $NaC_2H_3O_2$ and 0.2 N in $HC_2H_3O_2$, what change in pH will occur? Assume 100 ml is the final volume.

Step 1. The pH before the addition of the acid must be found by substituting all known values in the ionization constant equation for acetic acid,

Equation (9-12). Solving for the hydronium ion concentration and then the pH, using Equation (9-7), gives the initial pH.

$$1.8 \times 10^{-5} = \frac{[H_3O^+]0.20}{0.20}.$$
$$[H_3O^+] = 1.8 \times 10^{-5}.$$
$$pH = \log \frac{1}{1.8 \times 10^{-5}} = \log 0.555 \times 10^5$$
$$= \log 5.55 \times 10^4 = 4.74, \text{ the initial pH.}$$

Step 2. Find the pH after the acid is added. This is done in several steps. First find the amount of the acetate ion in the 100 ml of buffer that was changed to acetic acid. Assume (although this is not absolutely true) that all the acid added as HCl converts an equivalent quantity of acetate ions to acetic acid molecules. The amount of the acetate converted is found by applying Equation (7-3).

$$2.0 \times 1.0 = V_2 \times 0.20.$$

Here 2.0 is the volume of HCl solution added, 1.0 is the normality of this solution, $V_2$ is the volume of 0.2 N acetate solution converted, and 0.20 is the normality of the original acetate solution. Solving for $V_2$:

$$V_2 = \frac{2.0 \times 1.0}{0.20} = 10.$$

10 ml of the 0.20 N acetate was converted to acetic acid by the HCl. This is one-tenth of the amount that was in the original 100 ml. Therefore the molarity of the acetate left is only nine-tenths its initial molarity.

$$0.20 \times \tfrac{9}{10} = 0.18 \text{ M.}$$

This is the molarity of the remaining acetate in the buffer solution.

The acetic acid concentration is increased proportionately to eleven-tenths its initial concentration.

$$0.20 \times \tfrac{11}{10} = 0.22 \text{ M.}$$

This is the molarity of the acetic acid in the buffer solution.

Substituting these values in the equation for the ionization constant for acetic acid, Equation (9-12), we get:

$$1.8 \times 10^{-5} = \frac{[H_3O^+]0.18}{0.22}.$$
$$[H_3O^+] = \frac{1.8 \times 10^{-5} \times 0.22}{0.18} = 2.2 \times 10^{-5}.$$

The pH is found from this by using Equation (9-7).

$$pH = \log \frac{1}{2.2 \times 10^{-5}} = \log 0.455 \times 10^5 = \log 4.55 \times 10^4 = 4.66.$$

Step 3.  Find the change in pH by taking the difference in pH before and after the addition of acid.

$$4.74 - 4.66 = 0.08 \text{ pH units change.}$$

This is a very small change in pH with the addition of an appreciable quantity of strong acid.  Addition of strong base changes the pH in an exactly similar manner, except that the pH becomes higher.

**pH of a Solution of a Salt of a Weak Acid and a Strong Base.**  The solution of a salt of a weak acid and a strong base is the same as a solution in which chemically equivalent quantities of the acid and base have been added to water.  In this type of solution the hydroxide ions tend to acquire hydronium ions to form slightly ionized water molecules.  At the same time the negative ions of the salt tend to acquire hydronium ions which form the slightly ionized, weak acid.  In a solution of a salt of acetic acid, for example, the following reactions would be in competition:

$$H_3O^+ + OH^- \rightleftharpoons 2H_2O.$$
$$H_3O^+ + C_2H_3O_2^- \rightleftharpoons HC_2H_3O_2 + H_2O.$$

In all solutions in which two such equilibria are both established in the same vessel, the $[H_3O^+]$ is always the same value in any equations involving either equilibrium.  Thus in Equation (9–6):

$$[H_3O^+] = \frac{K_w}{[OH^-]}$$

but from Equation (9–12):

$$[H_3O^+] = \frac{K_A[HC_2H_3O_2]}{[C_2H_3O_2^-]}.$$

Since $[H_3O^+]$ can have but one value in the same beaker, the following equation would be true:

$$\frac{K_w}{[OH^-]} = \frac{K_A[HC_2H_3O_2]}{[C_2H_3O_2^-]}. \tag{9–14}$$

But if we put sodium acetate into water, the only $HC_2H_3O_2$ molecules in the solution will come from the following reaction:

$$C_2H_3O_2^- + H_2O \rightarrow HC_2H_3O_2 + OH^-.$$

From this equation it can be seen that there will be as many acetic acid molecules as hydroxide ions in such a solution.  Substituting $[OH^-]$ for $[HC_2H_3O_2]$ in Equation (9–14), we get:

$$\frac{K_w}{[OH^-]} = \frac{K_A[OH^-]}{[C_2H_3O_2^-]}$$

where $K_w$ is the ion product constant for water and $K_A$ is the ionization constant for the weak acid, in this case acetic acid. Solving for $[OH^-]$:

$$[OH^-]^2 = \frac{K_w[C_2H_3O_2^-]}{K_A}.$$

$$OH^- = \sqrt{\frac{K_w[C_2H_3O_2^-]}{K_A}}. \qquad (9\text{--}15)$$

This is a general equation where the concentration of any anion (negative ion) may be substituted for $[C_2H_3O_2^-]$. For practical purposes the amount of negative ion changed to the acid by reaction with water is usually negligible. Therefore the $[C_2H_3O_2^-]$ in solution is assumed to be the molar concentration calculated from the amount of salt added to the solution.

**Example.** Find the pH of a solution of 0.20 N sodium acetate. Disregard the change of acetate ions to acetic acid molecules.

Step 1. Solve for the $[OH^-]$ after substituting in Equation (9–15).

$$[OH^-] = \sqrt{\frac{10^{-14} \times 0.20}{1.8 \times 10^{-5}}}$$

$$= \sqrt{\frac{2 \times 10^{-15}}{1.8 \times 10^{-5}}}$$

$$= \sqrt{1.11 \times 10^{-10}}$$

$$= 1.05 \times 10^{-5}.$$

Step 2. Solve for the pOH of the solution, using Equation (9–8).

$$pOH = \log \frac{1}{1.05 \times 10^{-5}} = \log 0.95 \times 10^5 = \log 9.5 \times 10^4 = 4.98.$$

Step 3. Calculate the pH, using Equation (9–9).

$$pH = 14 - 4.98 = 9.02.$$

This is also the pH at the equivalence point during a titration of acetic acid with sodium hydroxide.

**pH of a Solution of a Salt of a Weak Base and a Strong Acid.** In the solution of the salt of a weak base and a strong acid, the positive ions of the salt compete with the hydronium ions of the water for hydroxide ions in the solution. The equations for the reactions, where $NH_4Cl$ is taken as an example, are:

$$NH_4^+ + OH^- \rightleftharpoons NH_4OH$$

and:

$$H_3O^+ + OH^- \rightleftharpoons H_2O.$$

Slightly ionized substances are formed in both reactions. With exactly the same reasoning as was used for finding the $[OH^-]$ of a sodium acetate solution, the $[H_3O^+]$ for an ammonium chloride solution can be found thus:

$$[H_3O^+] = \sqrt{\frac{K_w[NH_4^+]}{K_B}}. \qquad (9\text{--}16)$$

This is a general equation where the concentration of cations (positive ions) of a salt of any weak base may be substituted for the $[NH_4^+]$. $K_w$ is the ion product constant for water, and $K_B$ is the ionization constant for a weak base.

**Example.** Calculate the pH of a 0.20 N solution of hydrazine hydrochloride. $K_B$ for hydrazine is $3 \times 10^{-6}$.

Step 1. Substitute all values known in Equation (9–16).

$$\begin{aligned}
[H_3O^+] &= \sqrt{\frac{10^{-14} \times 0.20}{3 \times 10^{-6}}} \\
&= \sqrt{\frac{2 \times 10^{-15}}{3 \times 10^{-6}}} \\
&= \sqrt{0.667 \times 10^{-9}} \\
&= \sqrt{6.67 \times 10^{-10}} \\
&= 2.6 \times 10^{-5}.
\end{aligned}$$

Step 2. Calculate the pH, using Equation (9–7).

$$pH = \log \frac{1}{2.6 \times 10^{-5}} = \log 0.385 \times 10^5 = \log 3.85 \times 10^4 = 4.59.$$

This is the pH at the equivalence point in titrating hydrazine with hydrochloric acid.

**pH of the Salt of a Weak Base and a Weak Acid.** Using reasoning similar to that used for deriving Equation (9–15), the following equation can be obtained. It, like Equations (9–15) and (9–16), is an approximation that is very close to the exact value.

$$[H_3O^+] = \sqrt{\frac{K_A K_w}{K_B}}. \qquad (9\text{--}17)$$

$K_A$ is the ionization constant for a weak acid, $K_B$ is the ionization constant for a weak base, and $K_w$ is the ion product constant for water.

**Example 1.** Calculate the pH of a 0.10 N solution of $NH_4C_2H_3O_2$.

Step 1. Substitute all known values in Equation (9–17). $K_A$ for acetic acid is $1.8 \times 10^{-5}$, $K_B$ for $NH_4OH$ is $1.8 \times 10^{-5}$, and $K_w$ is $1 \times 10^{-14}$.

$$[H_3O^+] = \sqrt{\frac{1.8 \times 10^{-5} \times 1 \times 10^{-14}}{1.8 \times 10^{-5}}}.$$

Step 2. Solve for $[H_3O^+]$.

$$[H_3O^+] = \sqrt{1 \times 10^{-14}} = 1 \times 10^{-7}.$$

Step 3. Calculate the pH of the solution, using Equation (9-7).

$$pH = \log \frac{1}{1 \times 10^{-7}} = \log 10^7 = 7.$$

This is the pH at the equivalence point.

**Example 2.** What is the pH at the equivalence point during the titration of hydrazine with acetic acid? $K_A$ for acetic acid = $1.8 \times 10^{-5}$, $K_B$ for hydrazine = $3 \times 10^{-6}$.

Step 1. Substitute known values in Equation (9-17) and solve for the $[H_3O^+]$.

$$\begin{aligned} [H_3O^+] &= \sqrt{\frac{1.8 \times 10^{-5} \times 1 \times 10^{-14}}{3 \times 10^{-6}}} \\ &= \sqrt{6 \times 10^{-14}} \\ &= 2.45 \times 10^{-7}. \end{aligned}$$

Step 2. Calculate the pH, using Equation (9-7).

$$pH = \log \frac{1}{2.45 \times 10^{-7}} = \log 0.408 \times 10^7 = \log 4.08 \times 10^6 = 6.61.$$

This is the pH of a solution of a salt of hydrazine with acetic acid.

A series of calculations or measurements of pH, throughout the complete titration of a weak acid with a weak base, would show that the point of inflection at the equivalence point on the titration curve is not well defined. Weak acids are therefore titrated against strong bases, and weak bases against strong acids. Calculations such as the ones above are useful in determining the pH of buffer solutions containing such salts.

**Polyprotic Acids and Their Salts.** Such acids as $H_2S$, $H_2SO_3$, $H_2CO_3$, and $H_3PO_4$ are able to ionize, giving up two or more hydronium ions per mole of acid. These acids and others like them are polyprotic acids, and they play an important role in analytical chemistry. Using $H_2CO_3$ as a typical polyprotic acid, it can be seen that ionization takes place in two steps.

Step 1. $\qquad H_2CO_3 + H_2O \rightleftharpoons H_3O^+ + HCO_3^-.$

The ionization constant for this first step is designated as $K_1$ and is:

$$K_1 = \frac{[H_3O^+][HCO_3^-]}{[H_2CO_3]} \quad (9\text{--}18)$$

$$= 3.1 \times 10^{-7}.$$

Step 2.        $HCO_3^- + H_2O \rightleftharpoons H_3O^+ + CO_3^{-2}.$

The ionization constant for this step is designated as $K_2$ and is:

$$K_2 = \frac{[H_3O^+][CO_3^{-2}]}{[HCO_3^-]} \quad (9\text{--}19)$$

$$= 4.2 \times 10^{-11}.$$

The values for $K_1$ and $K_2$, $3.1 \times 10^{-7}$ and $4.2 \times 10^{-11}$ respectively, are taken from the table in Appendix IV.

**Titration Curve of a Polyprotic Acid.** A curve, such as in Fig. 18, is obtained if the pH is plotted against the volume of base during the titration of carbonic acid with a strong base such as sodium hydroxide. This curve shows two points of inflection, one at each equivalence

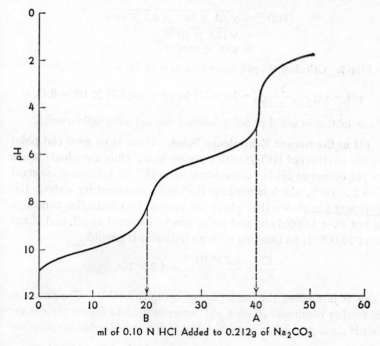

Fig. 18. Titration Curve: Diequivalent Base — Strong Acid. At $B$, the $CO_3^{-2}$ has been converted to $HCO_3^-$. At $A$, the $HCO_3^-$ has been converted to $H_2CO_3$.

point. Note that the first equivalence point at $A$ has a more marked inflection than the second equivalence point at $B$. The solubility of carbonic acid is too small to permit titrating it directly. The curve shown is the reverse, the titration of sodium carbonate with a strong acid.

**pH at the Equivalence Point for Polyprotic Acids.** The pH at the first equivalence point for carbonic acid is the same thing as the pH of a sodium bicarbonate solution. A rather involved derivation gives an approximate hydronium ion concentration of such a solution.

$$[H_3O^+] = \sqrt{K_1 K_2}, \tag{9-20}$$

where $K_1$ and $K_2$ are the two ionization constants for $H_2CO_3$.

**Example.** Calculate the pH of a sodium bicarbonate solution. All but very dilute solutions will have the same pH.

Step 1. Substitute known values in Equation (9-20) and solve for the hydronium ion concentration.

$$
\begin{aligned}
[H_3O^+] &= \sqrt{3.1 \times 10^{-7} \times 4.2 \times 10^{-11}} \\
&= \sqrt{13.0 \times 10^{-18}} \\
&= 3.61 \times 10^{-9}.
\end{aligned}
$$

Step 2. Calculate the pH, using Equation (9-7).

$$pH = \log \frac{1}{3.61 \times 10^{-9}} = \log 0.277 \times 10^9 = \log 2.77 \times 10^8 = 8.44.$$

Phenolphthalein would probably indicate this end point satisfactorily.

**pH at the Second Equivalence Point.** There is no good end point in the titration of $HCO_3^-$ with a strong base. Only a gradual change in pH occurs as $HCO_3^-$ is too weak an acid. Its ionization constant is $4.2 \times 10^{-11}$, which is too near that of the constant for water. Experiment has shown that where the ratio of two ionization constants is not over 1,000:1, no end point can be detected at all, and if not over 10,000:1, no titration with an indicator is possible.

$$\frac{K_2}{K_w} = \frac{4.2 \times 10^{-11}}{1 \times 10^{-14}} = 4.2 \times 10^3.$$

This is just below the borderline of being titratable. The situation is further confirmed when a pH meter is used to follow the change in pH during the addition of NaOH solution to a bicarbonate solution.

**Example.** Calculate the pH of a solution obtained by adding 1.0 ml of a 1.0 M NaOH solution to 100 ml of a 0.10 M NaHCO$_3$ solution. Assume that the volume is 100 ml even after the 1 ml of NaOH is added.

Step 1. Substitute the known value of $K_2$ in the second ionization constant equation for carbonic acid, Equation (9–19).

$$4.2 \times 10^{-11} = \frac{[H_3O^+][CO_3^{-2}]}{[HCO_3^-]}.$$

Step 2. Find the values of $[CO_3^{-2}]$ and $[HCO_3^-]$ and substitute these also in Equation (9–19).

In the original 100 ml (0.1 liter) there was 0.01 mole of $HCO_3^-$. In 1.0 ml of 1.0 M $OH^-$ there is $1 \times \frac{1}{1000} = 0.001$ mole of $OH^-$. If 0.001 mole of $OH^-$ reacts with an equal number of moles of $HCO_3^-$ thus:

$$HCO_3^- + OH^- \rightarrow CO_3^{-2} + H_2O$$

then there would be left in solution $0.01 - 0.001 = 0.009$ mole of $HCO_3^-$ in 100 ml, which would, if we assume no volume change, leave the solution 0.09 molar in bicarbonate. If we consider the volume change from 100 to 101 ml, then the new molarity would be:

$$\frac{0.09 \times 100}{101} = 0.0891 \text{ M},$$

a negligible difference from 0.09. Similarly the concentration of $CO_3^{-2}$ can be shown to be nearly 0.01 M after the $OH^-$ is added. This assumes that all $OH^-$ is converted to $CO_3^{-2}$. Substituting these values in Equation (9–19) we get:

$$4.2 \times 10^{-11} = \frac{[H_3O^+]0.01}{0.09}.$$

Step 3. Solve for the $[H_3O^+]$.

$$[H_3O^+] = \frac{4.2 \times 10^{-11} \times 0.09}{0.01} = 3.78 \times 10^{-10}.$$

Step 4. Calculate the pH, using Equation (9–7).

$$pH = \log \frac{1}{3.78 \times 10^{-10}} = \log 0.265 \times 10^{10} = \log 2.65 \times 10^9 = 9.42.$$

Successive additions of $OH^-$ solution should cause a more rapid increase in pH as the equivalence point is neared, but because $K_2$, for carbonic acid, is so near $K_w$ in value, instead of a sharp change in direction of the titration curve at the equivalence point, one finds that addition of NaOH solution is like adding the $OH^-$ to a weak solution of sodium hydroxide. Thus, to calculate the pH of solutions of $HCO_3^-$ with $CO_3^{-2}$, except when $[HCO_3^-]$ exceeds $[CO_3^{-2}]$, both the $K_2$ for carbonic acid and $K_w$ need to be considered. Practical problems involving carbonate and strongly basic solutions rarely occur in analytical chemistry. If they should arise, a good physical chemistry textbook should be consulted.

**pH of a Solution of Carbonic Acid.** Bicarbonate ions can be titrated with a strong acid with the following reaction occurring:

$$HCO_3^- + H_3O^+ \rightarrow H_2CO_3 + H_2O.$$

$K_1$ for carbonic acid is $3.1 \times 10^{-7}$. The $[H_3O^+]$ of the solution in which $H_2CO_3$ is formed is dependent upon the solubility of carbonic acid, which, in a saturated solution at room pressure and temperature, is about 0.05 M.

The titration is begun by adding acid to $HCO_3^-$, a buffer. Only a slight change in pH occurs until the $[HCO_3^-]$ becomes very small. From the point where the $[HCO_3^-]$ is $10^{-2}$, with a pH of 5.8, to where the $[HCO_3^-]$ is $10^{-5}$, at a pH of 1.8, a virtually completed reaction, the pH changes very quickly with only a small volume of acid solution added. This gives a good titratable end point.

**Example.** Calculate the pH of a solution of $NaHCO_3$ that is titrated with HCl until the concentration of $HCO_3^-$ is $10^{-4}$ molar. This is practically all gone. Assume the solution to be saturated with $H_2CO_3$, 0.05 M.

Step 1. Substitute known values in the equation for $K_1$ for carbonic acid, Equation (9–18), and solve for the $[H_3O^+]$.

$$3.1 \times 10^{-7} = \frac{[H_3O^+]10^{-4}}{5 \times 10^{-2}}.$$

$$[H_3O^+] = \frac{3.1 \times 10^{-7} \times 5 \times 10^{-2}}{10^{-4}} = 15.5 \times 10^{-5} = 1.55 \times 10^{-4}.$$

Step 2. Calculate the pH, using Equation (9–7).

$$pH = \log \frac{1}{1.55 \times 10^{-4}} = \log 0.645 \times 10^4 = \log 6.45 \times 10^3 = 3.81.$$

## Acid-Base Indicators

Acid-base or neutralization indicators are colored materials, often dyes, which are one color in one pH range and another color, or colorless, in a different pH range. All acid-base indicators are either weak acids or weak bases with a characteristic ionization constant value. Therefore they show a color change at a pH which is characteristic for each. It is clear that changes in color are due to changes from ions to molecules, or the reverse.

**General Indicator Reactions.** For an acid type of indicator the following equation represents the chemical change that causes the color change:

$$\underset{\text{Color } A}{HInd} + H_2O \rightleftharpoons H_3O^+ + \underset{\text{Color } B}{Ind^-}. \qquad (9\text{–}21)$$

HInd represents the molecular form as an acid with color $A$. Ind$^-$ represents the ion derived from the acid, the ion having a color $B$.

For a base type of indicator:

$$\text{IndOH} \underset{\text{Color } A}{\rightleftharpoons} \underset{\text{Color } B}{\text{Ind}^+} + \text{OH}^-. \qquad (9\text{--}22)$$

IndOH represents the molecular form of the base indicator. Ind$^+$ represents the ion derived from the base.

For either acid or base indicators, colors $A$ and $B$ may be two different colors, or one may be colorless.

**Ionization Constants for Indicators.** For each reversible reaction such as is indicated above, an ionization constant, $K_{Ind}$, can be found. For an acid indicator, as an example:

$$K_{Ind} = \frac{[\text{H}_3\text{O}^+][\text{Ind}^-]}{[\text{HInd}]}. \qquad (9\text{--}23)$$

The numerical value of $K_{Ind}$ for either an acid or a base is seldom applied as such, even though its magnitude determines the pH at which a color change will occur.

**pH of Indicator Color Change.** Rearranging Equation (9–23) thus:

$$[\text{H}_3\text{O}^+] = K_{Ind} \frac{[\text{HInd}]}{[\text{Ind}^-]}$$

it becomes clear that where $[\text{HInd}] = [\text{Ind}^-]$, the hydronium ion concentration becomes equal to the numerical value of $K_{Ind}$. At this point half the indicator is in the ionic state and the other half is in the molecular state. The indicator is changing color at the fastest rate during the titration, per unit of volume of reagent being added, and its color will be neither $A$ nor $B$, but half-way between. In addition:

$$\text{pH} = \text{p}K_{Ind}.$$

This is true because at this point $[\text{H}_3\text{O}^+] = K_{Ind}$ and

$$\log \frac{1}{[\text{H}_3\text{O}^+]} = \log \frac{1}{K_{Ind}}.$$

**Range of Color Change of Indicators.** Along with properties of indicators one generally finds listed a range of pH through which the indicator changes color. The pH of the middle of the range listed is approximately equal to the p$K$ of the indicator.

From the rearrangement of Equation (9–23) to:

$$[H_3O^+] = K_{Ind} \frac{[HInd]}{[Ind^-]}$$

it is obvious that increasing the value of the ratio $\frac{[HInd]}{[Ind^-]}$ from 1 to 10 increases the pH one unit. Changing this same ratio from 1 to 0.1 decreases the pH one unit. Experiment has shown that when the intensity of one color of the indicator reaches about 10% of that of the other color, a change in color is detectable. Thus most indicators have a range of visible change of about 2 pH units, from one above to one below the point of equal concentrations of both colors of the indicator.

**Concentration of Indicator.** The concentration of the indicator should be as low as is consistent with a good visible color change. The indicator uses reagent while undergoing change of form and color. The error introduced into a titration by such a reaction can usually be neglected. If the error might be appreciable, however, a blank should be run with the proper quantity of indicator to be used.

**Effect of Temperature.** Temperature affects the value of $K_w$ and also the $K_{Ind}$ for indicators. The indicator should be calibrated if it is to be used at other than near-room temperature.

TABLE 6

SOME ACID-BASE INDICATORS

| INDICATOR | ACID COLOR | ALKALINE COLOR | pH RANGE OF CHANGE |
|---|---|---|---|
| Picric acid | Colorless | Yellow | 0.1– 0.8 |
| Thymol blue | Red | Yellow | 1.2– 2.8 |
| 2,6-Dinitrophenol | Colorless | Yellow | 2.0– 4.0 |
| Congo red | Blue | Red | 3.0– 5.0 |
| Methyl orange | Red | Yellow | 3.2– 4.4 |
| Bromcresol green | Yellow | Blue | 3.8– 5.4 |
| Methyl red | Red | Yellow | 4.2– 6.2 |
| Methyl purple | Purple | Green | 4.8– 5.4 |
| Bromthymol blue | Yellow | Blue | 6.0– 7.6 |
| Litmus | Red | Blue | 4.5– 8.3 |
| Phenol red | Yellow | Red | 6.4– 8.2 |
| Phenolphthalein | Colorless | Red | 8.3–10.0 |
| Thymolphthalein | Colorless | Blue | 9.3–10.5 |
| Alizarin yellow | Yellow | Violet | 10.1–12.0 |
| 2,4,6-Trinitrotoluene | Colorless | Orange | 12.0–14.0 |

**Effect of Solvent.** Solvents other than water may cause alteration in the value of $K_{Ind}$. If nonaqueous solvents are involved, the indicator should be calibrated for the conditions of the analysis.

**Mixed Indicators.** A mixed indicator is a solution containing an indicator and either another indicator or an inert dyestuff.

The indicator, sensitive to changes in pH, will change color when it changes from acid to base form. This change in color can be made easier to see and more spectacular over a narrower range of pH if the indicator and background colors are complementary at a certain concentration ratio of the two forms of indicator. The complementary colors give a light gray or nearly colorless appearance over only a few tenths of a pH range. Sometimes a dye, insensitive to pH change, is mixed with an indicator to give a background color that is complementary to the indicator at a certain pH, or else the background color accentuates a certain color of the indicator at a definite pH.

**Example 1.** When phenolphthalein, which is colorless in acid and red in alkaline form, is mixed with methylene green, greenish blue in any pH, there is a color change from green, in acid, to pale blue at pH 8.8, and violet at pH 9.

**Example 2.** Methyl purple contains methyl red, which is red below pH 4.2 and yellow above pH 6.2. An inert blue dye is added to the methyl red. The blue dye with the red of the indicator gives a purple color below pH 4.8. The blue dye with the yellow of the indicator gives a green above pH 5.4. Between pH 4.8 and 5.4 the red-orange of methyl red and the blue are complementary, giving a light gray color over a very short range of pH. Care must be exercised, in titrating, not to allow this gray color to pass unobserved.

**Choosing an Indicator.** Three factors must be considered in choosing an indicator:

1. pH at the equivalence point.

2. pH range of the indicator.

3. Direction of titration, whether approaching the equivalence point from the acid side or the alkaline side.

STRONG ACID, STRONG BASE TITRATIONS. The pH at the equivalence point is 7, but only a very small amount of reagent causes a change in pH from about 3 to 10. See Fig. 15. From Table 6, any indicator can be chosen between methyl orange, 3.2–4.4, and phenolphthalein, 8.3–10.0. Dissolved carbon dioxide acts as an acid on phenolphthalein. Therefore, if phenolphthalein is used as an indicator, $CO_2$ should be absent during a titration of a strong base with a strong acid. Indicators with pH ranges nearer 7 can be used without any concern for the direction of titration. Titrating an acid with a base, using methyl orange, gives an end point on the acid side of the range of pH for methyl orange. Titrating a base with an acid gives an end point on the alkaline side of the range of pH for methyl orange. This difference is usually negligible.

STRONG ACID, WEAK BASE TITRATIONS. These have equivalence points at a pH less than 7. Indicators such as methyl orange should be considered. During titration a color change can be detected in the indicator when about one-tenth of it has been changed from one form to another. Therefore the indicator chosen, when titrating acid with base, should have a range of pH from a few tenths of a unit below the equivalence point to a higher pH. Conversely, when titrating base with acid, the best indicator has a pH range from a few tenths of a pH unit above the equivalence point to a lower pH.

WEAK ACID, STRONG BASE TITRATIONS. These have equivalence points at a pH greater than 7. For these titrations, indicators such as phenolphthalein should be considered. During a titration the indicator will show a visible change of color when one-tenth of it has changed from one form to the other. Therefore, in titrating a weak acid with a strong base, the best indicator has a pH range from a few tenths of a pH unit below the equivalence point to above the equivalence point. Titrating from the alkaline side with acid, the indicator should have a range from a few tenths of a pH unit above the equivalence point to below the equivalence point. Generally, the direction of titration makes very little difference in the choice of indicator except in rather dilute solutions such as 0.01 N or less.

## Review Questions and Problems

1. Define the terms *acid*, *base*, and *neutralization* according to both the Lewis electron pair concept and the Brønsted-Lowry concept.
2. How does a strong acid or base differ from a weak acid or base?
3. Calculate the pH of:
   a. A 0.2 N solution of NaOH.
   b. A solution of 50 ml of 0.2 N NaOH to which 25 ml of 0.2 N HCl has been added. Total volume is 75 ml.
   c. The same solution after 40 ml of 0.2 N HCl has been added, instead of 25 ml. Total volume is 90 ml.
   d. The same solution after 49 ml of 0.2 N HCl has been added. Consider the total volume to be 100 ml.

e. The same solution after 49.9 ml of 0.2 N HCl has been added. Consider the total volume to be 100 ml.

f. The same solution after 50.1 ml of 0.2 N HCl has been added. Consider the total volume to be 100 ml.

g. Plot the above values on a graph with pH values on the vertical axis and volume of HCl added on the horizontal axis.

4. If 25 ml of 0.09811 N HCl is titrated to an end point with 24.02 ml of NaOH, what is the normality of the solution of base?

5. Find the pH of a 0.01 N solution of lactic acid. $K_A$ for lactic acid is $1.4 \times 10^{-4}$.

6. $K_A$ for hydrofluoric acid, HF, is $1.7 \times 10^{-5}$. Find the pH of a solution that is 0.2 N with respect to NaF and 0.1 N with respect to HF.

7. If a solution is 0.05 N with respect to HF and 0.03 N with respect to NaF, what pH would the solution have?

8. If to 100 ml of the solution in question 7, 1 ml of 1.0 N NaOH were added, what would the pH be?

9. The $K_B$ of aniline is $2.70 \times 10^{-10}$. What is the pH of a 0.1 N solution of aniline hydrochloride?

10. Calculate the pH at the equivalence point during the titration with HCl of:

a. Diethylamine; $K_B$ is $8.92 \times 10^{-4}$.

b. Triethylamine; $K_B$ is $6.53 \times 10^{-4}$.

Assume the solutions are 0.05 N at the equivalence point.

11. What is the pH of a 0.01 N solution of potassium acid phthalate? $K_1 = 1.29 \times 10^{-3}$ and $K_2 = 3.8 \times 10^{-6}$.

12. What conditions of concentration of the chemical forms of an acid-base indicator must exist if the $[H_3O^+] = K_{Ind}$?

13. Explain why the total range of visible change of an indicator is generally about 2 pH units.

14. What are mixed indicators?

15. Give an example of a mixed indicator and explain how it functions to give a color change over a narrow range of pH.

16. In choosing an indicator what three factors should be considered?

17. Under what conditions may the direction of titration, acid to base or vice versa, be of no importance? Under what conditions may it be important enough to be considered?

# 10

# Typical Volumetric Analyses

Volumetric analytical procedures are rapid and are therefore preferable to gravimetric methods. Consequently many standard volumetric procedures have been developed. Those given here were chosen because they illustrate standard operations applicable to many analyses.

## Preparation of a Standard Silver Nitrate Solution

This preparation is an application of operations discussed in Chap. 6. Two different types of procedure are available. Procedure 1 does not take so much time, but an error made in the preparation would not be discovered unless the strength of the solution were tested against a primary standard, as in procedure 2. Procedure 2 is therefore far more reliable than procedure 1.

**Procedure 1.** This method makes use of a primary standard material as the active reagent in a standard solution.

1. Weigh to 0.1 mg about 17 g of primary standard silver nitrate which has been dried at 140° C for one hour. Reagent grade is usually of sufficient purity for ordinary work.

2. Dissolve the silver nitrate in distilled water in a one liter volumetric flask and dilute to the mark.

3. Calculate the normality of the solution by dividing the weight of silver nitrate in solution by the equivalent weight of silver nitrate thus:

$$\frac{\text{Weight of AgNO}_3}{169.89} = \text{normality.} \qquad (10\text{--}1)$$

**Errors in the Method.** Errors might occur through lack of purity or dryness of the silver nitrate. Carefully prepared silver nitrate is very pure. Errors from weighing should be extremely small.

**Procedure 2.** This method makes use of a primary standard material for checking the strength of the standard solution as discussed in Chap. 7.

1. Dissolve about 17 g of silver nitrate in about a liter of water as in Procedure 1. Neither the weight of silver nitrate nor the volume of solution need be known exactly, but if these two values are known, then the strength of the solution as calculated from them can be checked against primary standard sodium chloride.

2. Weigh to 0.1 mg three 0.2 g–0.25 g samples of primary standard NaCl, previously dried at least one hour at 105° C, in separate 250 ml Erlenmeyer flasks.

3. Dissolve each sample of sodium chloride in about 75 ml of water.

4. Add 1 ml of 5% $K_2CrO_4$ solution to each sample.

5. Titrate the NaCl solutions with the silver nitrate solution to the first perceptible reddish tint of color on the precipitate that persists after 40 seconds of vigorous shaking.

6. Determine the blank. The blank is relatively large but varies somewhat with the volume of the titration. To determine the blank, add about 1 g of chloride-free $CaCO_3$ powder to 100 ml of water in a 250 ml Erlenmeyer flask. To this add 1 ml of 5% $K_2CrO_4$ solution, and then add small parts of a drop of the silver nitrate solution until a definite change in color is visible. The volume of silver nitrate added is the blank. Subtract this volume from that found in step 5. The result is the corrected volume of titration, used in the next step.

7. Calculate the normality of the silver nitrate solution:

$$\text{Normality} = \frac{\text{weight of primary standard} \times \% \text{ purity}}{\text{gme of NaCl} \times \text{volume of tit.} \times 100}. \quad (10\text{--}2)$$

This is also equation (7–1), which see. The volume of titration in this equation is the corrected volume.

8. Average the three values, obtained by the three titrations, in order to find the most probable value for the normality of the silver nitrate solution.

**Example.** Find the normality of a silver nitrate solution if 0.2372 g of 100% pure NaCl was exactly titrated with 36.12 ml. The blank was found to be 0.04 ml.

Step 1. Subtract the blank to find the corrected volume.

$$36.12 - 0.04 = 36.08.$$

Step 2. Substitute in Equation (10–2) and solve for N. The gme of NaCl is 0.05845.

$$N = \frac{0.2372 \times 100}{0.05845 \times 36.08 \times 100} = 0.1125.$$

**Errors in the Method.** Small errors are possible even though this is a very precise procedure.

THE BLANK. An excess of silver ions is needed at the end point to produce some visible colored material. The volume of solution at the end point varies, resulting in varying concentrations of $CrO_4^{-2}$. Errors caused by these two factors can be reduced by determining and applying a blank.

POSSIBLE FALSE END POINT. Adsorption of the ion being titrated on the precipitate removes some of the ion from solution. Thorough shaking gives adsorbed ions time to diffuse into the solution again where they react with slight excesses of the titrating reagent.

## Analysis of a Soluble Chloride

This analysis applies principles similar to those applied in the gravimetric analysis of a chloride (Chap. 6). In addition, it illustrates the use of a colored precipitate, $Ag_2CrO_4$, as a material that indicates the end point. It is known as the Mohr method.

**Procedure.**

1. Dry the sample of soluble chloride, if it is a solid, for one hour at 105° C. This prepares the material for weighing in a way that is easily reproduced.

2. Weigh three 0.3–0.5 g samples to the nearest 0.1 mg and place each sample in a 250 ml Erlenmeyer flask.

3. Add, to each sample, 75 ml of distilled water and 1 ml of 5% $K_2CrO_4$ solution.

4. Titrate the solution with standard silver nitrate solution until a faint reddish color persists after about one minute of vigorous shaking.

5. Determine the blank and subtract it from the titration volume to get the corrected volume of titration.

6. Calculate the per cent of chloride as follows, using Equation (7–5):

$$\frac{\text{Corrected volume of titration} \times N \times \text{gme of } Cl^- \times 100}{\text{weight of the sample}} = \% \ Cl^-.$$

**Example.** Calculate the per cent of chloride in a sample of salt if 0.3764 g, when dissolved, was found by titration to be equivalent to 28.68 ml of 0.1125 N silver nitrate. The blank is 0.04 ml.

Substitute in Equation (7–5) above and solve for % chloride. The gme of $Cl^-$ is 0.03545.

$$\frac{(28.68 - 0.04) \times 0.1125 \times 0.03545 \times 100}{0.3764} = 38.19\% \text{ Cl}^-.$$

The results of three or more such calculations should be averaged to find the most probable value for the per cent of chloride in the sample.

**Errors in the Method.** Errors due to solubility, coprecipitation, and supersaturation can occur in volumetric precipitation analyses. The solubilities of the precipitates in this analysis result in a fairly large error which can be corrected by means of a blank.

THE BLANK. The blank is the volume of silver nitrate solution needed to give a detectable color after the equivalence point is reached. The indication of the end point depends upon $Ag_2CrO_4$ being more soluble than AgCl. The $Ag_2CrO_4$ must still be insoluble enough so that only a very small volume of silver ion solution is needed to give a precipitate that is visible. The blank may be found experimentally as outlined in the procedure.

*Finding the Blank by Calculation.* The blank may be partially calculated by applying the solubility product principle discussed in Chap. 5. There are three factors involved:

a. The quantity of $Ag^+$ solution needed to increase the silver ion concentration, $[Ag^+]$, from that in saturated silver chloride to that in saturated silver chromate.

b. The quantity of $Ag^+$ used up in precipitating out the $Cl^-$ in a saturated AgCl solution in which the change in concentration of $Ag^+$, calculated above, is made.

c. The quantity of $Ag^+$ needed to produce a precipitate of $Ag_2CrO_4$ large enough to be visible. This cannot be calculated because it varies with the amount of AgCl precipitated. It is generally in the range of 0.03 ml of 0.1 N solution in 100 ml.

The blank is the sum of these three factors, calculated in ml of the standard solution.

*Correction for the Blank.* The blank should be determined for any volumetric analysis where its value is not known to be negligible. The volume of titration less the volume of the blank is the corrected volume. The corrected volume is then used in calculations.

**Example.** What is the per cent chloride in a 0.5070 g sample which required 34.27 ml of 0.100 N $AgNO_3$ solution to titrate to an end point? The blank, found experimentally, is 0.04 ml.

Step 1. Find the corrected volume by subtracting the blank from the titration.

$$34.27 - 0.04 = 34.23 \text{ ml.}$$

Step 2. Calculate the per cent of chloride, using Equation (7–5).

$$\% \, Cl^- = \frac{34.23 \times 0.100 \times 0.03545 \times 100}{0.5070}$$
$$= 23.93\%.$$

COPRECIPITATION ERRORS. Precipitation of ions other than chloride can occur if ions of a slightly soluble salt are mixed with the chloride. In such a case the chloride would have to be separated from the possible contaminant before titration. Bromides, iodides, thiocyanates, cyanides, and other ions that form insoluble silver salts can cause errors by simultaneous precipitation with chloride.

Coprecipitation by adsorption of soluble ions is not a serious problem with silver precipitates. Silver and chloride ions are adsorbed most strongly, since they are common to the precipitate. But if chloride or silver ions are adsorbed on the first particles of precipitate to form, the adsorbed ions slowly diffuse into the solution as the end point is neared. This slow diffusion from within clumps of crystals takes time. Therefore the solution should be shaken thoroughly for thirty to sixty seconds after the indicator changes, to avoid a false end point. Silver ion diffuses more slowly than chloride.

Supersaturation of silver precipitates is seldom a problem. Silver precipitates are usually colloidal when first formed, but they coagulate readily when the end point is neared.

## Analysis of a Silver Alloy

In addition to the principles applied in the analysis of a chloride, the end point is indicated by formation of a soluble, colored complex ion, $FeCNS^{+2}$, rather than by an insoluble colored substance.

**Preparation and Standardization of Solutions.** (See also Chap. 7.)

1. Prepare a solution of thiocyanate by dissolving about 9.7 g of KCNS in water and diluting to 1 liter.

2. Standardize the thiocyanate solution, using pure silver as the primary standard.

a. Weigh three samples of pure silver of about 0.4 g size in 250 ml Erlenmeyer flasks.

b. Dissolve the silver by warming it with 10 to 15 ml of 1:1 nitric acid.

c. Boil out the oxides of nitrogen from the solution until no more brown fumes are visible.

d. Dilute to about 75 ml.

e. Add 2 ml of saturated ferric alum solution as an indicator.

f. Titrate with the thiocyanate solution to the first permanent pink color that persists after at least one minute of vigorous shaking.

g. Calculate the normality of the thiocyanate solution, using Equation (10–2) but with the gme of Ag substituted for that of chloride.

**Example.** What is the normality of a solution of thiocyanate if 42.77 ml of the solution was used in titrating 0.4529 g of 100% pure silver?

$$N = \frac{0.4529 \times 100}{0.10788 \times 42.77 \times 100} = 0.09816.$$

h. Average the results of three such calculations to find the most probable normality of the solution.

3. Prepare a solution of ferric alum indicator by making a saturated solution of ferric alum acid with nitric acid to prevent the ferric ion from hydrolyzing. Add nitric acid until the brown color is reduced to a light yellow.

**Analysis of a Sample.** The analysis is identical with the standardization procedure.

1. Weigh three samples of silver alloy of such size that they require at least 25 ml of the standard thiocyanate solution for the titration.

2. Dissolve the samples in 15–20 ml of 1:1 nitric acid solution.

3. Boil out the oxides of nitrogen until the vapor above the solution is colorless.

4. Dilute to about 75 ml.

5. Add 2 ml of ferric alum indicator solution.

6. Titrate as in step 2f under standardization of thiocyanate solution.

7. Calculate the per cent of silver, using Equation (7–5) with the gme of Ag in place of the gme of chloride.

**Example.** If a 3.1719 g sample of silver alloy, when dissolved, was titrated to an end point with 38.37 ml of 0.09816 N potassium thiocyanate solution, what is the per cent of silver in the alloy?

Substituting in Equation (7–5):

$$\% \text{ Ag} = \frac{38.37 \times 0.09816 \times 0.10788 \times 100}{3.1719} = 12.81\%.$$

8. Average the results of three samples to find the most probable per cent of silver in the alloy.

The equations for reactions used during the analysis are:

1. Dissolving the silver contained in the sample, using nitric acid.

$$3Ag + 4H^+ + NO_3^- \rightarrow 3Ag^+ + NO + 2H_2O.$$

2. Reaction during the titration with thiocyanate in which $Ag^+$ is precipitated.

$$Ag^+ + CNS^- \rightarrow AgCNS.$$

3. Reaction of the indicator, $Fe^{+3}$, to give a colored complex substance.

$$Fe^{+3} + CNS^- \rightarrow FeCNS^{+2}.$$

**Errors in the Method.** The errors in this analysis parallel those in the chloride analysis. The formation of a soluble, slightly colored complex ion is used to indicate the end point. Calculation of the blank involves not only solubility products but the instability constant of the $FeCNS^{+2}$. Such calculations, however, are not within the scope of this book. The blank can be measured experimentally but is so small that it is usually not applied.

If an attempt is made to determine chloride by adding an excess of $Ag^+$ and then titrating the excess of $Ag^+$ with standard $CNS^-$ solution, the AgCNS formed is less soluble than the AgCl. Therefore, during the titration, AgCl dissolves to give more $Ag^+$ for the $CNS^-$ to precipitate. This makes large errors that can be reduced by adding nitrobenzene to coat the precipitated AgCl and reduce the rate at which the AgCl dissolves.

## Other Methods of Detecting End Points for Precipitation Reactions

Several methods, other than the use of a colored precipitate or a colored complex ion, are available for indicating the end point.

**The Clear Point Method.** The end point can be found by carefully observing the point at which all colloidal particles flocculate and where the solution above the precipitate becomes clear and free of all colloidal particles. As precipitates form they adsorb from the solution whatever ion is common to the precipitate more strongly than they adsorb any other ions. Only one ion common to the precipitate is in excess in the solution at the beginning of the titration. This ion is adsorbed on the small particles of the precipitate, causing them to become charged and to remain suspended. The equilibrium between ions in the solution and ions adsorbed on the precipitated particles is disturbed by the titration. The concentration of the ions in solution that give the charge to the precipitated particles is reduced as the equivalence point is neared. At the equivalence point, ions of opposite charge are in equal abundance. Therefore the two oppositely charged ions are adsorbed at nearly the same rate, leaving the colloidal particles uncharged. The colloidal particles unite with each other to form larger particles which settle, leaving the solution clear. It takes a little time for the adsorbed ions to diffuse to the outside of floccules formed. It is therefore easy to pass the end point.

**The Equal Turbidity Method.** The equivalence point is indicated by removing two small samples of solution from the titration flask and adding a little of a solution of one ion being precipitated to one sample and a little of a solution of the other ion to the other sample. On either side of the equivalence point one sample will become more turbid than the other. At the equivalence point both samples will show an equal amount of turbidity. Carefully standardized test solutions of ions must be added from burets. Great care and patience are required in this method, but it can give very precise results.

**Adsorption Indicators.** Certain organic acids such as fluorescein, or organic bases such as the rhodamines, produce ions in solution of one color or nearly no color. When these ions are adsorbed on a precipitate of opposite charge, the ion of the acid or base changes color.

For example, if chloride ions are being titrated with silver ions, the precipitate first formed will adsorb chloride ions and the AgCl particles will acquire a negative charge. Such particles will not adsorb the fluorescein ion, which is also negatively charged. At the equivalence point the chloride and silver ions are adsorbed nearly equally, and a very slight excess of silver ion changes the charge on the precipitated particles to positive. The positively charged particles attract and adsorb the negative fluorescein ions and the latter become pink in color, indicating that the end point has been passed. Similarly, positively charged ions can be adsorbed by a negatively charged particle, the change in color, on being adsorbed, indicating that an equivalence point has been passed.

**Instrumental Methods.** Several instrumental methods of locating end points are available, but only two are mentioned here.

POTENTIOMETRIC. A silver electrode in a solution of silver ions produces a single electrode potential against a standard electrode that is measurable with a potentiometer. As the titration of $Ag^+$ with $Cl^-$ proceeds, the potential on the silver electrode will vary so that if a plot of $Ag^+$ concentration against the electrode potential is made, there will be a sharp point of inflection at the equivalence point. The curve resembles any oxidation-reduction titration curve or acid-base titration curve.   Fig. 14, p. 90, shows such a curve. Other electrodes for other reactions can be applied similarly.

CONDUCTOMETRIC.   The conductance of a solution during certain titration reactions, such as the chloride-silver ion titration, reaches a minimum at the equivalence point.   This minimum point on a graph indicates the volume of titration at the equivalence point.

### Preparation of a Standard HCl Solution

Concentrated HCl which is about 12 N is diluted to approximately 0.1 N with boiled, cooled, carbon dioxide free, distilled water.   The solution is then standardized against primary standard $Na_2CO_3$.   If constant boiling HCl solution is available, it may be measured out and diluted accurately, in which case standardization, although advisable, is not necessary.

Constant boiling HCl is prepared by diluting the best available commercial grade of concentrated HCl to a density of 1.10 and distilling the solution until the boiling point becomes constant.   After the first 60–70% is discarded, the distillate is collected until either sufficient solution is obtained or the residue is nearly gone.   The barometer is read, and a table in any chemical handbook is consulted for the composition of the distilled acid.   The concentrations given in the tables are remarkably reliable.   At 750 mm pressure the composition is about 20.20% HCl, and 18.015 g of the solution can be weighed out and diluted to produce one liter of 0.100 N HCl. The constant boiling solution is neither hygroscopic nor seriously volatile, and can be weighed in a weighing bottle or small flask.

The following steps can be taken in standardizing any solution of acid against primary standard sodium carbonate.

1. Dry the primary standard sodium carbonate in a weighing bottle for at least one hour at 140° C.

2. Cool the sodium carbonate and weigh out three samples, each about 0.25 g, into 250 ml Erlenmeyer flasks.

3. To each, add 75 ml of boiled, cooled, carbon dioxide free water, and dissolve the sodium carbonate.

4. Add a few drops of methyl orange indicator solution.

5. Titrate with the prepared HCl solution until the first change from a straw color to pink is detectable.   If preferred, a mixed indicator, methyl orange-indigo carmine may be used instead of methyl orange.   This produces a gray color that indicates the end point.

6. Calculate the normality, as found from the three titrations, and

average the three values to find the most probable normality.    Store the solution in a glass-stoppered bottle.

**Example.**    The volume of concentrated HCl needed to prepare one liter of 0.1 N HCl solution is calculated by using Equation (7–3).    Concentrated HCl is about 12 N.

$$V \times 12 \text{ N} = 1000 \text{ ml} \times 0.1 \text{ N}.$$
$$V = \frac{1000 \times 0.1}{12} = 8.33 \text{ ml}.$$

About 8.33 ml of concentrated HCl solution makes one liter of 0.1 N HCl.

In standardizing the above solution, 36.37 ml of it is needed to titrate 0.2236 g of $Na_2CO_3$ with a purity factor of 99.83%.    Find the normality of the solution.

Step 1.    Find the weight of pure sodium carbonate by multiplying the sample weight by the purity factor, after the purity factor has been changed to a decimal number.

$$0.2236 \times 0.9983 = 0.2232 \text{ g}.$$

Step 2.    Find the number of gme of sodium carbonate in the sample. The gme of sodium carbonate is 0.053 g.

$$\frac{0.2232}{0.053} = 4.21 \text{ gme of } Na_2CO_3.$$

4.21 is the number of ml of 1 N solution equivalent to this much $Na_2CO_3$.

Step 3.    Calculate the normality of the solution using Equation (7–3).

$$36.37 \times \text{N} = 4.21 \times 1.$$
$$\text{N} = \frac{4.21 \times 1}{36.37} = 0.1158.$$

## Analysis of a Sodium Carbonate Mixture

This analysis is an application of the same process as that used in standardizing the HCl solution.

**Procedure.**    The unknown sodium carbonate is weighed and titrated with standard HCl solution, and the per cent of $Na_2CO_3$ is calculated.

1. Dry the unknown sample for at least one hour at 140° C.

2. Weigh three samples of sodium carbonate to the nearest 0.1 mg. Each sample should be about 0.3 g or at least large enough to require more than 25 ml of the standard acid.

3. Place each sample in a 250 ml Erlenmeyer flask.

4. Dissolve each sample in 75 ml of freshly boiled, cooled, carbon dioxide free water.

5. Add the indicator (two or three drops of methyl orange or three drops of mixed methyl orange-indigo carmine).

6. Titrate with the standard HCl solution to the first perceptible change from yellow to pink, if methyl orange is used as the indicator, or to a light gray color if methyl orange-indigo carmine is used.

7. Calculate the per cent of sodium carbonate in each sample.

**Example.** If a sample containing sodium carbonate and weighing 0.3066 g is dissolved in carbon dioxide free water and titrated to an end point with 29.87 ml of 0.1158 N HCl, what is the per cent of sodium carbonate in the sample?

Step 1. Find the number of gme of $Na_2CO_3$ in the sample and in 29.87 ml of 0.1158 N HCl solution, since they are equivalent to each other.

$$29.87 \times 0.1158 = 3.46 \text{ gme of } Na_2CO_3.$$

Step 2. Find the weight of sodium carbonate in the sample by multiplying the number of gme by the weight of one gme. The gme of $Na_2CO_3$ is 0.053 g.

$$3.46 \times 0.053 = 0.1833 \text{ g } Na_2CO_3.$$

Step 3. Calculate the per cent of $Na_2CO_3$ by dividing the part which is $Na_2CO_3$ by the weight of the entire sample and multiplying by 100, thus:

$$\frac{0.1833 \times 100}{0.3066} = 59.78\% \ Na_2CO_3.$$

Combining the three steps we have:

$$\frac{29.87 \times 0.1158 \times 0.053 \times 100}{0.3066} = 59.78\% \ Na_2CO_3.$$

8. Average the three values found, to get the most probable value for the per cent of sodium carbonate.

**Errors in the Method.** The errors in this analysis are kept relatively small by careful adjustment of conditions. The blank is usually so small as to be negligible since the standardization and analysis blanks tend to cancel each other.

END POINT DETECTION. When using methyl orange as an indicator for carbonate titrations, the color change is gradual and some error may occur because the rate of change of pH at the equivalence point is not so rapid as with an HCl-NaOH titration. This is made clear by comparing Fig. 18 with Fig. 15. It is obvious that the steepest part of the curve in Fig. 18 is not so nearly vertical as the steepest part of the curve in Fig. 15. It can be shown that a 0.1 N solution of strong acid is the most dilute that one can safely use for titrating sodium carbonate. With less concentrated solutions an error in detecting the end point can be made because of the very large volume of acid needed to give a visible color change to methyl orange. Mixed indicators greatly reduce this source of error.

HIGH IONIC STRENGTH. Whenever an acid-base titration is made, the presence of ions other than those taking part in the reaction may change ionic activities. This can result in a change in pH at which the equivalence point occurs. Further, such extraneous ions can alter the nature of reactants by forming complex ions, thereby changing the effectiveness of ions in reactions.

## Analysis of an Acid Phthalate Mixture

A mixture of potassium acid phthalate with some neutral substance is analyzed for its potassium acid phthalate content. The analysis is made by titrating weighed samples of the unknown with a carefully standardized sodium hydroxide solution. Standardization of the sodium hydroxide is described in detail in Chap. 7.

**Procedure.** The steps in this analysis are similar to those for the standardization given in Chap. 7.

1. Prepare a 0.1 N NaOH solution as nearly carbonate free as possible.

2. Standardize the solution against 0.4–0.5 g samples of accurately weighed, primary standard potassium acid phthalate. With phenolphthalein as the indicator the titration is carried to the first perceptible pink color that persists for about 30 seconds.

3. Calculate the normality of the sodium hydroxide solution. See Chap. 7, pp. 70–71.

4. Weigh accurately three samples of about 1.0 g each of the unknown substance containing acid phthalate.

5. Dissolve the samples in about 75 ml of freshly boiled and cooled, carbonate free water in 250 ml Erlenmeyer flasks.

6. Add the indicator and titrate the samples with the standard sodium hydroxide solution until the first perceptible pink color persists for about 30 seconds.

7. Calculate the per cent of potassium acid phthalate in the unknown sample.

**Example.** If a sample of material containing potassium acid phthalate and weighing 0.9884 g is dissolved and titrated to the first perceptible pink color of phenolphthalein with 27.22 ml of 0.09577 N NaOH solution, what per cent of the sample is potassium acid phthalate? The gme of potassium acid phthalate is 0.20422 g.

Step 1. Find the number of gme of the potassium acid phthalate in the sample by calculating the number of gme of NaOH that are in the titrating solution. This is done by multiplying the normality of the solution by the number of ml used in the titration.

$$27.22 \times 0.09577 = 2.607 \text{ gme.}$$

Step 2. Find the weight of potassium acid phthalate in the sample by multiplying the number of gme by the weight of each gme.

$$2.607 \times 0.20422 = 0.5323 \text{ g.}$$

Step 3. Calculate the per cent of potassium acid phthalate in the sample.

$$\frac{0.5323 \times 100}{0.9884} = 53.86\%.$$

Combining all the above three steps into one:

$$\frac{27.22 \times 0.09577 \times 0.20422 \times 100}{0.9884} = 53.86\%.$$

8. Average the three values found, to get the most probable value for the per cent of potassium acid phthalate.

**Errors in the Method.** In this analysis, carelessness and limitation of measurements by instruments are the major causes of errors. End point detection is far more precise than with methyl orange in the carbonate titration, but at concentrations of titrating agent lower than 0.02 N some considerable variations in end point arise.

WEIGHING ERRORS. These are negligible because of the very high equivalent weight of the potassium acid phthalate. The acid phthalate does not absorb moisture and can be dried easily and safely at 110° C.

BLANK ERROR. This is so small as to be negligible. With phenolphthalein there should be less than 0.03 ml of 0.1 N NaOH needed to give a perceptible color in 100 ml of carbonate free water.

## pH Meter Indication of End Points for Acid-Base Titrations

Instead of colored indicators it is often desirable to use a pH meter for indicating end points, especially when a gradual change in pH occurs at the end point. This happens when titrating very dilute solutions or weak acids and bases, or when the pH at the end point is unknown and a choice of indicator is difficult to make.

**The Semi-log Plot.** The pH meter is a modified potentiometer designed to read the pH of a solution directly when standard electrodes are dipping into the solution tested. Plotting pH, a logarithmic function, against the volume of reagent added, an arithmetic function, gives a semi-log plot such as Figs. 15, 16, and 17, pp. 101 and 106.

THE EQUIVALENCE POINT. The equivalence point on a semi-log plot is the point on the volume axis where the rate of change of pH is at a maximum. This is the steepest point of the curve, known as the point of inflection.

PROCEDURE. An analysis by this procedure is the same as that used if an indicator is employed. The difference is that the electrodes of a pH meter are dipping in the solution throughout the titration and readings of the pH are taken after each addition of titrant.

STANDARDIZATION OF A 0.1 N ACID SOLUTION. This can be done by titrating a weighed quantity of a primary standard base or by titrating a measured volume of standard base solution.

1. Weigh out properly dried samples of primary standard sodium carbonate, each about 0.2–0.25 g in weight, or pipet out, into 400 ml beakers, a given volume of standard base solution. If sodium carbonate is weighed out, dissolve it in about 75 ml of boiled, distilled water. If standard base is used, it may be diluted to about 75 ml.

2. It is best not to immerse a glass electrode or pH meter in solutions of pH over 10 or 11. Therefore add about half, or more than half, as much acid as will be needed for titrating the base; then lower the electrodes into the solution.

3. Read the pH, then add 1 ml of acid, read the pH again, and repeat this until the end point is neared. One sample may have to be run as a test to estimate where the end point will be in later titrations. Record the pH at each volume of acid added. This record, of pH and volume titrated, can be plotted on a previously prepared graph. Near the point of inflection the volume of acid added should be no more than 0.10 ml between pH readings.

4. After the points are plotted, draw a smooth curve, and estimate the steepest point. This point is usually halfway between the two points where the steepest tangent to the curve appears to depart from the curve. See Fig. 19, p. 136.

5. Calculate the normality of the acid by following the method illustrated in the example on p. 131 if a primary standard is used, or by applying Equation (7–3) (see example, p. 76) if a standard solution is used for standardizing.

ADVANTAGE. This method gives the equivalence point without regard to the pH at which the end point occurs, and consequently is more reliable than titration to a fixed pH by use of an indicator. An indicator changes at a certain pH whether that is the titration end point or not.

**Differential Plot.** A curve with a peak that indicates the end point very accurately is made by plotting the differential of the change in

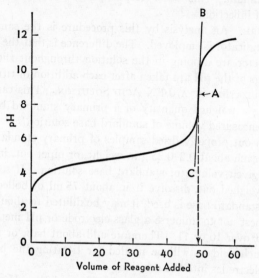

Fig. 19. Finding the End Point on a Titration Curve. *A* is the point of greatest slope; *BC* is the line tangent to the curve.

pH, at different points during the titration, with respect to a given volume of titrant.

The operation of the analysis is nearly identical with that followed for the semi-log plot. The difference is in the way of plotting the results. The vertical axis plots the *change* of pH per unit of volume of solution added, and the horizontal axis plots the volume of titration solution. Each point plotted is connected by a smooth curve and, since there is a maximum rate of change in pH at the equivalence point, the equivalence point is indicated by a sharp peak where two parts of the curve intersect. See Fig. 20, p. 137.

Calculations and other procedures are no different from those in which other methods are used for finding the equivalence point

## Analysis of Iron in an Ore

The analysis of iron in an ore applies so many principles of analytical chemistry that it has become a standard analysis.

**Preparation and Standardization of Reagents.** The first step in any analysis is the preparation of all solutions needed so that the procedure can be completed with as little interruption as possible.

MERCURIC CHLORIDE SOLUTION. Saturate water with $HgCl_2$ by dissolving the mercuric chloride in warm water and allowing it to

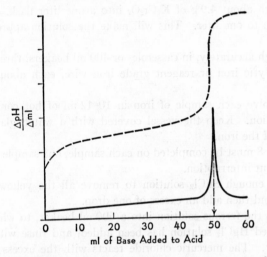

Fig. 20. Differential Plot. The dotted line is a conventional pH curve for comparison.

cool. Crystallization of mercuric chloride during cooling assures one that the solution is saturated.

STANNOUS CHLORIDE SOLUTION. Dissolve 100 g of $SnCl_2 \cdot 2H_2O$ in 180 ml of concentrated HCl solution and dilute to 1000 ml. Add a few pieces of metallic tin to prevent oxidation of the tin.

OXYGEN FREE WATER. Boil water for about two minutes in a Florence flask, stopper loosely by inverting a small beaker over the neck of the flask, and cool to room temperature in cold water or ice. Then stopper the flask tightly to prevent oxygen from the air redissolving. This water is used for diluting the iron solutions before titrations are made.

DIPHENYLAMINE SULFONATE SOLUTION. Dissolve 3.2 g of barium diphenylamine sulfonate in about 900 ml of water. Add about 5 g of $Na_2SO_4$ dissolved in 75 ml of water. Allow the $BaSO_4$ to settle, and siphon off the clear solution for use as indicator.

STANDARDIZATION OF A SOLUTION OF OXIDIZING AGENT. Several oxidizing agents are suitable. The choice depends on convenience and cost. Potassium dichromate is chosen for this analysis.

Although reagent grade (ACS standard) potassium dichromate is usually satisfactory, it may vary in oxidizing capacity as much as 0.5% from theoretical. Solutions should be prepared and standardized in the following steps.

1. Weigh about 4.9 g of $K_2Cr_2O_7$ into a one liter flask. Dissolve and dilute to one liter. This will make the solution approximately 0.1 N.

2. Weigh accurately, in casseroles or 400 ml beakers, three samples of electrolytic iron or reagent grade iron wire, each about 0.20 to 0.25 g.

3. Dissolve each sample of iron in 10–12 ml of hot concentrated HCl solution. Keep the vessel covered with a watch glass during solution of the iron.

Steps 4–8 must be completed on each sample, one sample at a time and without interruption.

4. Add enough $SnCl_2$ solution to remove all the yellow color of $FeCl_6^{-3}$, and then add an excess of one drop.

5. Pour the ferrous solution into a 600 ml beaker, to which 15 ml of saturated $HgCl_2$ solution has been added, and rinse with oxygen free water. The mercuric chloride reacts with the excess stannous chloride thus:

$$2HgCl_2 + Sn^{+2} + 4Cl^- \rightarrow Hg_2Cl_2 + SnCl_6^{-2}.$$

If the precipitated $Hg_2Cl_2$ is not white and silky in appearance, but gray or black, too much excess stannous chloride solution was added and the sample must be discarded. The gray or black free Hg hides the end point color change and reacts with the oxidizing agent. If no precipitate forms, not enough stannous chloride was added to reduce all the ferric ions to ferrous ions and the sample must be discarded. The $Hg_2Cl_2$ precipitate is insoluble so that it reacts extremely slowly with the oxidizing agent. The amount of oxidizing agent reacting with the precipitate is so small as to be negligible during a fairly rapid titration.

6. Add 20 ml of concentrated $H_2SO_4$, 15 ml of syrupy phosphoric acid, and oxygen free water to make about 300 ml.

7. Add about 8–10 drops of diphenylamine sulfonate indicator.

8. Titrate with the dichromate solution until the first permanent tint of blue appears. The green of the chromic ion $(Cr^{+3})$ formed during the titration tends to hide the end point and to give a peculiar, almost gray color with the first appearance of blue.

9. Calculate the normality of the dichromate solution, using Equation (7–2).

**Example.** What would be the normality of a dichromate solution if 38.47 ml of it were needed to titrate the iron in 0.2446 g of electrolytic iron of 100% purity?

Step 1. Normally, the first step is to calculate the weight of pure primary standard from the weight of the sample and the purity factor. The purity factor, in per cent, is converted to a decimal and then multiplied by the weight of the sample of primary standard. This value is used in Equation (7–2). The step is not needed in this example since the purity factor of the iron is 100%.

Step 2. Substitute known values in Equation (7–2) and solve for the normality. The gme of iron is 0.05585.

$$N = \frac{0.2446}{0.05585 \times 38.47} = 0.1139.$$

10. Instead of the normality, the Fe titer (see p. 79) of the dichromate solution may be desired. This is calculated by multiplying the gme of the substance by the normality, thus:

$$0.05585 \times 0.1139 = 0.006358 \text{ g of Fe}$$

each ml of dichromate solution will titrate.

STANDARDIZATION OF CERIC SOLUTION. The acid sulfate solution of ceric ion is often preferred. The $Ce^{+4}$ probably exists in solution as the trisulfato cerate ion, $Ce(SO_4)_3^{-2}$, but for convenience it is usually referred to as the ceric ion, $Ce^{+4}$ or $Ce^{IV}$.

1. Dissolve 76 to 80 g of ammonium sulfate cerate in 500 ml of water to which 28 ml of concentrated sulfuric acid has been added. When solution is complete, dilute to one liter.

2–6. Follow steps 2 through 6 for dichromate standardization above.

7. Add 2 drops of 0.01 M ferroin as the indicator. Ferroin is a complex compound made up of 3 molecules of 1,10-phenanthroline with one ferrous ion. It has an intense red color. When the ferrous ion in the complex is oxidized to ferric ion the color changes to a faint blue.

8. Titrate with the ceric solution to the point where the red-orange color is gone for at least 5 seconds. The faint blue of the indicator may not be visible. $Hg_2Cl_2$ precipitate will reduce ceric ion slowly. The end point color, therefore, reverts rather rapidly to the original orange color.

9. Calculate the normality of the ceric solution as in step 9 or calculate the Fe titer as in step 10 under dichromate standardization above.

**Analysis of an Iron Ore.** The iron compounds in the ore must be dissolved, the iron reduced to the ferrous oxidation state, and the latter titrated with a standard solution of a suitable oxidizing agent.

EQUATIONS FOR REACTIONS USED DURING THE ANALYSIS.

1. Dissolving the iron oxides in the ore with hydrochloric acid:

$$Fe_2O_3 + 6H^+ + 12Cl^- \rightarrow 2FeCl_6^{-3} + 3H_2O$$

and:

$$Fe_3O_4 + 8H^+ + 12Cl^- \rightarrow 2FeCl_6^{-3} + Fe^{+2} + 4H_2O.$$

2. Reduction to ferrous ion:

$$2FeCl_6^{-3} + Sn^{+2} \rightarrow 2Fe^{+2} + SnCl_6^{-2} + 6Cl^-.$$

3. Oxidation of ferrous ion during titration:

$$6Fe^{+2} + Cr_2O_7^{-2} + 14H^+ \rightarrow 2Cr^{+3} + 6Fe^{+3} + 7H_2O,$$

or with ceric ion:

$$Fe^{+2} + Ce^{+4} \rightarrow Fe^{+3} + Ce^{+3}.$$

PROCEDURE. The steps are similar to those for preparing a standard solution.

Iron ores contain, along with other minerals, mainly $Fe_2O_3$ and $Fe_3O_4$. These compounds can be dissolved in hot HCl solution and, if stannous chloride is added while the ore is entering solution, the dissolving takes place very rapidly.

1. Dry the ore in a drying oven at 105° to 110° C, for at least one hour.

2. Weigh out three samples of the ore of such size that more than 25 ml of standard oxidizing solution will be required for titration. Usually 0.4–0.6 g is satisfactory.

3. Place the samples in clean casseroles.

4. Add 15 ml of concentrated HCl solution, warm gently, and as the HCl solution turns yellow add stannous chloride solution to reduce the yellow $FeCl_6^{-3}$ to the nearly colorless $FeCl_2$. Be careful

not to add more than one or two drops more of stannous chloride than is needed to reduce the $Fe^{III}$ to $Fe^{II}$. All of the ore is dissolved when no black or red specks are left in the bottom of the casserole or when no little yellow streamers of $Fe^{III}$ solution can be seen coming from the undissolved particles.

5. As soon as the solution is complete, transfer, by washing with oxygen free water, all the reduced iron ore in solution to a 600 ml beaker containing 15 ml of saturated mercuric chloride solution. A white silky precipitate should form. If no precipitate forms, insufficient stannous chloride was probably added to reduce all of the ferric iron, and the sample should be discarded.

6. Add the indicator, either 8–10 drops of diphenylamine sulfonate solution or 2 drops of ferroin. The former is used if the oxidizing agent is dichromate, the latter if it is ceric ion.

7. Add 20 ml of concentrated sulfuric acid and 15 ml of syrupy phosphoric acid.

8. Dilute to about 300 ml with oxygen free water.

9. Titrate with the standard solution of oxidizing agent as in the standardization.

10. Calculate the per cent of iron in the ore, using Equation (7–5).

**Example.** What is the per cent of iron in an ore if a 0.5181 g sample, when dissolved, required 29.07 ml of 0.0987 N ceric ion for the titration?

Substitute all known values in Equation (7–5) and solve for the per cent of iron. The gme of Fe is 0.05585.

$$\% \text{ Fe} = \frac{29.07 \times 0.0987 \times 0.05585 \times 100}{0.5181} = 30.93.$$

If the iron titer of the solution is used for the calculation, the product of the titer and the volume of titration gives the weight of iron in the sample. This, divided by the weight of the sample and multiplied by 100, gives the per cent of iron in the sample. Thus, for an iron titer of 0.00551:

$$\% \text{ Fe} = \frac{29.07 \times 0.00551 \times 100}{0.5181} = 30.93.$$

**Errors in the Method.** Several possible errors can occur.

UNDISSOLVED ORE. Not all iron-containing minerals are soluble in HCl solution. Should any appreciable amount of dark-colored material be left in the casserole after all action with HCl has ceased, there may be undissolved iron left. To assure no loss of iron in such insoluble minerals:

1. Filter off the residue on filter paper, catching the filtrate in a 500 ml Erlenmeyer flask.

2. Wash the paper and undissolved solids with water until the yellow $FeCl_6^{-3}$ color is completely removed.

3. Dry and burn off the paper slowly in a crucible.

4. Add about 3 g of potassium pyrosulfate to the crucible.

5. Heat, to melt the pyrosulfate, and continue heating just enough to keep it liquid. Keep molten until action ceases.

6. Cool the crucible and add a few ml of HCl solution.

7. Transfer to the filtrate in step 1.

8. Boil until the cake is dissolved and until the volume is reduced to no more than 50 ml. From this point on, the procedure is the same as if all the ore had dissolved in the HCl solution. $SnCl_2$ solution is added, the excess is destroyed with $HgCl_2$ solution, and the titration is carried out normally. Some minerals require treatment with hydrofluoric acid rather than with potassium pyrosulfate. Such treatment should be made in a platinum crucible in a well-ventilated hood.

OXYGEN OF THE AIR. Ferrous iron solutions absorb oxygen from the air which oxidizes ferrous iron to the ferric oxidation state. This gives low results in an iron analysis. After the excess of stannous chloride is destroyed, the analysis should be made without delay to avoid any appreciable oxidation by the air.

EXCESS OF STANNOUS CHLORIDE. Too great an excess of stannous chloride, or the addition of mercuric chloride solution to the stannous chloride rather than the reverse, can cause reduction of $HgCl_2$ to Hg. The metallic mercury reacts with oxidizing agents to give high results. Adding the mercuric chloride to the solution containing a small excess of $Sn^{+2}$ can develop areas where a relatively large excess of $Sn^{+2}$ in contact with the $HgCl_2$ can reduce the mercury to the metal. Pouring the dilute $Sn^{+2}$ into the $HgCl_2$ solution prevents any local excess of $Sn^{+2}$.

INSTABILITY OF REAGENTS. Dichromate is perfectly stable. Ceric ions, especially if in the nitrate form, often precipitate from dilute acid solution as basic salts. Sulfate does not exhibit this instability and can be kept indefinitely.

INDICATOR BLANK. The indicator diphenylamine sulfonate has a small blank error but, since ferrous ion is required if the indicator is to give an end point color, the blank is not easy to determine. Ferroin has so small a blank it is inconsiderable.

**Alternate Reagents.** Other oxidizing and reducing agents are frequently employed.

POTASSIUM PERMANGANATE. Permanganate is a common reagent which is used instead of dichromate or ceric ion. Dissolved as the potassium salt, it makes a solution which is a powerful oxidizer and is its own indicator. Its instability on storage requires frequent

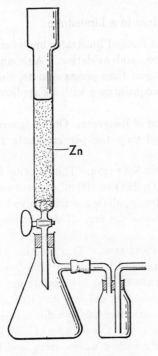

Fig. 21. Jones Reductor.

standardization (p. 144), and its preparation requires long standing to permit $MnO_2$ to settle, or filtration to remove suspended solids. It is subject to many side reactions. One of these reactions is decomposition of the permanganate ion itself. Permanganate can be standardized against pure iron and used for titrating in exactly the same way as is dichromate, except that no indicator is needed. Permanganate is especially effective in oxidizing chloride ions, a reaction difficult to prevent. This can be a serious source of error.

THE JONES REDUCTOR. Instead of using $SnCl_2$ as the reducing agent, amalgamated zinc, in a Jones reductor (see Fig. 21), is often used. The Jones reductor is useful for reducing dilute ferric solutions in a rather large volume. $SnCl_2$ can be used only on relatively small volumes of solution. The reaction in the Jones reductor is:

$$2Fe^{+3} + Zn \rightarrow 2Fe^{+2} + Zn^{+2}.$$

The Jones reductor avoids the presence of $Hg_2Cl_2$ and other contaminants, and it can reduce ions in a much larger volume and more dilute solution than can stannous ion.

## Analysis of Calcium in a Limestone

The analysis of calcium by this method illustrates important principles of separation, precipitation, and oxidation. Although ceric ion is a more reliable oxidizing agent than permanganate, the latter is so commonly used that some acquaintance with its applications is necessary.

**Preparation and Standardization of Reagents.** Only a few reagents are needed for this analysis, and only the permanganate requires standardization.

SATURATED AMMONIUM OXALATE SOLUTION. This solution is made by adding about 5 g of $(NH_4)_2C_2O_4 \cdot H_2O$ to 100 ml of distilled water. After half an hour or more of stirring, allow the undissolved solid to settle, and siphon off the clear liquid for use. This solution is best prepared fresh.

DILUTE AMMONIUM OXALATE SOLUTION. This solution contains 1 g of ammonium oxalate per liter and is used for transferring and preliminary washing of the precipitate. The low oxalate ion concentration greatly reduces the solubility of calcium oxalate. A satisfactory wash solution is 20 ml of saturated solution diluted to 1 liter.

STANDARD PERMANGANATE SOLUTION. Dissolve 3 g of solid $KMnO_4$ in 500 ml of distilled water, cover with a watch glass, and heat to just under boiling for an hour. Allow this solution to stand in the dark for at least a day. Then filter it through a Gooch crucible with an asbestos mat (see p. 54 and Fig. 10) or through a sintered-glass crucible. A sintered-glass crucible is one with a bottom made of small pieces of glass heated until they partially fuse together; it may also be called a fritted-glass crucible. Store in a clean glass bottle that has been rinsed with dilute sulfuric acid and thoroughly washed with water.

Equations for reactions involved in standardizing permanganate solution are given under Separation and Analysis of Calcium; see next section. Steps in the standardization are as follows.

1. Dry primary standard sodium oxalate for an hour at 105–110° C.

2. Weigh out three 0.25–0.30 g samples into 600 ml beakers.

3. Dissolve the sodium oxalate in 250 ml of a solution of sulfuric acid made by pouring 50 ml of concentrated acid into 950 ml of water.

4. Add about 25–30 ml of permanganate rapidly, but avoid spattering.

5. As soon as the pink color has faded, heat the solution to 60° C.

6. Slowly complete the titration with permanganate to a pink color that persists for 30 seconds at 60° C.

7. Determine the blank by measuring the volume of permanganate needed to give a perceptible pink color to an equal volume of oxalate free sulfuric acid at 60° C. The blank is to be subtracted from the volume of each titration made with the same permanganate and sulfuric acid.

8. Calculate the normality of the permanganate, or else calculate the CaO titer.

**Example.** With a sample of primary standard sodium oxalate which weighs 0.2619 g and has a purity factor of 99.78%, calculate (a) the normality, and (b) the CaO titer of the permanganate, if 42.97 ml of the permanganate was needed for the titration.

(a) Substitute all known values in Equation (7–1) and solve for the normality. The gme of sodium oxalate is 0.067.

$$N = \frac{0.2619 \times 99.78}{0.067 \times 42.97 \times 100}.$$

The 100 in the denominator changes the purity factor from per cent to a decimal.

$$N = 0.09078.$$

(b) Find the CaO titer of the solution by multiplying the normality by the gme of CaO.

$$0.09078 \times 0.028 = 0.002542.$$

0.028 is the gme of CaO.

**Separation and Analysis of Calcium.** The sample must be dried, weighed out, and ignited to drive off $CO_2$, and the residue dissolved with hot HCl solution. This solution is diluted, oxalate is added, and urea is added and allowed to hydrolyze, permitting the $CaC_2O_4$ to be precipitated. The latter is filtered, washed, and then dissolved in dilute sulfuric acid. The solution of oxalic acid thus obtained is titrated with the standard permanganate solution.

EQUATIONS FOR REACTIONS.

1. Ignition of the sample.

$$CaCO_3 \rightarrow CaO + CO_2.$$

2. Solution of the sample in HCl.

$$CaO + 2H^+ \rightarrow Ca^{+2} + H_2O.$$

3. The hydrolysis of urea.

$$CO(NH_2)_2 + H_2O \rightarrow CO_2 + 2NH_3.$$

4. Precipitation of calcium as oxalate.

$$Ca^{+2} + C_2O_4^{-2} \rightarrow CaC_2O_4.$$

5. Solution of the precipitate in $H_2SO_4$ solution.

$$CaC_2O_4 + 2H^+ \rightarrow H_2C_2O_4 + Ca^{+2}.$$

6. Titration with permanganate.

$$5H_2C_2O_4 + 2MnO_4^- + 6H^+ \rightarrow 10CO_2 + 2Mn^{+2} + 8H_2O.$$

PROCEDURE.

1. Dry the sample for at least one hour at 105–110° C.

2. Weigh out separate portions of from 0.25 g to 0.50 g of sample.

3. Ignite each sample, preferably in a platinum crucible, at 900° C, starting cold and raising the temperature slowly. The temperature of 900° C should not be reached before 20 minutes.

4. Cool, and place the crucibles in 250 ml beakers.

5. Add 5 ml of $H_2O$ and 10 ml of concentrated HCl.

6. Heat to dissolve all calcium salts.

7. Wash off crucibles and remove from beakers. Do not proceed further unless there is time to complete all operations of the analysis.

8. Heat the 5% $(NH_4)_2C_2O_4$ solution to 90° C and add 100 ml of the solution to each sample.

9. Add 2 drops of methyl red indicator.

10. Add 10 g of solid urea to each sample.

11. Heat to boiling and boil until the indicator changes to yellow. The urea hydrolyzes, giving $NH_3$ and $CO_2$. The $NH_3$ neutralizes the acid slowly and increases the pH uniformly throughout the solution.

12. Filter, first by decanting the clear solution, then by transferring the $CaC_2O_4$ to a Gooch crucible with an asbestos mat. A fritted-glass crucible may be used (see p. 144).

13. Transfer the precipitate to the crucible using a wash bottle

containing dilute ammonium oxalate solution. Then wash the precipitate thoroughly with dilute ammonium oxalate solution. The precipitate is only slightly soluble in the dilute ammonium oxalate.

14. Finally, wash the precipitate with cold distilled water no more than 4 times.

15. Remove the Gooch or fritted-glass crucible, wash off its outside, and place it in a 250 ml beaker.

16. Add about 100 ml of water, stir the crucible, and then add 5–6 ml of concentrated $H_2SO_4$.

17. Run in about 25 ml of permanganate.

18. Heat to 50–60° C and finish the titration at about 60° C.

19. Calculate the per cent of CaO in the sample.

**Example.** A sample of limestone weighing 0.4421 g was treated as in the above steps. The titration with 0.09078 N permanganate solution required 40.03 ml. What is the per cent of CaO in the sample?

Step 1. Calculate the per cent of CaO in the sample by substituting known values in Equation (7–5).

$$\% \text{ CaO} = \frac{40.03 \times 0.09078 \times 0.028 \times 100}{0.4421} = 23.02.$$

Step 2. Calculate the per cent of CaO, using the CaO titer. The titer multiplied by the volume of solution gives the weight of CaO in the sample. This, divided by the weight of the sample and multiplied by 100, gives the per cent of CaO. Combining these into one operation:

$$\frac{40.03 \times 0.002542 \times 100}{0.4421} = 23.03\%.$$

The slight difference in values is due to the small variations in the logarithms used for solving the problems.

**Errors in the Method.** Although there are many possible errors in this analysis, all of them can be minimized or eliminated so that excellent results can be obtained.

INSTABILITY OF REAGENTS. Permanganate solutions are unstable if they are overheated, are stored in the light, or are in the presence of $MnO_2$, decomposing thus:

$$4MnO_4^- + 4H^+ \rightarrow 4MnO_2 + 2H_2O + 3O_2.$$

By standardizing solutions on the same day that they are used, any error from this source can be eliminated.

Oxalate is not stable in strong, hot sulfuric acid. The oxalic acid formed can become dehydrated thus:

$$H_2C_2O_4 + H_2SO_4 \rightarrow CO + CO_2 + H_2SO_4 \cdot H_2O.$$

Oxalic acid also decomposes into $CO + CO_2 + H_2O$ if the walls of the vessel containing it are heated above 120° C.

COPRECIPITATION. Calcium oxalate has little tendency to coprecipitate soluble ions. The main contaminant is likely to be $MgC_2O_4$, which postprecipitates on the calcium oxalate if filtration is not completed in less than an hour after precipitation. Homogeneous precipitation of the $CaC_2O_4$ gives large, filterable, and quite pure crystals. They are made by mixing the $Ca^{+2}$ and $C_2O_4^{-2}$ in a strongly acid solution, then hydrolyzing urea to carbon dioxide and ammonia by boiling. The ammonia formed by the hydrolysis of the urea neutralizes the acid and decreases the solubility of the $CaC_2O_4$.

## Analysis of Manganese in Pyrolusite

Permanganate is able to react in neutral or slightly alkaline solutions as well as acid solutions. The product of reduction of the permanganate is $MnO_2$ instead of $Mn^{+2}$.

$$MnO_4^- + 3e + 4H^+ \rightarrow MnO_2 + 2H_2O.$$

### Preparation and Standardization of Reagents.

STANDARD PERMANGANATE SOLUTION. This solution is prepared and standardized in the same way as for calcium in limestone. The normality of the solution, as calculated when it is standardized against $Na_2C_2O_4$, must be corrected for the different reaction employed in analyzing the pyrolusite for manganese. Against oxalate ion, $MnO_4^-$ forms $Mn^{+2}$, a change of 5 oxidation units or electrons. With $Mn^{+2}$, $MnO_4^-$ reacts to form $MnO_2$, a change of 3 oxidation units or electrons. Thus, whatever normality is found for the permanganate in acid solution must be multiplied by $\frac{3}{5}$.

ZINC OXIDE PASTE. The only reagent required, other than the common laboratory acids, is a paste made of ZnO and water, to be prepared when needed. Add a little water to about 10 g of ZnO and mix. Add one or two more ml of water and mix again. Add more small portions of water and mix until a paste, the consistency of a fairly thick cream, is attained.

**Analysis of the Sample.** The sample is dissolved in concentrated HCl to reduce the $MnO_2$ to $Mn^{+2}$. The HCl and $Cl_2$ are driven off by boiling with $H_2SO_4$. The excess $H_2SO_4$ is neutralized with sodium carbonate, zinc oxide paste is added, and the solution is titrated at near boiling with a standard permanganate solution.

REACTIONS DURING THE ANALYSIS.  The following reactions occur during the analysis.

1. $MnO_2$ is dissolved by HCl.

$$MnO_2 + 4H^+ + 2Cl^- \rightarrow Mn^{+2} + Cl_2 + 2H_2O.$$

2. The evaporation of the HCl is not considered a chemical reaction.  Partial neutralization of the sulfuric acid with sodium carbonate is a step in the analysis.

$$CO_3^{-2} + 2H^+ \rightarrow CO_2 + H_2O.$$

3. Further neutralization of the sulfuric acid is accomplished with ZnO.

$$ZnO + 2H^+ \rightarrow Zn^{+2} + H_2O.$$

The zinc ions in solution are useful because they displace any $Mn^{+2}$ that might be adsorbed on the precipitated $MnO_2$ during the titration.

4. ZnO reduces the concentration of $H^+$ so much that $Fe^{+3}$, if present, precipitates out by reacting with the $OH^-$ thus produced.

$$Fe^{+3} + 3OH^- \rightarrow Fe(OH)_3.$$

The ferric hydroxide is, of course, hydrated.

5. The reaction that occurs during titration, that of $MnO_4^-$ with $Mn^{+2}$ in a nearly neutral solution, is:

$$2MnO_4^- + 3Mn^{+2} + 2H_2O \rightarrow 5MnO_2 + 4H^+.$$

PROCEDURE.  The steps in the analysis are:

1. Dry the manganese ore for one hour at 105–110° C.

2. Weigh out about 1 g of ore into a 500 ml Erlenmeyer flask.

3. Add 25 ml of concentrated HCl solution and boil gently until all black particles are gone or until no further change occurs in the undissolved material.

4. Add 10 ml of concentrated $H_2SO_4$ and, under the hood, boil until dense white fumes pour from the mouth of the flask.

5. Cool and, while stirring, slowly add 50 ml of water.

6. Transfer to a 500 ml volumetric flask.

7. Add 5 g of solid zinc sulfate, dissolved in 100 ml of water.

8. Add $Na_2CO_3$, a little at a time, stirring thoroughly between each addition to prevent excess foaming.  Add enough $Na_2CO_3$ to nearly neutralize all of the acid but, if a precipitate forms, redissolve it by adding a drop of concentrated $H_2SO_4$.

9. Add enough ZnO paste so that not all of it is dissolved. This precipitates out all ferric iron.

10. Cool to room temperature, dilute to the 500 ml mark, shake, and allow to settle.

11. Pipet out 100 ml of the clear solution from the 500 ml volumetric flask into a 500 ml Florence flask.

12. Heat to 95° C and add standard permanganate solution. The $MnO_2$ that precipitates tends to hide the end point. Near the end point, if shaken vigorously and allowed to settle, the $MnO_2$ coagulates, so that any pink color can be seen in the liquid at the edge where the solution climbs up the wall of the flask. The end point is reached when a visible pink color persists for 10 seconds at boiling temperature.

13. Calculate the per cent of manganese in the sample, remembering that only one-fifth of the sample was removed by the pipet from the volumetric flask.

**Example.** A sample of pyrolusite (manganese ore) weighing 1.1092 g was dissolved and diluted to 500 ml. Of this solution 100 ml was pipetted out and titrated with 34.61 ml of permanganate which was 0.09078 N when standardized against sodium oxalate in acid solution. Calculate the per cent of manganese in the sample.

Step 1. Calculate the normality of the permanganate in neutral solution, remembering that it is $\frac{3}{5}$ of what it is in acid solution.

$$0.09078 \times \tfrac{3}{5} = 0.05446 \text{ N.}$$

Step 2. Calculate the per cent of Mn in the sample. Since only $\frac{1}{5}$ of the sample weighed out and dissolved was titrated, $\frac{1}{5}$ of the weight of the sample is used in Equation (7–5). The gme of Mn is 0.05494.

$$\frac{34.61 \times 0.05446 \times 0.05494 \times 100}{\dfrac{1.1092}{5}} = 46.68\% \text{ Mn.}$$

**Errors in the Method.** The common errors in this analysis are the usual ones found in permanganate titrations. In addition there are a few that are specific for this method.

SOLUBILITY OF THE ORE. If sulfides are present it is possible that, in addition to HCl, some $HNO_3$ should be added to assure complete decomposition. Fuming with sulfuric acid will volatilize both hydrochloric and nitric acids.

ADSORPTION OF $Mn^{+2}$ BY $MnO_2$. When $MnO_2$ precipitates from a solution containing $Mn^{+2}$, the $Mn^{+2}$ is strongly adsorbed. To reduce this adsorption $Zn^{+2}$ is added in high concentration to displace the $Mn^{+2}$, making the latter available for reaction with $MnO_4^-$.

FERRIC IONS. The presence of $Fe^{+3}$ in solution must be avoided. The $Fe^{+3}$ can oxidize $Mn^{+2}$, thus giving low results during the titration. The ZnO increases the pH so that the hydrated ferric oxide precipitates.

OXIDATION BY OXYGEN OF THE AIR. After ZnO paste is added, the oxygen of the air will oxidize $Mn^{+2}$. Therefore, after ZnO paste is added there should be no delay in completing the analysis. If overnight storage of the $Mn^{+2}$ unknown solution is necessary, acidify the solution with sulfuric acid and add excess ZnO the next time the analysis is continued.

INSTABILITY OF PERMANGANATE. The precipitated $MnO_2$ catalyzes the decomposition of permanganate at the boiling point of water. The reaction is slow, but titrating slowly can cause an appreciable error.

*Note.* This analysis gives the per cent of Mn in the ore. Frequently the oxidizing power of manganese dioxide is measured instead. The sample and a weighed quantity of sodium oxalate are treated together with sulfuric acid. The $MnO_2$ in the sample oxidizes some of the oxalate. The remaining oxalate is titrated with standard permanganate. The difference between the amount of sodium oxalate added and that titrated is equivalent to the amount of $MnO_2$ in the sample.

## Analysis of Copper in an Ore

Determining the per cent of copper in an ore is an example of an analysis which employs iodide as a reducing agent, and iodine as an oxidizing agent.

**Preparation and Standardization of Solutions.** The solutions needed are bromine water, starch suspension, and standard thiosulfate solution.

STARCH SUSPENSION. Starch suspension should be freshly prepared. Make a thin paste with 1 g of soluble starch by adding water, a little at a time, to the starch. Pour the starch into 100 ml of boiling water while stirring vigorously. Cool, add 2 g of solid KI, and stir until dissolved. When this is complete the suspension is ready for use.

STANDARD THIOSULFATE SOLUTION. It is best to use the solution within a few days of its preparation. Standardization of the solution should be done simultaneously with the titrations of unknowns if results of highest precision are desired.

1. Dissolve 20 g of $Na_2S_2O_3$ in about 500 ml of cool, distilled water that has been boiled free of $CO_2$.

2. Add about 0.5 g of NaOH and dilute to one liter.

3. Clean 2 g of pure electrolytic copper, first with steel wool and then with HCl solution.

4. Weigh the copper accurately into a 250 ml Erlenmeyer flask.

5. Add 10 ml of concentrated $HNO_3$.

6. When action ceases, add 5 ml of saturated bromine water and boil for about 2 minutes.

7. Dilute to 50 ml and cool.

8. Add ammonium hydroxide, drop by drop, until the whitish copper hydroxide, formed first, starts to dissolve, as indicated by the solution beginning to turn darker blue. Do not add ammonia until the solution is dark blue.

9. Add about 5 ml of glacial acetic acid.

10. Transfer to a 500 ml volumetric flask, cool, and dilute to the mark.

11. Pipet out 50 ml of this solution into a 250 ml Erlenmeyer flask.

12. Dilute to 100 ml, and add 3 g of KI that has been dissolved in about 10 ml of water.

13. Titrate with thiosulfate solution until the brown color of the iodine is nearly gone.

14. Add one ml of starch solution and titrate until the blue color begins to fade.

15. Add one more ml of starch solution and 2 g of $NH_4CNS$ (ammonium thiocyanate), dissolved in water. The thiocyanate ion displaces $I_2$, adsorbed on $Cu_2I_2$ (cuprous iodide), which was formed as a precipitate during the titration.

16. Titrate to the point where the blue changes to a very light tan color.

17. Calculate the copper titer of the thiosulfate solution.

$$\text{Cu titer} = \frac{\text{weight of Cu}}{\text{ml of titration}}.$$

**Example.** A 1.8909 g sample of pure copper is dissolved in $HNO_3$ and diluted to 500 ml. If 50 ml of that solution required 41.77 ml of thiosulfate solution for titration of the liberated iodine, what is the copper titer of the thiosulfate solution?

**Step 1.** One-tenth of the pure copper weighed out is in the titrated 50 ml.

$$\frac{1.8909}{10} = 0.18909 \text{ g of Cu in the solution titrated.}$$

**Step 2.** Calculate the titer, using the equation given under step 17, above.

$$\frac{0.18909}{41.77} = 0.004527 \text{ g of Cu per ml of thiosulfate.}$$

BROMINE WATER. Add liquid bromine to distilled water in a glass-stoppered bottle and shake until the water is saturated with bromine.

**Analysis of the Ore.** The treatment described will dissolve ores containing sulfides, oxides, or copper metal.

REACTIONS DURING THE ANALYSIS. The following reactions may occur during the analysis.

1. Copper oxide will dissolve in HCl solution thus:

$$CuO + 2HCl \rightarrow Cu^{+2} + 2Cl^- + H_2O.$$

2. Copper sulfide will dissolve only if nitric acid is added. The nitrate oxidizes $S^{-2}$ to free sulfur.

$$S^{-2} + 2NO_3^- + 4H^+ \rightarrow 2NO_2 + S + 2H_2O.$$

The sulfur may be further oxidized to $SO_2$.

$$S + 4NO_3^- + 4H^+ \rightarrow SO_2 + 4NO_2 + 2H_2O.$$

These two reactions reduce the sulfide ion concentration below that in the solubility product constant for CuS. The $Cu^{+2}$ concentration increases greatly and the CuS dissolves.

3. Addition of ammonia solution (ammonium hydroxide) neutralizes excess acid.

$$NH_3 + H^+ \rightarrow NH_4^+.$$

It also increases the $OH^-$ concentration so that copper hydroxide precipitates.

$$NH_3 + H_2O \rightarrow NH_4^+ + OH^-$$

and:

$$Cu^{+2} + 2OH^- \rightarrow Cu(OH)_2.$$

If too much ammonia is added it will redissolve the $Cu(OH)_2$, forming a dark blue complex ion.

$$Cu(OH)_2 + 4NH_3 \rightarrow Cu(NH_3)_4^{+2} + 2OH^-.$$

4. Ammonium bifluoride is added to form a very stable complex

ion with ferric ions. Otherwise the ferric ions would react with iodide to give free iodine.

$$Fe^{+3} + 6F^- \rightarrow FeF_6^{-3}.$$

This reaction reduces the $Fe^{+3}$ concentration below that needed to oxidize iodide ions.

5. Potassium acid phthalate contains the biphthalate ion which can react with an excess of either $H^+$ or $OH^-$, holding the pH between 3.5 and 4.5. The biphthalate ion is therefore a buffer.

$$HC_8H_4O_4^- + H^+ \rightarrow H_2C_8H_4O_4.$$

This reaction occurs if there is an excess of acid in the solution. The following reaction occurs if there is an excess of hydroxide ions.

$$HC_8H_4O_4^- + OH^- \rightarrow C_8H_4O_4^{-2} + H_2O.$$

6. Cupric ions oxidize iodide to free iodine.

$$2Cu^{+2} + 4I^- \rightarrow Cu_2I_2 + I_2.$$

The cuprous iodide is insoluble and precipitates out, strongly adsorbing $I_2$ unless there are many thiocyanate ions present to displace the iodine. Iodine molecules react with iodide ions to form a loose complex ion, the tri-iodide ion:

$$I_2 + I^- \rightarrow I_3^-.$$

7. The tri-iodide ion is reduced to iodide by the thiosulfate ions in the standard solution.

$$I_3^- + 2S_2O_3^{-2} \rightarrow 3I^- + S_4O_6^{-2}.$$

PROCEDURE. The ore is dissolved and analyzed in the following steps.

1. Dry the ore no more than one hour at 105–110 °C. Overdrying can cause air oxidation of sulfides in the ore.

2. Weigh 1 g samples of ore into 500 ml Erlenmeyer flasks, if copper flasks are not available.

3. Add 10 ml of concentrated HCl.

4. Boil down to about 5 ml.

5. Add 10 ml of concentrated $HNO_3$.

6. Boil down to about 10 ml.

7. Add 10 ml of concentrated HCl and boil down to about 10 ml.

8. Cool, and add 10 ml of concentrated $H_2SO_4$, slowly.

9. Boil off at least 5 ml of the liquid in the flask. Continue boiling until dense white fumes of sulfuric acid have poured from the mouth of the flask for at least 30 seconds. All of the HCl must be volatilized.

10. Cool, add 20 ml of water, and heat until dense white fumes again pour out of the mouth of the flask.

11. Cool, and dilute to 25–30 ml.

12. Add ammonium hydroxide (ammonia solution) until the green color starts to turn blue.

13. Add 2 g of ammonium bifluoride, $NH_4HF_2$, and stir until it is dissolved.

14. Add 3 g of potassium iodide and dissolve it.

15. One gram of potassium acid phthalate may be added and dissolved at this point to act as a buffer. It is seldom needed, however.

16. Using starch as the indicator, titrate with thiosulfate exactly as in steps 13 to 16 under standardization of the thiosulfate solution.

17. Calculate the per cent of copper in the ore, using Equation (7–6).

**Example.** If a sample of ore weighing 0.9743 g is dissolved and the liberated iodine is titrated with 34.62 ml of a thiosulfate solution having a copper titer of 0.004527, what is the per cent of Cu in the ore?

Substitute known values in Equation (7–6) and solve for the per cent of Cu. Multiplying the titer by the number of ml of titration gives the weight of Cu in the sample titrated. Dividing this weight of Cu by the weight of the sample and multiplying by 100 gives the per cent of Cu.

$$\frac{34.62 \times 0.004527 \times 100}{0.9743} = 16.09\% \text{ Cu.}$$

**Errors in the Method.** There are many possible sources of error in this analysis but, with proper precautions, excellent results may be obtained.

FERRIC IONS. $Fe^{+3}$ oxidizes $I^-$ just as $Cu^{+2}$ does unless it is removed from solution.

$$2Fe^{+3} + 2I^- \longrightarrow 2Fe^{+2} + I_2.$$

To prevent this reaction, fluoride ions are added in $NH_4HF$ to form the stable complex ion described under Reactions during the Analysis, No. 4.

pH CONTROL. Above pH 4.5 $Cu^{+2}$ reacts with $OH^-$, precipitating out of solution and causing incomplete oxidation of $I^-$.

$$Cu^{+2} + 2OH^- \longrightarrow Cu(OH)_2.$$

Below pH 3.5 both $As^{+5}$ and $Sb^{+5}$, if present, can oxidize $I^-$.

$$As^{+5} + 2I^- \longrightarrow As^{+3} + I_2.$$

Antimony reacts similarly. Therefore the analysis solution must be buffered to a pH between 3.5 and 4.5. The bifluoride ion in $NH_4HF_2$ is usually a sufficient buffering agent although potassium acid phthalate is often added as an additional buffering aid. The bifluoride ion buffers in the same way as the biphthalate ion. With excess $H^+$:

$$HF_2^- + H^+ \rightarrow H_2F_2,$$

and with excess $OH^-$:

$$HF_2^- + OH^- \rightarrow 2F^- + H_2O.$$

ADSORPTION OF $I_2$ ON $Cu_2I_2$. The cuprous iodide precipitate adsorbs $I_2$ strongly unless relatively large numbers of $CNS^-$ are present to be adsorbed, thus displacing the $I_2$ from the surfaces of the cuprous iodide crystals.

INSTABILITY OF THIOSULFATE SOLUTION. Thiosulfate decomposes in acid or neutral solutions and with $O_2$ of the air, producing sulfur and sulfates or sulfites. The addition of NaOH or $Na_2CO_3$ stabilizes the solution somewhat, but titrations and standardizations are best completed the same day.

## Review Questions and Problems

1. What are the normality and the chloride titer of a silver nitrate solution made up by dissolving 15.4191 g of pure $AgNO_3$ in water and diluting to one liter?

2. If 32.51 ml of a silver nitrate solution was used to titrate 0.2400 g of 99.72% pure NaCl, what is the normality of the silver nitrate solution?

3. A chloride sample weighing 0.3176 g was dissolved and titrated with 41.98 ml of a silver nitrate solution that was 0.1044 N. What per cent of chloride was in the sample?

4. How is a false end point avoided in a silver or chloride analysis?

5. What is the normality of a thiocyanate solution if a 0.4117 g sample of pure silver required 42.09 ml of the thiocyanate solution for the titration? What is the silver titer of the thiocyanate solution?

6. While making a titration of a solution containing 1.1728 g of a silver alloy, 28.48 ml of a 0.09848 N solution of thiocyanate was used. What is the per cent of silver in the alloy?

7. What is meant by the clear point method of finding the end point in a titration?

8. What is the principle of adsorption indicators?

9. How is $CO_2$ free water prepared?

10. What is a mixed indicator? Give an example and explain how it functions.

11. To standardize an HCl solution, an analyst weighed out 0.2557 g of

99.91% pure $Na_2CO_3$. He titrated the carbonate with 39.17 ml of the acid. What was the normality of the acid?

12. What per cent of sodium carbonate is in a sample of salt, 0.3215 g of which required 27.92 ml of 0.1131 N HCl for titration?

13. A 0.6469 g sample of solid, containing potassium acid phthalate, needed 40.82 ml of 0.09544 N NaOH solution for the titration. What is the per cent of potassium acid phthalate in the sample?

14. What advantage does a differential plot of a potentiometric titration have over a semi-log plot?

15. What indicator is usually used when titrating with dichromate as the oxidizing agent? Why not use ferroin?

16. What is the iron titer of a ceric solution if 34.91 ml of the solution was required for titrating a 0.2817 g sample of pure electrolytic iron?

17. Find the per cent of iron in an ore if 0.4936 g of the ore, after being dissolved and reduced, required 25.78 ml of ceric solution for titration. The ceric solution had an iron titer of 0.005902.

18. How is iron ore treated if it does not dissolve in HCl solution?

19. How does a Jones reductor function? What advantage does a Jones reductor have over $SnCl_2$?

20. Why is the calcium oxalate precipitate not washed with plain distilled water? Why is the precipitate less soluble in dilute ammonium oxalate solution?

21. Write equations for the reactions occurring during the analysis of calcium in a limestone.

22. What are the CaO titer and the normality, in acid solution, of a permanganate solution, 36.41 ml of which was used to titrate 0.2438 g of 99.84% pure sodium oxalate?

23. How is urea used in the calcium analysis?

24. List some possible errors that might occur in the calcium analysis.

25. Why must the zinc ion concentration be high in the titration solution when $Mn^{+2}$ is titrated with permanganate?

26. Why is ZnO paste added to the titration solution before the titration is made in the manganese analysis?

27. What is the per cent of Mn in a sample if 1.1271 g of manganese ore is dissolved and diluted to 500 ml, and 100 ml of the diluted solution is titrated with 28.19 ml of permanganate which was found to be 0.09764 N when standardized against sodium oxalate in acid solution?

28. What per cent of copper is there in an ore if a 2.0192 g sample of ore is dissolved and the $I_2$ liberated by the copper is titrated with 43.07 ml of thiosulfate with a copper titer of 0.004228?

29. List all the reagents used in the copper analysis, and write equations for any reactions each undergoes during the analysis.

# 11

# Electrolytic Separations and Analyses

Because they are rapid and sometimes extremely precise, electrolytic methods are standard procedures in many laboratories. Refinements in instrument design for controlling electrolysis have improved procedures to a point where, once started, the analysis can be completed with little or no attention from the operator.

## Electrodeposition

The separation of substances, on electrodes, from a solution containing ions is commonly called electrodeposition. The separated material may be a solid element, a compound, a gas, or an alloy.

**Theory.** The theoretical problems in electrodeposition are the same as those encountered in oxidation-reduction reactions in general. In addition, overvoltages and decomposition potentials are specific problems of electrolytic operations.

FARADAY'S LAW. Faraday's second law states the quantitative relation of electric current to deposited material: The amounts of different substances deposited by the same current during the same time are proportional to their chemical equivalent weights. Each equivalent weight requires for its deposition one faraday, which is 96,500 coulombs of electricity.

One *coulomb* is the amount of electricity carried by a current of one ampere flowing for one second.

An *ampere* is a unit of current that will deposit, in one second, 0.001118 g of silver from a silver nitrate solution.

The *volt* is the electromotive force needed to push a current of one ampere through a resistance of one ohm.

**Example 1.** In two hours what weight of copper can be deposited from a $CuSO_4$ solution by a current of 0.5 ampere?

Step 1. Find the equivalent weight of copper. Copper has an atomic

158

weight of 63.54. The valence of copper in copper sulfate is +2. The equivalent weight is the atomic weight divided by the valence.

$$\frac{63.54}{2} = 31.77, \text{ the equivalent weight of Cu.}$$

Step 2. Find the number of coulombs of electricity that passed through the solution. This is found by multiplying the time in seconds by the current in amperes.

$$2 \times 60 \times 60 = 7200 \text{ seconds.}$$
$$7200 \text{ seconds} \times 0.5 \text{ ampere} = 3600 \text{ coulombs.}$$

Step 3. Calculate the weight of copper, using the faraday. If 96,500 coulombs will deposit 31.77 g of copper, then 3600 coulombs will deposit a proportional weight of copper.

$$\frac{96,500}{31.77} = \frac{3600}{x},$$

where $x$ is the weight of copper deposited.

$$x = \frac{3600 \times 31.77}{96,500} = 1.185 \text{ g of copper deposited.}$$

**Example 2.** (a) How many coulombs of current are needed to liberate 0.01429 g of chlorine? (b) What weight of $Na_2SO_3$ can be oxidized to $Na_2SO_4$ by this much chlorine?

(a) Find the coulombs needed by proportion. If 35.457 g of chlorine are liberated by 96,500 coulombs, then 0.01429 g of chlorine will need a proportional number of coulombs.

$$\frac{35.457}{96,500} = \frac{0.01429}{x},$$

where $x$ is the number of coulombs needed to liberate 0.01429 g of chlorine. Solving for $x$:

$$x = \frac{0.01429 \times 96,500}{35.457} = 38.91 \text{ coulombs.}$$

(b) Find the weight of $Na_2SO_3$ oxidized by this many coulombs.

Step 1. First find the equivalent weight of the $Na_2SO_3$. Since the valence change of sulfur will be from +4 to +6, when sulfite is oxidized to sulfate, the equivalent weight of $Na_2SO_3$ is one-half of the formula weight.

$$\frac{126.0}{2} = 63.0, \text{ the equivalent weight of } Na_2SO_3.$$

Step 2. By proportion find the weight of sodium sulfite oxidized. Since 63 g of sodium sulfite will be oxidized by 96,500 coulombs, then 38.91 coulombs will oxidize a proportionate number of grams of sulfite.

$$\frac{63.0}{96,500} = \frac{x}{38.91},$$

where $x$ is the number of grams of sodium sulfite oxidized by 38.91 coulombs of electricity. Solving for $x$:

$$x = \frac{38.91 \times 63.0}{96,500} = 0.02540 \text{ g of Na}_2\text{SO}_3.$$

THE NERNST EQUATION. During electrolysis reactions, reduction occurs at the cathode (− electrode) and oxidation occurs at the anode (+ electrode). The oxidation-reduction reactions at electrodes conform to the same laws as ordinary chemical oxidation and reduction. Therefore the Nernst equation is useful in predicting conditions, concentrations, and potentials of cells during electrolysis reactions.

*Calculating Single Electrode Potentials.* Using Equation (8–3), where the reduced form of the substance is a metal and the oxidized form is an ion, $E$, the potential of an electrode, is found from:

$$E = E^0 + \frac{0.059}{n} \log \frac{[M^{+n}]}{[M^0]}, \tag{11-1}$$

where $[M^{+n}]$ is the molar concentration of the metal ion and $[M^0]$ is the molar concentration of the metal. $M^0$ is arbitrarily given the value of one since the size of the electrode is immaterial in voltage production. Equation (11–1) then becomes:

$$E = E^0 + \frac{0.059}{n} \log [M^{+n}]. \tag{11-2}$$

**Example 1.** If the standard electrode potential for the Zn in a 1 M $Zn^{+2}$ solution is −0.762, find the electrode potential for a $Zn^{+2}$,Zn electrode (see Chap. 8, p. 88) in a 0.1 M $Zn^{+2}$ solution.

$$E = -0.762 + \frac{0.059}{2} \log 0.1$$
$$= -0.762 + (0.029 \times -1)$$
$$= -0.791 \text{ volt.}$$

After several such problems have been solved it becomes apparent that a tenfold change in the ionic concentration (from 1 M to 0.1 M, or 0.1 M to 0.01 M) of a monovalent ion changes the $E$ of an electrode 0.059 volt. For a divalent ion the change would be half as much, and for a trivalent ion the change would be but one-third as much.

**Example 2.** Find the theoretical potential of a silver electrode in an $Ag^+$ solution where the $[Ag^+]$ is 0.02. The standard electrode potential for $Ag^+$,Ag is +0.799 v.

Step 1. Substitute in Equation (11–2) the values given, and solve for $E$.

$$E = +0.799 + 0.059 \log 0.02$$
$$= +0.799 + (0.059 \times -1.699)$$
$$= +0.799 - 0.100$$
$$= +0.699 \text{ volt.}$$

This is 0.10 volt more negative than if the solution had been 1.0 M in $Ag^+$. Such a calculation can show the minimum theoretical voltage needed to reduce the concentration of an ion to any desired degree.

**Example 3.** At what voltage would a silver electrode be in equilibrium with a solution $10^{-5}$ M in silver ions?

Solve this problem exactly as the example above is solved.

$$E = 0.799 + 0.059 \log 10^{-5}$$
$$= 0.799 + (0.059 \times -5)$$
$$= 0.799 - 0.295$$
$$= 0.504 \text{ volt.}$$

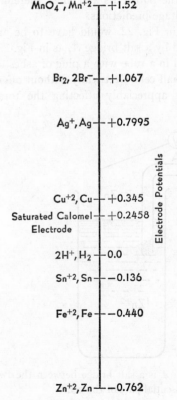

| | |
|---|---|
| $MnO_4^-, Mn^{+2}$ | +1.52 |
| $Br_2, 2Br^-$ | +1.067 |
| $Ag^+, Ag$ | +0.7995 |
| $Cu^{+2}, Cu$ | +0.345 |
| Saturated Calomel Electrode | +0.2458 |
| $2H^+, H_2$ | 0.0 |
| $Sn^{+2}, Sn$ | −0.136 |
| $Fe^{+2}, Fe$ | −0.440 |
| $Zn^{+2}, Zn$ | −0.762 |

Electrode Potentials

Fig. 22. Single Electrode Potentials. The potential of a cell made with any pair of electrodes will be the algebraic difference between the two electrode potentials.

It is apparent that to reduce the concentration of $Ag^+$ from 1 M to $1 \times 10^{-5}$ M a change of 0.295 v is needed during the electrolysis. This calculated value would be the minimum, but not necessarily the actual, change needed.

*Potentials of Cells.* The potential an electrolytic cell can produce is the sum of the two single electrode potentials developed at the cathode and at the anode. Fig. 22, p. 161, shows how combinations of single electrodes, in pairs, can be used to produce cells of differing potential. Stated mathematically,

$$E \text{ of cell} = E_2^0 - E_1^0. \tag{11-3}$$

All values given in Fig. 22 are standard electrode potentials where the concentrations of the ions are 1 M in activity. Other concentrations would give different potentials which could be calculated by using the Nernst equation. If ions other than those of the metal are present they will probably affect the potentials and must therefore be considered when making cell voltage predictions.

Cells with electrodes, indicated in Fig. 22, would have to be arranged with the half cells connected by a salt bridge $A$, as in Fig. 23. The salt bridge is a solution of KCl in a tube with a plug of asbestos in each end that connects the two half cells electrically without offering much resistance and without appreciably affecting the total

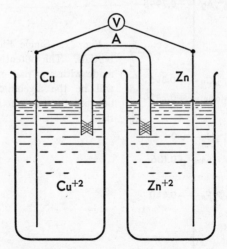

Fig. 23. An Electrochemical Cell. $A$ is a salt bridge between the two half cells. $V$ is a voltmeter, not an essential part of the cell.

voltage of the cell. The values found from Fig. 22 are the potentials that such a cell will produce.

Voltages required to electrolyze a solution in a cell must be larger than the cell potential, since the voltage produced by the cell must be overcome, and sufficient potential must be applied to decompose the electrolyte.

**Example.** Find the cell potential if two electrodes, one silver and the other zinc, are immersed in a solution that is 1 M activity in its ion.

Find the single electrode potentials for silver and zinc in Fig. 22, substitute them in Equation (11–3), and solve for $E$.

$$E = 0.799 - (-0.762) = 1.56 \text{ volts, the cell potential.}$$

DECOMPOSITION POTENTIAL. During electrolysis, deposition of a metal on the cathode occurs only when a sufficient potential is applied to the cell. The minimum voltage, between electrodes in an electrolytic cell, required to cause electrolysis of a solution is called the decomposition potential. Fig. 24 shows how a potential can be increased without any change in conductivity until the decomposition potential is reached. A further increase in potential produces decomposition of the electrolyte, resulting in an increase in the current through the cell.

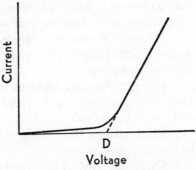

Fig. 24. Decomposition Potential. The decomposition potential, $D$, is found by extrapolation of the steep line to the $X$-axis.

POLARIZATION. The voltage drop across an electrolytic cell during electrolysis is caused by internal resistance of the cell solution combined with the resistances at the two electrode surfaces. There are two factors causing resistance and voltage drop at electrode surfaces. One factor is the reversible potential calculated by the Nernst equation. The other factor is irreversible and is due to polarization. The drop in potential across a cell due to polarization increases with increase in current while the reversible potential remains constant.

*Concentration Polarization.* One type of polarization is concentration polarization. It is due to the reduction in the number of ions in the immediate vicinity of the electrodes. As ions are removed from solution on the electrode, there are fewer to contact the electrode and the resistance is thereby increased.

*Chemical Polarization.* The other type of polarization is called chemical polarization, or overvoltage. Overvoltage is of sufficient importance to deserve special attention.

OVERVOLTAGE. Overvoltage is greatest when gases are liberated at electrodes. This may be partially, though not entirely, due to the gas bubbles on the surface reducing contact between the electrode and the solution. But even metals exhibit overvoltage, and they certainly do not form bubbles. Therefore overvoltage is probably partially due to slowness of chemical changes between the hydrated ions and the electrode. It may be due to slowness in the transfer of electrons from ions to electrodes, or from electrodes to ions. In the case of hydrogen, which has a very high overvoltage, it may also be due to slowness in forming hydrogen molecules from atoms.

Hydrogen overvoltage varies with:

1. Nature of the cathode. Hydrogen overvoltage is greatest with mercury as the cathode, least with catalytically active metals such as platinum and nickel.

2. Physical character of cathode surface. The overvoltage will vary with rough or smooth, rolled or hammered, porous or dense surfaces on the cathode.

3. Temperature. Overvoltage of hydrogen decreases with increase in temperature.

4. Current density. The current density is the current per unit of area of the cathode. Hydrogen overvoltage increases with increase in current density.

5. Time. Hydrogen overvoltage increases with time for a few minutes to perhaps an hour. It eventually becomes constant, however.

IMPORTANCE OF HYDROGEN OVERVOLTAGE. In electroanalysis, hydrogen overvoltage makes it possible to deposit, from water solutions, metals that are more active than hydrogen. Zinc, cadmium, tin, lead, and nickel, all more active than hydrogen, can be plated from various aqueous (water) solutions. The very high hydrogen overvoltage on mercury makes it possible to plate, on mercury cathodes, such an extremely active metal as sodium, where the metal dissolves, forming an amalgam as fast as it is deposited. Practically all metals can be plated out on mercury cathodes where high hydrogen overvoltage and the formation of amalgams combine to aid in the process.

REACTIONS AT THE ANODE. Besides reduction reactions at the cathode there are also oxidation reactions which occur at the anode that are useful in analytical chemistry. Lead can be deposited as nearly pure $PbO_2$ from a solution containing $Pb^{+2}$ and nitric acid. Cobalt can be deposited as nearly pure $Co_2O_3$ from a solution containing $Co^{+2}$, acetic acid, and acetate. Chloride, bromide, and iodide can be deposited as halides of silver on a silver anode.

**Electrolytic Operations.** The operations and equipment for electrolysis are simple in principle. The more automatic the equipment, the more elaborate it needs to be.

EQUIPMENT. Apparatus for electrolytic reactions consists of electrodes, a source of direct current, and an electrolyte.

*Electrodes.* Electrodes are usually made of platinum, which is unaffected by almost all the reagents employed in electrolytic analyses. Cathodes are usually of platinum gauze, which has a large surface area for a given weight. (See p. 167.) Anodes are generally of the same material, but smaller so that they can serve as stirrers as well as anodes. Rapid stirring increases the speed of deposition by reducing polarization caused by the accumulation of gases on the electrodes.

*Source of Direct Current.* The source may consist of a storage battery, a motor generator, or a rectifier which converts alternating current to direct current. Several dry plate varieties of rectifier are available. The voltage delivered should be controlled so as to deliver any desired current density. If the voltage between the cathode and solution is to be controlled, a standard electrode and potentiometer will also be needed.

*Electrolyte.* Only perchlorate, nitrate, and sulfate solutions can contain metal ions that are not almost completely associated with ions or molecules other than water molecules. In solutions containing fluoride, chloride, oxalate, cyanide, tartrate, and many other ions, highly associated compounds exist, with the metal ions, as such, occurring in very low concentration. This low concentration requires a greater potential applied to the cell in order to get electrolysis to occur. This fact can be applied to effect separations of some ions which would ordinarily be difficult to separate electrolytically. In cyanide solutions copper can be plated out, leaving silver in solution, even though silver is less active as a metal than copper. Although copper ions form rather stable complex ions with cyanide, the $Ag(CN)_2^-$ ion is even more stable so that simple copper ions are far more numerous than simple silver ions.

*Circuits.* There are two general kinds of circuits available for use in electrolysis. One is with uncontrolled cathode potential, Fig. 25, and the other is with controlled cathode potential, Fig. 26.

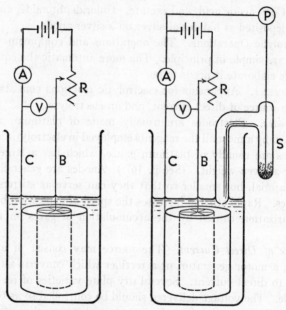

Figs. 25 and 26. Electrolysis Circuits. $A$ is the ammeter, $B$ is the anode, $C$ is the cathode, $V$ is the voltmeter, $S$ is the standard cell, and $P$ is a potentiometer.

Fig. 25 illustrates the commonest type of circuit in which only the potential between the electrodes is controllable.

Fig. 26 illustrates a circuit which permits the operator to control the potential between the cathode and the solution. This potential, as measured, includes the reversible cathode potential (Nernst equation) and the potential due to polarization on the cathode only. By limiting potential changes on the cathode, one metal can be deposited, leaving others in solution. The potential between the solution and the cathode is measured with the standard cell $S$ and the potentiometer as shown in Fig. 26. This potential is controlled by varying the voltage between the cathode and anode with adjustments in the variable resistance $R$. Separations can be made with little attention from the operator if the resistance $R$ is adjusted automatically so as to control the potentiometer reading within limits.

If decomposition potentials of two metals differ by as much as 0.3 v, they can be separated by controlled cathode potential electrolysis. This is clear if one considers that for every change of $0.059/n$ volts at the cathode a tenfold change occurs in the molar concentration of the metal ion being deposited.

NATURE OF THE DEPOSIT. Some deposits are smooth and adhere to the electrode; others are spongy and flaky or crystalline. Conditions that give good deposits (smooth) with one metal give poor ones (spongy) with other metals. No general rules have been found to apply to more than one metal.

*Ions in Solution.* Positive ions of metals as in nitrate and perchlorate solutions give good deposits with copper but not with silver. Most metals deposit best from solutions where the metal ion is part of a complex ion, causing slow deposition. Silver is thus best deposited from cyanide solutions containing $Ag(CN)_2^-$.

*Temperature.* Some elements deposit best at temperatures over 50° C. Others will give spongy deposits at such high temperatures.

*Current Density.* Like high temperature, high current density is possible with some elements but results in spongy or nonadherent deposits with others. Sometimes a change in current density during electrolysis is desirable, as with copper, which should be started at a low current density but can have the current increased after a short while. In general, rapid stirring permits higher current densities.

*Nature of Electrodes.* (See p. 165.) The electrode holds a deposit better if its surface is large and not too smooth. A gauze made of fine wire is usually more satisfactory than a sheet of metal.

*Evolution of Gases.* Most deposits adhere best if no gas is liberated at the electrode where deposition occurs.

TREATMENT OF DEPOSITS. Once the deposition is completed its amount must be determined. This requires cleaning, drying, and weighing the electrode and deposit.

*Removing Electrolyte from Electrodes.* Two methods are employed for washing the electrolyte.

First Method. The electrode with the deposit is raised slowly, with the current still flowing, and washed quickly and steadily by a stream of water from a wash bottle. This method is usually satisfactory for most metals, but copper often redissolves slightly when deposited from nitric acid solutions.

Second Method. The electrolyte is siphoned out and distilled water is added at the same rate, maintaining the original level of liquid while the current remains flowing. This method is preferred unless the electrolyte contains a constituent to be determined later. This method must be used wherever copper is deposited from nitric acid solutions.

*Drying Electrodes.* After the electrolyte is removed the electrodes are washed with alcohol and dried for a few minutes at 100° C. Amalgams are generally dried with ethyl ether at room temperature.

**Coulometric Analysis.** By measuring the amount of current that goes through a cell while a reaction is completed by the current, one can determine the amount of material that reacted. It is necessary to choose reactions which are quantitative and without side reactions.

MEASUREMENT OF CURRENT. The amount of current that passes through a cell is found by means of a coulometer cell in series with the analytical cell. In the coulometer cell either hydrogen or oxygen gas, or metallic silver may be deposited. The gases are measured by volume, the metal by weight.

DETECTING THE END POINT. If the potential at the electrode where the reaction is occurring is controlled carefully, the current will flow until the reaction is completed. Then the current will cease to flow because a higher potential would be needed to force current through the cell after the constituent being analyzed is used up. If a constant current flow is maintained through a cell, the completion of the reaction will be indicated by a change in potential between the electrode where the reaction occurs and the solution.

INDIRECT OXIDATION AND REDUCTION. An intermediate redox agent may be employed if a substance cannot be oxidized directly by the electrodes. In oxidizing thiocyanate ($CNS^-$) with bromine, the latter is formed electrolytically from a solution of bromide ions. Ferrous ions, electrolytically generated, have been used to reduce dichromate. Such coulometric procedures are especially adapted to micro or semi-micro methods.

## Applications of Electrolysis

A few analyses are typical of the major amount of work done by electrolytic procedures. The analysis of a brass or bronze that is low in lead is a procedure involving simultaneous separation on both cathode and anode, copper being plated on the cathode while lead dioxide is deposited on the anode. More than about 5% of lead in the alloy may give deposits of lead dioxide that are flaky and non-adherent.

**Analysis of a Brass or Bronze.** Brasses are essentially Cu-Zn alloys, and bronzes are essentially Cu-Sn alloys. Some lead is generally found in such alloys and must be determined. Tin must be separated by the filtering of $SnO_2$. Lead and copper are determined electrolytically, and the zinc is determined gravimetrically. No solutions need be standardized.

The procedure is a standard method that is rapid and accurate.

1. Weigh three 1–2 g samples of the brass or bronze into 250 ml beakers. Cover with watch glasses and add 30 ml of 6 N nitric acid (1 part acid to 2 parts water).

2. Warm gently to just under boiling for one hour, after the reaction ceases. This digests the white stannic oxide formed from tin in the alloy reacting with the nitric acid thus:

$$4H_3O^+ + 4NO_3^- + 3Sn + yH_2O \rightarrow 3SnO_2(H_2O)_x + 4NO + zH_2O.$$

3. Dilute to about 75 ml.

4. Add about half of a square of filter paper pulp.

5. Digest about 10 minutes at near boiling and filter without delay.

6. Prepare filters with fine pored filter paper.

7. Filter off the hydrated stannic oxide. If some seems to pass through the filters pour it through again until the filtrate is clear. Catch the filtrate, and later the washings, in a 400 ml beaker.

8. Wash the precipitate on the paper at least five times with hot 0.1 M $HNO_3$ solution. This prevents the precipitate from being peptized and helps to keep lead and copper in solution. (Peptizing is the formation of a colloid from a solid.) Washings and filtrate are to be saved and analyzed for copper and lead, procedure 14.

9. Prepare porcelain crucibles by heating them to constant weight at about 900° C.

10. Place the paper and tin oxide in the crucible, and burn off the paper carefully (not too hot).

11. Heat for 20 minute periods at 900° C to constant weight. Meker burners may be used if furnace is not available.

12. The precipitate is converted by ignition to $SnO_2$ thus:

$$SnO_2(H_2O)_x \rightarrow SnO_2 + xH_2O.$$

13. Calculate the per cent of tin in the original sample as follows:

Step 1. Calculate the gravimetric factor of Sn in $SnO_2$ by determining the value of the ratio:

$$\frac{\text{Atomic wt. of Sn}}{\text{Formula wt. of } SnO_2} = \frac{118.70}{150.70} = 0.7877,$$

the $Sn/SnO_2$ gravimetric factor.

Step 2. Find the weight of tin in $SnO_2$ by multiplying the weight of tin oxide by the gravimetric factor.

$$\text{Wt. of } SnO_2 \times 0.7877 = \text{weight of tin in sample.}$$

Step 3. Solve for the per cent of tin:

$$\frac{\text{Wt. of Sn in sample} \times 100}{\text{Wt. of sample}} = \% \text{ of Sn in sample.}$$

The steps may be combined:

$$\frac{\text{Wt. of } SnO_2 \times 0.7877 \times 100}{\text{Weight of sample}} = \% \text{ of Sn in sample.} \quad (11\text{--}4)$$

14. The filtrate and washings from procedures 7 and 8 are combined, and the acid is neutralized with 1:1 ammonia solution (1 part ammonium hydroxide and 1 part water). A precipitate which does not redissolve quickly and is almost white in color may be copper hydroxide. Do not add enough ammonia solution to dissolve the copper hydroxide and make a dark blue solution, but, if possible, add enough to precipitate $Cu(OH)_2$.

15. Add nitric acid until all copper hydroxide dissolves.

16. In addition to the amount added in procedure 15, add 3 ml of nitric acid for each 100 ml of solution.

17. Clean the platinum gauze anode and cathode in nitric acid, wash with water, and dry at 100° C.

18. Weigh the electrodes.

19. Lower the electrodes into the solution and connect them to the electric analyzing unit.

20. Cover the solutions with split watch glasses.

21. Start the stirring motor. The anode usually acts as the stirrer.

22. Adjust the voltage so that a current of 0.5 ampere passes for 30 minutes.

23. Increase the current to 1.0 ampere for 30 minutes.

24. Add 2 ml of concentrated sulfuric acid for each 100 ml of solution.

25. Increase the current to 1.5 amperes for about 30 minutes or until one ml of solution withdrawn shows no blue of copper ammonia complex when concentrated ammonia solution is added.

26. Siphon out the solution, adding water to maintain the level, until the current practically stops. Save the solution for the determination of zinc and add to it the rinse water from the electrodes.

27. Raise the electrodes, and, with the current still on, wash them gently until they are above the solution.

28. Rinse the electrodes gently in water.

29. Rinse the electrodes gently in alcohol.

30. Dry the electrodes for a few minutes (not more than five minutes) at 100° C.

31. Weigh both electrodes. The gain in weight of the cathode is the weight of copper in the sample. The gain in weight of the anode is the weight of nearly pure $PbO_2$, from lead in the sample.

32. Calculate the per cent of copper by dividing the weight of copper (gain in weight of the cathode) by the weight of the original sample, and then multiplying by 100:

$$\frac{\text{Wt. of Cu} \times 100}{\text{Wt. of sample}} = \% \text{ copper.} \qquad (11\text{--}5)$$

33. Calculate the per cent of lead in the sample.

Step 1. Find the gravimetric factor for Pb in $PbO_2$. This is 0.8662, but since anodic $PbO_2$ contains impurities, mostly $O_2$, experience has shown that the factor 0.864 is more nearly correct and is used universally as the gravimetric factor for lead in $PbO_2$ deposited on anodes.

Step 2. Calculate the weight of lead in the deposited $PbO_2$.

$$\text{Wt. of } PbO_2 \times 0.864 = \text{wt. of Pb in the sample.}$$

Step 3. Calculate the per cent of lead in the sample.

$$\frac{\text{Wt. of Pb} \times 100}{\text{Wt. of sample}} = \% \text{ of Pb in the sample.}$$

Combining these steps:

$$\frac{\text{Wt. of } PbO_2 \times 0.864 \times 100}{\text{Wt. of sample}} = \% \text{ of Pb.} \qquad (11\text{--}6)$$

34. If zinc is to be determined, the solutions from procedures 26–28 must be combined and boiled down under a watch glass to about 150 ml. Any iron or aluminum can be precipitated with ammonia and

the zinc can then be determined gravimetrically as the pyrophosphate, $Zn_2P_2O_7$. These gravimetric procedures will not be discussed here, however.

**Example.** A 1.3347 g sample of an alloy produced 0.1437 g of $SnO_2$ ignited to constant weight at 900° C, 0.9941 g of Cu on the cathode, and 0.1947 g of $PbO_2$ on the anode. Calculate the per cent of tin, copper, and lead.

Step 1. To find the per cent of tin, substitute known values in equation (11–4).

$$\frac{0.1437 \times 0.7877 \times 100}{1.3347} = 8.48\% \text{ tin.}$$

The $Sn/SnO_2$ gravimetric factor is 0.7877. (See procedure 13.)

Step 2. To find the per cent of copper divide the weight of copper deposited by the weight of the sample and multiply by 100, Equation (11–5).

$$\frac{0.9941 \times 100}{1.3347} = 74.41\% \text{ copper.}$$

To find the per cent of lead, substitute given and known values in Equation (11–6).

$$\frac{0.1947 \times 0.864 \times 100}{1.3347} = 12.61\% \text{ lead,}$$

where 0.864 is taken as the $Pb/PbO_2$ gravimetric factor. (See procedure 33.)

**Errors in the Method.** Electrolytic analyses are among the most accurate and precise methods known. This is true in spite of the fact that there are many possible sources of error in every determination.

NONADHERENT DEPOSITS. Rough, loosely held deposits flake off, causing losses. There are several ways of improving the quality of an electrolytic deposit. They are as follows.

*Low Current Density.* Some metals deposit more smoothly and firmly when the rate of deposition is reduced by lowering the current to only a few amperes per square decimeter. Too high a current density builds up the deposit unevenly.

*Stirring.* Stirring the solution by using one electrode as the stirrer improves the evenness of the deposit.

*Proper Temperature.* Some metals can be deposited best hot while others are best deposited cold. Each metal is different and there is no general rule.

*Complex Ions.* Formation of complex ions with a metal to be deposited lowers the activity of the ion itself. This reduces the rate of deposition and produces deposits, for most metals, that are more smooth and adherent.

INCOMPLETE DEPOSITION. The frequent occurrence of incomplete deposition is usually due to errors in making up solutions or in the adjustment of the voltage between electrodes.

*Effect of pH.* Deposition of metals will not be complete for solutions in which the concentration of acids is too high. Copper from nitric acid solutions plates satisfactorily only if the concentration of nitric acid is no greater than 3%.

*Negative Ions.* The presence or absence of certain negative ions may be essential for a complete deposit. Such effects are specific. Copper requires the presence of some nitrate ion for satisfactory deposition. Lead deposits on the anode best if some sulfate ion is in the electrolyte. Cobalt, deposited from solutions in which there is little or no nickel ion, can be deposited completely only if some sulfite ion is present.

*Insufficient Voltage.* The voltage applied between the cathode and anode must be sufficient to overcome the resistance of the solution and all other resistances in the cell. In addition, it must exceed the voltage as calculated from the Nernst equation for as low concentrations as are required. If these requirements are not met, then deposition of the substance will be incomplete. In general, the voltages required must be found by experimentation.

## Review Questions and Problems

1. Define: volt, coulomb, ampere, faraday, overvoltage, decomposition potential, ohm, and polarization.
2. How many coulombs of electricity will be needed to deposit (a) 0.9000 g of silver from silver nitrate; (b) 0.3247 g of copper from copper sulfate solution; (c) 0.8411 g of chlorine from a chloride solution?
3. How many grams of the following will be deposited by 800 coulombs: (a) silver from silver nitrate; (b) copper from cupric ion solution; (c) bromine from bromide ion solution?
4. Calculate, from Fig. 22 on p. 161, the voltage one could expect to have developed by a cell made up of copper in copper ions as one electrode and iron in ferrous ions as the other electrode. Concentrations of the ions are 1 M activity.
5. At what voltage would a copper electrode be in equilibrium with a solution of cupric ions which are: (a) 0.1 M; (b) 0.01 M; and (c) $10^{-5}$ M?
6. What factors affect the magnitude of hydrogen overvoltage?
7. Why is hydrogen overvoltage valuable to the analyst and metallurgist?

8. How does a circuit for electrolysis using a controlled cathode potential differ from one without controlled cathode potential?

9. Outline the main steps in the analysis of a brass.

10. Starting with a sample of brass weighing 0.8744 g an analyst found 0.0217 g of $SnO_2$, 0.7049 g of Cu, and 0.0831 g of $PbO_2$. Assuming the remainder to be zinc, calculate the per cent of Sn, Cu, Pb, and Zn in the brass.

11. How long would a current of 0.3 ampere need to pass through a solution of (a) $CuSO_4$ to deposit 0.5300 g of Cu; (b) $AgNO_3$ to deposit 0.403 g of Ag?

# 12

# General Methods of Separation

In analytical chemistry there are simple analyses in which the measurement of a constituent is direct. The per cent of alcohol in an alcohol-water solution can be determined from a table if the specific gravity of the solution has been measured. More often, a constituent of a sample must be separated from other constituents before any measurement can be made that will give the quantity of the analyzed constituent. Thus, carbon in steel must be separated from the steel as carbon dioxide, then absorbed and weighed. Such separations make up such a large part of analytical chemistry that several classes of separations are discussed here.

## Precipitation Methods

One of the commonest methods of separating a constituent from other materials is to dissolve all of them and form a solid compound of the desired constituent. The solid can then be allowed to settle or it can be filtered off, thus removing it from the other materials. A discussion of precipitation theory is given in Chap. 5.

**Inorganic Precipitating Agents.** The most commonly used inorganic precipitants are the common acids and salts.

In mineral analyses, hydrochloric acid may be used to precipitate silica from silicates or insoluble chlorides such as those of silver.

Sulfuric acid is used most commonly for precipitating, as sulfates, barium or lead salts.

Hydrogen sulfide is one of the most frequently used precipitants, though it is used in solutions where the pH is controlled by some other acid such as hydrochloric acid. By controlling the pH many elements can be separated from others by precipitating with hydrogen sulfide.

Ammonia solution, commonly called ammonium hydroxide, is frequently used to raise the pH of a solution to the point where hydroxides are precipitated out. By skillful use of buffers (see Chap. 9) many elements can be separated from others with ammonia.

Ammonium salts such as ammonium phosphate are used to precipitate elements in solutions that are properly buffered. Magnesium is thus precipitated as $MgNH_4PO_4$ from a solution containing $NH_4^+$, $NH_3$, and $PO_4^{-3}$ ions. Salts other than ammonium salts are seldom used as precipitating agents because ammonium salts are volatile whereas salts of metal ions are not.

**Organic Precipitating Agents.** Organic precipitating agents are useful in inorganic analyses. The precipitates formed are rarely ionic, which results in their being generally insoluble in water but soluble in organic solvents. There are some exceptions such as calcium oxalate and the pyridine copper complexes, which precipitate with thiocyanate. The former is like an inorganic substance whereas the latter is somewhat more covalent in structure.

COMPLEX FORMERS. By far the largest group of organic precipitating agents are those that form complex compounds. These agents are both acids and bases simultaneously. The acid part of the molecule has a hydrogen atom replaceable by a metal ion which forms an ionic bond, and the base part of the molecule has a pair of electrons to donate to the metal ion, forming a co-ordinate covalent bond. See the G. N. Lewis definition of a base, pp. 97–98. The most stable compounds formed are those in which the two bonds with the same metal ion form rings, with five or six atoms per ring. Rings of such size are the most free from strain. The arrangement in space which permits such a formation may be very selective, as in the case of dimethylglyoxime with nickel, or it may be unselective as with 8-hydroxyquinoline, which forms complexes with many metal ions.

Complex formers, in forming rings, make two bonds with the metal ion. Each bond tends to strengthen the forces of the other, and the resulting ring is called a chelate ring. The Greek word *chele* means "claw of a crab."

**Example.** The commonest and best known of the chelate ring compounds is the nickel-dimethylglyoxime compound, which is insoluble in water but soluble in organic solvents such as chloroform. Dimethylglyoxime has two oxime groups (=NOH). The hydrogen in this group can be replaced by a metal ion to form an ionic bond. The nitrogen in this group has a pair of unshared electrons that it can lend to form a co-ordinate bond. If one oxime group, like an acid, has a proton displaced, the other oxime group's nitrogen atom shares a pair of electrons with the metal atom. Thus two molecules of dimethylglyoxime form a complex compound with nickel ions that contains two five-membered rings and two six-membered rings per molecule.

$$
\begin{array}{c}
\text{H} \\
\diagup \quad \nwarrow \\
\text{O} \qquad \text{O} \\
| \quad A \quad \uparrow \\
\text{CH}_3\text{—C}{=}\text{N} \qquad \text{N}{=}\text{C—CH}_3 \\
\searrow \\
\text{B} \quad \text{Ni} \quad \text{B} \\
\nwarrow \\
\text{CH}_3\text{—C}{=}\text{N} \qquad \text{N}{=}\text{C—CH}_3 \\
\downarrow \quad A \quad | \\
\text{O} \qquad \text{O} \\
\nwarrow \\
\text{H}
\end{array}
$$

Arrows indicate co-ordinate bonds. Rings labeled *A* are six-membered; rings labeled *B* are five-membered. It is clear that the nickel atom is a member of all four rings.

Dipicrylamine has been used for precipitating potassium, and benzidine has been found useful in precipitating sulfate. The properties of many other organic precipitants can be found in J. F. Flagg, *Organic Reagents Used in Gravimetric and Volumetric Analysis*, Interscience, 1948.

ADVANTAGES OF ORGANIC PRECIPITATING AGENTS. There are several ways in which organic precipitants are better than inorganic agents.

*Selectivity.* In many cases organic reagents are somewhat specific, as dimethylglyoxime with nickel. In other cases adjustment of the pH will often cause precipitation of one constituent alone. By changing pH and solvent conditions, one constituent after another can sometimes be quickly precipitated out.

*Ease of Drying.* Organic reagents produce compounds that have little affinity for water and are dried easily at temperatures low enough to prevent decomposition.

*Coprecipitation.* Lack of ionic character of organic precipitation products greatly reduces coprecipitation, in most cases. Exceptions occur but are beyond the scope of this book. See P. W. West and L. J. Conrad, "Coprecipitation of Cations by Organic and Inorganic Precipitants," *Anal. Chem. Acta*, IV (1950), 561.

*High Molecular Weight.* The very high molecular weight of chelate complexes formed with metal ions reduces, proportionately, small errors in precipitation and weighing.

*Colored Compounds.* Chelate compounds are often highly colored, and since they are usually soluble in organic solvents, they lend themselves well to colorimetric or photometric methods of analysis.

DISADVANTAGES OF ORGANIC PRECIPITANTS. There are, unfortunately, disadvantages to using organic reagents.

*Impurities in Reagents.* Complicated organic molecules needed to form chelate rings are difficult to prepare in very pure form, and impurities often cause undesirable reactions.

*Volatility.* Often the precipitated compound will evaporate upon being dried. Most, however, can be safely dried at 110° C.

*Insolubility of Agent in Water.* The precipitating agents are usually insoluble in water. Therefore it is important not to add an excess of reagent. This is difficult because there is no way to tell when sufficient reagent, without excess, has been added. Any excess that is insoluble would add to the weight of the precipitate.

**Electrolytic Methods of Separation.** The principles of these methods have been discussed in Chap. 11. In general they are methods of causing an ion to separate out, as an element, onto an electrode. This is not true precipitation, but it can be a very useful method of separation.

## Volatilization Methods

The nonmetallic elements such as carbon, boron, fluorine, and arsenic are regularly separated from other elements by forming, and distilling off, compounds that boil at a low temperature. Mercury is commonly distilled, and even zinc and lead can be selectively evaporated from a brass by using low pressure and high temperature techniques.

**Nonmetals.** Of the nonmetals, several are nearly always separated from other materials by distilling either the element itself or a volatile compound of it.

NITROGEN. In the Kjeldahl method, most frequently applied to foodstuffs, fertilizers, and organic products in general, the nitrogen is converted to ammonium sulfate by digestion with sulfuric acid, using selenium oxide, $SeO_2$, copper selenite, $CuSeO_3 \cdot 2H_2O$, or some other material as a catalyst. The cooled solution is then made alkaline with NaOH. The liberated ammonia is distilled into a receiver containing either standard acid or boric acid. If standard acid is used the excess can be titrated with standard base to find the amount of acid not neutralized by the ammonia. Convenient indicators are methyl red and methyl purple. (See p. 119.) If boric acid is used to absorb the ammonia the $H_2BO_3^-$ formed is titrated with standard acid, using brom cresol green as indicator. The analyst titrates the solution with the acid until its color is identical with a solution of boric acid to which brom cresol green has been added.

CARBON. Carbon in carbonates is determined by heating the compound to decompose the carbonate, producing $CO_2$ gas. For calcium carbonate the reaction is:

$$CaCO_3 \rightarrow CaO + CO_2.$$

The loss in weight is carbon dioxide.

For carbon in steels and other substances, where carbon occurs as graphite or as carbides, the material is burned at a high temperature in oxygen. The carbon and carbides burn to $CO_2$ which is absorbed on a strongly alkaline medium such as ascarite. The gain in weight of the absorbing material is the weight of the $CO_2$ produced.

BORON. Boron usually occurs as borate or as the oxide. In either case the compound, with methanol and sulfuric acid, forms methyl borate, $CH_3BO_2$, which can easily be distilled. This substance is absorbed in sodium hydroxide to form a borate, $BO_2^-$, which is then converted to boric acid by adding a strong acid until methyl red becomes red (acid). At this point a sugar, mannitol, is added to give a monoequivalent acid with a ring structure containing the boric acid. This substance is an acid about equal in strength to acetic acid. It is easily titrated with standard NaOH solution.

**Metalloids.** Substances such as arsenic, antimony, selenium, and tellurium are usually distilled away from other materials as chlorides or oxychlorides. The separation of As, Sb, and Sn by distillation from each other has been worked out by J. A. Scherrer, "Distillation and Separation of Arsenic, Antimony, and Tin," *Journal of Research*, National Bureau of Standards, XVI (1936), 253–259, and also by W. D. Mogerman, "Determination of Sn in Nonferrous Metals by Distillation as $SnBr_4$ and Precipitation with Cupferron," *ibid.*, XXXIII (1944), 307–314.

**Metals.** Under about 0.001 mm of mercury pressure, samples of about 0.2 g of a brass can be heated, in silica vessels, so that zinc and lead together can be distilled away from copper and tin. Metal oxides as well as metals may be analyzed by volatilization in a stream of hydrogen at high temperatures. Low pressures are not needed. See E. W. Colbeck, *et al.*, "Determination of Bismuth in Copper," *Analyst*, LIX (1934), 395–399.

## Extraction or Partition Methods

Extraction methods can be clean and rapid in effecting separations. Not many common separations involve extractions, however, because there are more convenient methods available.

**Extraction of Solids.** Many constituents that are soluble in solvents can be removed from other constituents by dissolving the soluble one with a suitable solvent.

**Example.** The classical separation of potassium and sodium by precipitation of the perchlorates, with subsequent dissolving of the sodium salt away from the potassium salt, is typical of an extraction of solid inorganic materials. The potassium perchlorate is made less soluble by adding alcohol to the water used to extract the sodium perchlorate.

**Extraction of Liquids.** Where two immiscible (insoluble) liquids are in contact, and a solute is somewhat soluble in both but more soluble in one than in the other, an equilibrium can be established in which the solute distributes itself through both liquids in proportion to its solubility in each.

THE THEORY OF PARTITION. Partition is the separation of a solute from one liquid by extracting it with another. The efficiency of such an extraction depends on the partition coefficient.

$$\frac{\text{Concentration in solvent 1}}{\text{Concentration in solvent 2}} = K, \qquad (12\text{-}1)$$

where $K$ is the partition or distribution coefficient, and, in extraction of water solutions, solvent 2 is water and solvent 1 is the liquid immiscible with water. Complete equilibrium between the two solvents on the part of the solute is understood.

One extraction of solvent 2 with a given volume of solvent 1 removes a fraction of the solute from solvent 2. Repeating the extraction with the same volume of solvent 1 removes the same fraction of solute that is left in solvent 2.

**Example.** In extracting iodine from water with carbon tetrachloride:

$$\frac{[I_2] \text{ in } CCl_4}{[I_2] \text{ in } H_2O} = 85,$$

where $[I_2]$ is the concentration of iodine in the solvent. This equation means that, where equal volumes of water and carbon tetrachloride are in contact until the iodine has distributed itself between them, the concentration of iodine in the carbon tetrachloride layer will be 85 times as great as in the water layer. Extracting one liter of water containing 0.1 g of iodine with one liter of carbon tetrachloride would leave:

$$0.1 \times \tfrac{1}{85} = 0.001176 \text{ g of iodine}$$

in the water layer. A second extraction would leave one eighty-fifth of that, or:

$$0.1 \times [\tfrac{1}{85}]^2 = 0.00001266 \text{ g of iodine}$$

in the water layer. Similarly, $n$ extractions would leave:

$$0.1 \times [\tfrac{1}{85}]^n \text{ g of iodine in the water layer.}$$

*Volumes of Solvent.* If instead of equal volumes, different volumes of the two solvents are employed, it is obvious that smaller volumes of an extracting solvent like carbon tetrachloride would be less effective. One eighty-fifth of a liter of carbon tetrachloride would extract iodine from a liter of water solution until an equal weight of iodine was in each solvent. Three factors determine the efficiency of an extraction: the partition coefficient, the volume of extraction solvent, and the number of extractions.

The equation for the partition coefficient can be expressed by expanding concentrations to include volumes of solvent as well as weights of solute at equilibrium:

$$\frac{\dfrac{M_0 - M_2}{V_{s_1}}}{\dfrac{M_2}{V_{s_2}}} = \frac{\text{Conc. in solvent 1}}{\text{Conc. in solvent 2}} = K, \qquad (12\text{--}2)$$

where  $M_0$ is the total mass or weight of the solute in both layers of solvent;

$M_2$ is the mass or weight of solute left in solvent 2;

$V_{s_1}$ is the volume of solvent 1;

$V_{s_2}$ is the volume of solvent 2;

$M_0 - M_2$ is the weight of solute in solvent 1 at equilibrium because the total amount of solute, less what went into solvent 2, is what was left in solvent 1.

Equation (12–2) can be solved for $M_2$, the weight of solute left in the solvent 2 layer after one extraction, to give:

$$M_2 = M_0 \left[ \frac{V_{s_2}}{K V_{s_1} + V_{s_2}} \right]. \qquad (12\text{--}3)$$

For $n$ extractions it can be shown that:

$$M_{2_n} = M_0 \left[ \frac{V_{s_2}}{KV_{s_1} + V_{s_2}} \right]^n, \qquad (12\text{--}4)$$

where $M_{2_n}$ is the mass of solute left in solvent 2 after $n$ extractions.

**Example.** Which is more efficient, one extraction by 50 ml of carbon tetrachloride of 100 ml of water containing 0.01 g of dissolved iodine, or two extractions of 25 ml each by carbon tetrachloride?

Step 1.    Calculate the weight of iodine left in the water layer, $V_{s_2}$, by substituting known values in equation (12–3) and solving for $M_2$.  $V_{s_1}$ is 50 ml of carbon tetrachloride and $V_{s_2}$ is 100 ml of water.

$$M_2 = 0.01 \left[ \frac{100 \text{ ml H}_2\text{O}}{85 \times 50 \text{ ml CCl}_4 + 100} \right]$$
$$= \tfrac{1}{4350}$$
$$= 0.00023 \text{ or } 2.3 \times 10^{-4} \text{ g of iodine left in the water layer.}$$

Step 2.    Substitute known values in Equation (12–4) where $n$ is 2 and $V_{s_1}$ is 25 ml of carbon tetrachloride; then solve for $M_2$.

$$M_2 = 0.01 \left[ \frac{100}{85 \times 25 + 100} \right]^2$$
$$= 0.01 \left[ \tfrac{100}{2225} \right]^2$$
$$= 0.01 \times 0.00202$$
$$= 2.02 \times 10^{-5} \text{ g of iodine left in the water layer.}$$

It is obvious that two extractions are about 10 times as effective as one, in spite of the fact that the same total volume of extracting solvent is used.

*Rinsing Glassware.*    The rinsing of glassware with distilled water follows this same law.    Several rinsings with small portions of distilled water are far more effective than one rinsing with a large volume.

APPLICATIONS OF EXTRACTION METHODS.    Many chelating agents, and other ions that form complex molecules or ions, have been applied in the separation of ions from each other by extraction.

*Dithizone (Diphenylthiocarbazone).*    Most metal ions that form sulfides which are insoluble in water also form compounds with dithizone that are insoluble in water but soluble in chloroform.    By adjusting the pH in the water layer certain ions can be extracted with chloroform, leaving others behind.    The chloroform solutions are usually colored, so that many separations and colorimetric determinations have been worked out.    See E. B. Sandell, *The Colorimetric Determination of Traces of Metals*, Interscience, 1950.

*8-Hydroxyquinoline.* This compound, when dissolved in chloroform, can be used for extracting metals from buffered solutions in much the same way as dithizone.

*Thiocyanates.* A few thiocyanates are colored and soluble in organic solvents. Molybdenum in steel is commonly determined by extracting the thiocyanate from a water solution with butyl acetate or some such solvent. The solution is colored so that besides the separation, the amount of molybdenum in a sample can be determined colorimetrically.

## Adsorption Methods

Adsorption is the process of gathering a substance on the surface of a solid material and holding it there without any chemical change apparently occurring.

**Carriers.** Examples of this sort of adsorption are the precipitation of radium sulfate along with barium sulfate, or the precipitation of arsenic and antimony by adsorption on hydrous ferric oxide precipitated with ammonia.

**Differential Adsorption or Chromatography.** For separations such as these a column or tube is packed with clay, charcoal, silica gel, alumina gel, or other inert material. The substances in solution to be separated are poured through the tube; another solution or solvent is then poured through slowly so that the material least strongly adsorbed is washed through most rapidly. If the tube is long enough a separation of almost any two similar substances is possible. See H. G. Cassidy, *Adsorption and Chromatography*, Interscience, 1951.

Paper chromatography is the use of paper, or paper impregnated with an adsorbing agent such as alumina gel or starch, for adsorption separations.

## Ion Exchange Methods

In contrast to adsorption, ion exchange occurs when one ion is replaced by another at some position on a resin molecule. Positive ions replace positive ions only, and negative ions replace negative ions only. This reaction is a true chemical change in which concentrations, ionic diameters, valencies of ions, and the nature of the resin involved combine to determine the extent of replacement of one ion by another. See R. O. Samuelson, *Ion Exchangers in Analytical Chemistry*, Wiley, 1953. A great many separations of ions have been worked out. A few typical ones are mentioned here.

**Deionizing Water.** Water containing dissolved salts can be circulated through a bed of a resin where positive ions of the salt replace hydrogen ions (from a cation exchange resin), then through another bed where the negative ions replace hydroxide ions (from an anion exchange resin). The replaced hydrogen and hydroxide ions combine to yield water. By mixing both kinds of resin in one bed only one container is needed. Regeneration of the resins in separate beds is accomplished by passing an acid solution, HCl, through the cation exchanger, and a basic solution, $NH_3$, through the anion exchanger. Single-bed exchangers are regenerated in the same way, after the two types of resins are first separated, by making use of the difference in their density.

**Preparation of Carbonate Free Base.** Allowing a 0.1 N solution of sodium hydroxide or potassium hydroxide to percolate through a strong base (anion) exchange resin results in replacement of hydroxide ions on the resin by carbonate ions in the solution. Similarly, if the resin is in chloride form, the carbonate replaces the chloride and the chloride is harmless in the subsequent acid-base titration.

**Concentration of Traces.** If proper precautions are taken, ions can be concentrated and purified by passing very dilute solutions through ion exchange resins. Nickel, manganese, and zinc in foodstuffs, and copper in milk, have been concentrated on ion exchange resins so that they can be determined by standard methods.

**Titration of Salts with Acids and Bases.** Passing a salt through either a cation or anion exchange resin, in the acid or base form, will produce either an acid or base solution, respectively, chemically equivalent to the amount of salt. This acid or base solution can be titrated with standard base or acid to determine the amount of the original salt. These reactions can be quantitative.

**Separation of Similar Ions.** Ions similar to each other, as those of the rare earth metals, have been separated in pure form by ion exchange. Separating sodium ions from potassium ions is a much simpler operation. See J. Beukenkamp and W. Rieman, "Determination of Sodium and Potassium, Employing Ion-Exchange Separations," *Anal. Chem.*, XXII (1950), 582–585.

**Example.** A solution containing 8 milliequivalents each of $Na^+$ and $K^+$ was poured through a column containing 60 g of finely divided cation exchange resin. The resin was capable of holding about 240 milliequivalents of metal ion. A solution of 0.7 M HCl was allowed to percolate slowly through the resin to wash out (elute) the ions from the resin. The first

370 ml contained nothing but HCl, the next 160 ml contained all of the Na$^+$, and the next 190 ml contained all of the K$^+$. About 5 hours were required for the passage of 720 ml through the column. Fig. 27 shows graphically how this operation proceeded.

One advantage of ion exchange methods is that 100% separations are possible.

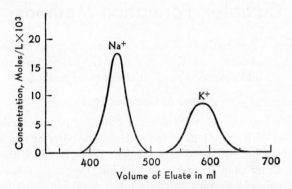

Fig. 27. Separation of Sodium and Potassium
from Each Other, by Ion Exchange.

From John Beukenkamp and William Rieman III, "Determination of Sodium and Potassium, Employing Ion-Exchange Separation," *Analytical Chemistry*, XXII (1950), 582.

## Review Questions and Problems

1. List five general methods of separating a constituent from other materials in a sample.
2. What are chelate compounds?
3. What are four advantages of organic precipitating agents?
4. Give three disadvantages which organic precipitants may have.
5. Name several elements usually separated in analyses by volatilization methods, and describe the reactions involved in each case.
6. Explain how chromatography differs from ion exchange.
7. What are some applications of ion exchange to analytical methods?
8. What are some applications of adsorption methods?
9. Explain why several extractions with small amounts of solvent are more effective in separations by extraction than one extraction with a large amount of solvent.

# 13

# Complex Formation Methods

Although a few methods of analysis involving complex formation have been known for a long time, recent studies have uncovered many new reagents and some new applications of older methods.

## Nature of Complex Ions

Complex ions are generally thought of as compounds made up of a metal ion with other ions or molecules. The parts of the complex are held together by co-ordinate covalent bonds in which the ion or molecule, other than the central metal ion, forms the bond by donating a pair of electrons to the central metal ion. According to the G. N. Lewis conception of acids and bases (pp. 97–98), the central metal ion acts as an acid, and the other ions or molecules act as bases.

**A Complex with Ammonia.** One of the best known of complex ions is the copper ammonia complex:

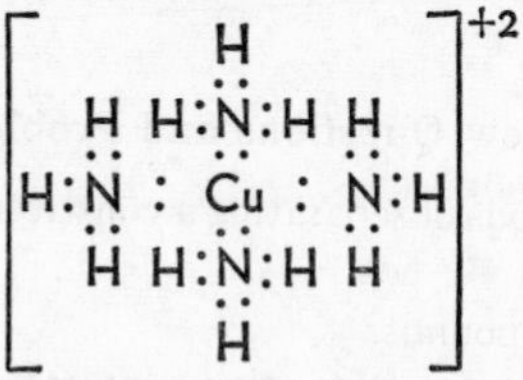

$$
\left[
\begin{array}{c}
\text{H} \\
\text{H H:N:H H} \\
\text{H:N : Cu : N:H} \\
\text{H H:N:H H} \\
\text{H}
\end{array}
\right]^{+2}
$$

In place of ammonia molecules, water molecules or cyanide, fluoride, chloride, iodide, oxalate, and sulfate ions also form similar complex ions, either with copper or with other metal ions.

**A Complex with Chloride.** Cadmium, with chloride ions, forms a complex ion much like the complex with ammonia. The $Cd^{+2}$ with four $Cl^-$ produces an ion with a $-2$ charge.

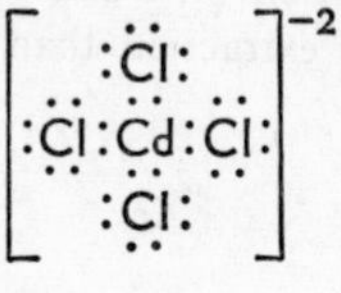

$$
\left[
\begin{array}{c}
\text{:Cl:} \\
\text{:Cl:Cd:Cl:} \\
\text{:Cl:}
\end{array}
\right]^{-2}
$$

**A Complex with Fluoride.** Fluorides form very stable complexes with $Al^{+3}$, $Fe^{+3}$, and many other metal ions, due to the small radius of the fluoride ion. It is possible, in many cases, that fluoride complexes are very stable because there is an actual exchange of electrons, with the result that the fluoride complexes are held together by electrostatic forces as ionic pairs, rather than by co-ordinate covalent bonds alone. See R. M. Fuoss, *Chem. Rev.*, XVII (1935). The structural formula of the aluminum fluoride complex is:

**General Rules of Complex Formation.** Several general statements can be made about complex ions and their formation. There are sometimes exceptions to these statements.

1. The number of ions or molecules that are held about the central atom is the coordination number. This is dependent upon the radius of the central atom relative to the radius of the coordinating particle. The elements in the first period of the periodic table have a maximum coordination number of 4. The second and third period elements have a maximum coordination number of 6, and other atoms have higher possible coordination numbers.

2. The ions do not always make use of their maximum coordination numbers. $Ag^+$ forms $Ag(NH_3)_2^+$ with a coordination number of 2, $Ni^{+2}$ often has a coordination number of 4, and $Cu^{+2}$ exhibits a coordination number of 2.

3. According to Fajans and Sidgwick the most easily deformed negative ions form the most stable complexes. Therefore, the following contribute to stability in complex ion formation.

a. Small radius of cation (central atom).

b. Large radius of anion (except $F^-$, where ion pairs form — see Complex with Fluoride, above). Iodides form more stable complex ions than chlorides, and perchlorate, the least deformable of the common ions, forms the least stable complexes.

c. High charge on both cation and anion.

d. Metal ions that do not have 8 electrons in the outer energy level of the ion as in an inert gas. $K^+$ has 8 electrons in its outer energy level. It forms few complexes. $Ag^+$ has 18 electrons in its outer energy level. It forms many stable complexes.

## Analytical Applications of Complex Ion Formation

There are many such applications. Only a few will be mentioned here.

**Mercuric Ion Titration.** Mercuric nitrate solution can be used to titrate chloride, bromide, iodide, thiocyanate, and cyanide.

**Example 1.** Chloride, bromide, and thiocyanate can be titrated with $Hg(NO_3)_2$. The reactions, using chloride as an example, are:

$$Hg^{+2} + 2Cl^- \rightarrow HgCl_2 \text{ (slightly ionized)}.$$

At the end point a slight excess of $Hg^{+2}$, with diphenyl carbazide as an indicator, yields an intense violet color.

$$Hg^{+2} + \text{diphenyl carbazide} \xrightarrow{\text{pH 1.5–2.0}} \text{violet color.}$$

ADVANTAGES OF THE METHOD:

1. Speed.
2. Wide range of chloride concentrations can be determined in this way.

DISADVANTAGES OF THE METHOD:

1. Any substance that can form a complex with diphenyl carbazide or mercuric ion interferes with the titration.
2. The narrow range of pH where the indicator functions requires time for preparation of the solution for titration.

**Other Variations:**

1. Instead of diphenyl carbazide, diphenyl carbazone can be used as indicator at pH 3.2–3.3.
2. Sodium nitroprusside forms a precipitate with any excess of $Hg^{+2}$, which indicates the end point.

**Example 2.** Iodide can be determined by titration with $Hg^{+2}$ solution. The reaction is:

$$Hg^{+2} + 4I^- \rightarrow HgI_4^{-2}.$$

The indication of the end point is formation of the red $HgI_2$ with the first trace of excess of $Hg^{+2}$.

$$HgI_4^{-2} + Hg^{+2} \rightarrow 2HgI_2.$$

DISADVANTAGES OF THE METHOD:

1. $HgI_4^{-2}$ dissociates somewhat, giving an end point with low results. Since this error is partially offset by using $HgCl_2$ solution rather than $Hg(NO_3)_2$ solution, the former, although not very soluble, is most often used.

2. Because of errors mentioned in 1, the standardization and analysis require more time and care than are usually available.

**Example 3.** Cyanide, in cyanide plating baths, must be determined frequently. Titration with standard silver ion solutions is commonly used, but it requires some special modifications. The main reaction is:

$$Ag^+ + 2CN^- \rightarrow Ag(CN)_2^-.$$

A slight excess of $Ag^+$ causes AgCN to precipitate out at just past the equivalence point. The equation for the reaction is:

$$Ag(CN)_2^- + Ag^+ \rightarrow 2AgCN.$$

During the titration an excess of $Ag^+$ builds up in parts of the solution, producing the AgCN precipitate which redissolves very slowly in the excess cyanide. Therefore ammonia is added to the cyanide solution to prevent AgCN from precipitating, and KI is added to give a precipitate of AgI (insoluble in the ammonia solution) as an indicator of the end point. The AgI that forms during the titration is yellowish and quickly soluble in any excess of $CN^-$, and gives a permanent opalescence at the end point. The end point reaction between excess $Ag^+$ and $I^-$ is:

$$Ag^+ + I^- \rightarrow AgI.$$

ADVANTAGE OF THE METHOD:

This analysis gives one of the sharpest and most precise end points known.

DISADVANTAGES OF THE METHOD:

1. One disadvantage, not really serious, is that only one ion of silver is chemically equivalent to two cyanide ions.

2. The extremely poisonous nature of cyanides makes them dangerous to handle. They must never be allowed to become acid, or deadly HCN gas may be formed.

**The Analysis of a Cyanide.** Caution: never use a pipet to measure solutions containing cyanide. Either use a buret, or weigh the solutions. Solutions of cyanide used as unknowns decompose when left standing. *Never acidify a solution containing cyanide!* Dispose of all solutions, under a hood, in specially provided containers.

PREPARATION AND STANDARDIZATION OF SOLUTION. Only one solution need be prepared and standardized, an approximately 0.10 N silver nitrate solution. Weigh out 8.4944 g of primary standard silver nitrate into a 500 ml volumetric flask. Dissolve in water and dilute to the mark on the flask.

PROCEDURE.

1. Weigh three clean, dry Erlenmeyer flasks.

2. Add to each a sample of cyanide, provided by the instructor.

3. Weigh the flasks again. The difference in weight will be the weight of the sample.

4. Dilute to 50 ml.

5. Add 0.10 g of solid KI.

6. Add 3 ml of concentrated ammonia solution (ammonium hydroxide).

7. Titrate with the standard 0.1 N silver nitrate solution to a permanent faint opalescence.

Calculate the per cent of cyanide ($CN^-$) in the sample, using 0.05204 as the gme of cyanide.

**Example.** If a sample of cyanide solution weighing 9.434 g is titrated to an end point with 31.49 ml of 0.09411 N silver nitrate, what is the per cent of $CN^-$ in the unknown solution?

Step 1. Find the number of gme of $CN^-$ in the titrating solution, and therefore in the unknown, by multiplying the normality of the titrating solution by its volume.

$$31.49 \times 0.09411 = 2.964 \text{ gme.}$$

Step 2. Find the weight of $CN^-$ in the sample by multiplying the number of gme by the weight of one gme.

$$2.964 \times 0.05204 = 0.1542 \text{ g of } CN^-.$$

Step 3. Find the per cent of cyanide ion in the sample by dividing the weight of cyanide by the weight of the sample and multiplying by 100.

$$\frac{0.1542 \times 100}{9.434} = 1.635\% \ CN^- \text{ in the solution.}$$

Combining all three steps in one:

$$\frac{31.49 \times 0.09411 \times 0.05204 \times 100}{9.434} = 1.635\% \ CN^-.$$

## Analytical Application of Chelate Complexing

**Versene or EDTA.** Of the chelate complexing agents, ethylene-diaminetetracetic acid, EDTA (known also as versene), is one of the commonest and most useful.

FUNCTION OF THE REAGENT. The EDTA, or versene, has the following structural formula:

$$\text{HOOCCH}_2 \diagdown \qquad\qquad \diagup \text{CH}_2\text{COOH}$$
$$\text{NCH}_2\text{—CH}_2\text{N}$$
$$\text{HOOCCH}_2 \diagup \qquad\qquad \diagdown \text{CH}_2\text{COOH}$$

The disodium salt, written $Na_2H_2Ver \cdot 2H_2O$, ionizes to give $H_2Ver^{-2}$ ions which react with $Ca^{+2}$ or $Mg^{+2}$ as well as with other divalent ions thus:

$$Ca^{+2} + H_2Ver^{-2} \rightarrow CaVer^{-2} + 2H^+$$

or:

$$Mg^{+2} + H_2Ver^{-2} \rightarrow MgVer^{-2} + 2H^+.$$

The $CaVer^{-2}$ and $MgVer^{-2}$ are chelate compounds (see Chap. 12) which are so slightly ionized that $Ca^{+2}$ and $Mg^{+2}$ are effectually removed from solution by the disodium versenate. This gives the chemist a method of determining the hardness of water.

INDICATOR. The indicator for the reaction, when titrating $Ca^{+2}$ and $Mg^{+2}$ in water, must show the presence of a slight excess of the $Na_2Ver^{-2}$. Such a compound is eriochrome black T or F241, a triequivalent acid, $H_3In$, where In is the indicator ion. The functioning of the indicator depends upon several reactions and conditions:

a. The pH of the solution:

$$\underset{\text{red}}{H_2In^-} \underset{}{\overset{\text{pH 6.3}}{\rightleftharpoons}} \underset{\text{blue}}{HIn^{-2}} \overset{\text{pH 11.5}}{\rightleftharpoons} \underset{\text{orange}}{In^{-3}}.$$

b. $Mg^{+2}$ must be present during the titration if the indicator is to function. At pH 8–10:

$$HIn^{-2} + Mg^{+2} \overset{\text{pH 10}}{\rightleftharpoons} MgIn^- + H^+.$$

During a titration of a solution containing both $Ca^{+2}$ and $Mg^{+2}$ the versenate, $H_2Ver^{-2}$, reacts:

1. First with $Ca^{+2}$ until the $Ca^{+2}$ concentration is **very low**:

$$Ca^{+2} + H_2Ver^{-2} \rightleftharpoons CaVer^{-2} + 2H^+.$$

2. Then with $Mg^{+2}$:

$$Mg^{+2} + H_2Ver^{-2} \rightleftharpoons MgVer^{-2} + 2H^+.$$

3. Then with the red magnesium-indicator complex, $MgIn^-$:

$$\underset{\text{red}}{MgIn^-} + H_2Ver^{-2} \rightleftharpoons MgVer^{-2} + \underset{\text{blue}}{HIn^{-2}} + H^+.$$

The disappearance of any of the red color identifies the end point. It is brought about by the slight excess of versene which removes $Mg^{+2}$ from the red $MgIn^-$, leaving the blue $HIn^{-2}$ (stable at pH 10 or 11).

**The Analysis of Water for $Ca^{+2}$ and $Mg^{+2}$.** The analysis of water for calcium and magnesium hardness is chosen as an example of a titration with a chelating agent (versene).

PREPARATION OF SOLUTIONS. The following solutions should be prepared in advance of the analysis.

*Buffer Solution.* Weigh out 6.8 g of solid $NH_4Cl$. To this add 57.0 ml of concentrated ammonia (ammonium hydroxide), and dilute to 10 ml.

*Indicator.* Dissolve 0.250 g of eriochrome black T in 50 ml of alcohol.

*Versene Solution.* Dissolve in water and dilute to one liter 4.0 g of disodium hydrogen versenate dihydrate and 0.10 g of $MgCl_2 \cdot 6H_2O$.

*Standard Calcium Solution.* Dissolve 1.0000 g of the purest available $CaCO_3$ in enough dilute (1:3) hydrochloric acid to effect solution. Transfer to a one liter volumetric flask and dilute to the mark. Each ml of this is equivalent to 1.00 mg of calcium carbonate.

STANDARDIZATION OF VERSENE SOLUTION. The versene solution is standardized against the standard calcium carbonate solution.

1. Pipet 25.0 ml of the standard calcium solution into a 250 ml Erlenmeyer flask, and dilute to 50 ml.

2. Add 1.0 ml of buffer solution.

3. Add 4 drops of indicator solution.

4. Titrate with the versenate solution until all of the reddish color is gone and a pure blue color remains in the solution. Near the end point add two drops of the versene solution at a time, reading the buret each time before the solution is added. The end point is passed when no further color change from red to blue can be discerned. The reading before the last two drops were added is taken as the titration volume.

5. Calculate the volume of versenate solution needed to make up

exactly 500 ml of solution of a strength equal to 1.0 mg of $CaCO_3$ per ml. Measure this volume out carefully into a 500 ml volumetric flask, dilute to the mark, and check its strength by titrating 25 ml of the standard calcium solution.

HARDNESS OF WATER. The hardness of water, due to $Ca^{+2}$ and $Mg^{+2}$, is found in the same way as the calcium solution is standardized. The steps are:.

1. Pipet out 50 ml of the water into a 250 ml Erlenmeyer flask.
2. Add 4 ml of buffer solution.
3. Add 0.02 g of hydroxylammonium chloride.
4. Add 0.25 g of solid NaCN.
5. Add 4 drops of indicator solution.
6. Titrate with the standard versenate solution.
7. Calculate the hardness of the water by finding the parts per million of calcium carbonate in the water.

Step 1. Since the volume of sample taken (50 ml) is $\frac{1}{20}$ of a liter, multiply the volume of titration by 20 to find the volume needed to titrate one liter of the water. One liter of water is assumed to weigh 1000 g.

Step 2. Since each ml of the versenate solution is equivalent to 1 mg of $CaCO_3$, the number of ml of versene, calculated in step 1, is also the number of mg of $CaCO_3$ hardness in a liter of water.

Step 3. Since there are one million mg of water in one liter of water, the number of mg of hardness per liter is the same as parts per million of $CaCO_3$ hardness in the sample. This is the total hardness due to $Ca^{+2}$ and $Mg^{+2}$ both, but it is reported as parts per million, ppm, of $CaCO_3$.

The NaCN (sodium cyanide) is added to form a very stable complex with any heavy metal ion that might be present. This prevents the metal ion from interfering by its reacting with the versene. The cyanide may be omitted if hardness due to calcium and magnesium only is not desired.

The hydroxylammonium chloride is added to reduce the ferric to ferrous ions, if any are present. In the ferrous state, the cyanide prevents the iron from interfering.

To determine hardness due to either $Ca^{+2}$ or $Mg^{+2}$ alone, titrate both together in one sample as described above. In another sample of water, precipitate out the $Ca^{+2}$ as $CaC_2O_4$ (calcium oxalate), and then titrate the remaining solution which will contain the $Mg^{+2}$. The hardness due to calcium only is then found by difference.

*Advantages of the Method:*

Despite the fact that this analysis represents an application of complex ion or chelate formation, it is quite practical. Thousands of such determinations are made daily in commercial laboratories. The main advantages are:

1. The determination is rapid, requiring only a few minutes.
2. The precision is good enough for almost all commercial needs.
3. Interfering ions can be controlled easily.
4. Only heavy metals and $Al^{+3}$ interfere.

*Disadvantages of the Method:*

1. The end point is not so sharply defined as it is in most titrations.
2. The end point is found by a change from one color to another and is the point where the first color disappears. This is unusual, as in most titrations the end point is indicated by the first, rather than the last, perceptible change.
3. The color changes are very difficult to see in certain kinds of light.

## Review Questions and Problems

1. Define: versene, complex ion, co-ordination number.
2. Draw electronic diagrams of some typical complex ions.
3. State the four rules of Fajans and Sidgwick concerning the stability of complexes.
4. Outline the essential steps in an analysis involving mercuric ion as a titrating agent.
5. What are some advantages of determinations made with mercuric ion?
6. Why should great care be exercised in analyses of cyanide?
7. What are the reactions that take place during the determination of the hardness of water by versene (EDTA) titration?
8. How can hardness of water due to either $Ca^{+2}$ or $Mg^{+2}$ be determined?
9. What indicator is employed in a versene titration and how does it function?
10. What advantages and disadvantages are there with a versene titration?
11. Why is iodide added to the solution during the titration of cyanide?
12. If a sample of solution containing cyanide weighs 4.981 g, and if upon dilution and titration with 0.1041 N $AgNO_3$ solution it requires 47.22 ml of the latter, what is the per cent of $CN^-$ in the sample? The gme of $CN^-$ is 0.05204.
13. Calculate the ppm (parts per million) of $CaCO_3$ hardness of a 50 ml sample of water that required 8.30 ml of versene for the titration. Each ml of the versene is equivalent to 1 mg of $CaCO_3$.

NOMENCLATURE. Confusion of terminology in photometric study by different authors led to formation of a committee with the goal of establishing a uniform system of symbols and terms. See H. K. Hughes, et al., "Suggested Nomenclature in Applied Spectroscopy," *Analytical Chemistry*, XXIV, No. 8, 1349 (1952). Their suggestions have been followed by many recent writers and will be the basis of the definitions in this chapter.

# 14

# Analysis by Instrumental Measurements

The introduction of electronic apparatus for measuring various physical properties of substances has greatly increased the number of analyses that can be done by instrumental methods. The ordinary instruments such as the balance and the buret are still used as much as ever, but applications of analytical methods have been extended by the use of new devices for making physico-chemical measurements.

## Absorptiometry

One of the very large fields of new analytical methods involves the estimation of quantities of constituents by measuring the degree of absorption, by colored substances, of light of certain wave lengths. At one time all such measurements were made visually. The photo-electric devices now available make the use of the unaided eye nearly obsolete, except for very hasty determinations.

**Basic Laws and Principles.** White light passing through a colored solution becomes "colored." Actually, certain wave lengths of light have been absorbed by the colored material in the solution. Those wave lengths not absorbed go on through and are observed as the hue of the solution. See Table 7.

TABLE 7

HUES ABSORBED AND TRANSMITTED

| HUE TRANSMITTED (SEEN) | HUE ABSORBED | WAVE LENGTH ABSORBED mμ |
|---|---|---|
| bluish green | red | 650–700 |
| greenish blue | orange | 600–650 |
| blue | yellow | 570–600 |
| purple | green | 490–570 |
| red | blue green | 475–490 |
| yellow | blue | 440–475 |
| yellow green | violet | 400–440 |

195

NOMENCLATURE.  Confusion of terminology in photometric studies by different authors led to formation of a committee with the goal of establishing a uniform system of symbols and terms.  See H. K. Hughes *et al.*, "Suggested Nomenclature in Applied Spectroscopy," *Analytical Chemistry*, XXIV (1952), 1349–1354.  Their suggestions have been followed by many recent writers and will be the basis of definitions in this chapter.

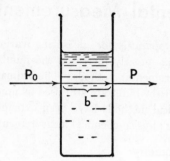

Fig. 28.  Relation of Incident Light, $P_0$, Transmitted Light, $P$, and Thickness of the Absorbing Layer, $b$.

BEER'S LAW.  This law (also called the Beer-Lambert law or the law of Beer and Bouguer) is concerned with four factors:

1. Incident radiant power, or a quantity proportional to it, as measured with a pure solvent in the beam of light and represented by $P_0$, or frequently by $I_0$.

2. Transmitted radiant power, represented by $P$, or frequently by $I$.

3. The thickness or breadth, usually in centimeters, of the absorbing liquid in the cell, represented by $b$ or the letter $l$.

4. The concentration of the substance in the solution, usually in moles per liter and represented by $c$.

Fig. 28 illustrates the relation of the first three factors to each other.

Beer's law is expressed mathematically:

$$P = P_0 10^{-abc}$$

or:

$$\log \frac{P}{P_0} = -abc, \qquad (14\text{--}1)$$

where $a$ is the absorptivity (also called the extinction coefficient, specific absorption, and absorbance index), which is equal to the ratio of the absorbance to the product of concentration and length of optical path.

The absorbance, represented by $A$, is given by the equation:

$$A = abc$$

from which the definition for absorptivity stated above is derived:

$$a = \frac{A}{bc}.$$

There is no name for the unit of absorptivity.

The absorbance, $A$ (sometimes called the optical density), is also defined as the logarithm to the base 10 of the reciprocal of the transmittance, $T$:

$$A = \log_{10}\left(\frac{1}{T}\right)$$

where $T$, the transmittance, is the ratio of the radiant power transmitted by a sample ($P$) to the radiant power incident on the sample ($P_0$). This statement can be expressed as the equation:

$$T = \frac{P}{P_0}.$$

The transmittance is stated either as a decimal or per cent transmittance and has no dimensions since $P$ and $P_0$ are expressed in the same units.

Another concept frequently used is the molar absorptivity (sometimes called the molar extinction coefficient) represented by $\epsilon$ (epsilon). It is simply the absorptivity expressed in units of $\frac{\text{liter}}{\text{mole} \times \text{cm}}$. The concentration is in moles per liter, and the cell length is in centimeters.

Beer's law is true when:

1. Light of a single wave length is used.

2. The solution contains only one species capable of absorbing the particular wave length. (A species is a single form of an ion or molecule. An ion with five molecules of water coordinated is a species that is different from the same ion with four molecules of water coordinated.)

3. Only light transmitted through the solution is measured as emergent light. None is due to fluorescence, scattering by suspended particles, or leakage by the instrument.

APPLICATIONS OF BEER'S LAW. Only a few applications can be considered here, and they are best explained by examples.

**Example 1.** Find the molar absorptivity for a substance in a solution where the per cent transmittance is 60% with a solution that is $10^{-3}$ molar, and the thickness of the cell $b$ is one cm.

Step 1. Substitute all known values in Equation (14–1) where 60% transmittance $\dfrac{P}{P_0} = 0.60$.

$$\log 0.60 = -a \times 1 \times 10^{-3}.$$

Step 2. Solve for $a$ by finding the log of 0.60 and setting it equal to the term containing $a$.

$$-1 + .7782 = -a \times 1 \times 10^{-3}.$$

Simplifying, we get:

$$-.2218 = -a \times 10^{-3}.$$
$$a = \frac{0.2218}{10^{-3}} = 221.8 = 2.22 \times 10^{2} = \text{the molar absorptivity.}$$

**Example 2.** With the absorptivity equal to $2.22 \times 10^{2}$, what would be the molar concentration of the same substance in a solution which has a transmittance of 30%? All other factors, except concentration, are the same as in example 1.

Step 1. Substitute all known values in Equation (14–1).

$$\log 0.30 = -2.22 \times 10^{2} \times 1 \times c.$$

Step 2. Solve for $c$ by finding the log of 0.30 and inserting it into the equation.

$$-1 + 0.4771 = -2.22 \times 10^{2} \times c.$$
$$-0.5229 = -2.22 \times 10^{2} \times c.$$
$$c = \frac{0.5229}{222} = 2.36 \times 10^{-3} \text{ molar,}$$

the concentration of the solution that would give a reading of 30% transmittance. This is 2.36 times as concentrated as the solution in example 1.

Example 2 indicates that the equation for Beer's law is useful for finding the concentration of a solution whose transmittance is different from the transmittance of the one measured. It can therefore be used for finding the range of concentration of a substance that will produce a specified range of per cent transmittance. The molar absorptivity must be known or calculable, and any change in concentration must not change the chemical nature of the absorbing substance or the amount of light absorbed at any given wave length will not be proportional to the sought-for constituent.

**Methods of Measurement of Transmitted Light.** The visual operator cannot remember hues or intensities, so he must compare the light transmitted through two solutions while they are side by side.

Fig. 29 shows Nessler tubes which can be viewed from above, enabling the viewer to match two solutions side by side.

METHODS USING NESSLER TUBES. There are several general methods of using Nessler tubes. The two most common ones are given here. If more precise instruments are available, Nessler tubes should not be used as their use is subject to errors due to eye fatigue or faulty judgment of the operator.

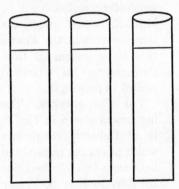

Fig. 29. Nessler Tubes with Clear Flat Bottoms.

*The Standard Series Method.* The following steps are taken.

1. A series of Nessler tubes are filled to the mark with solutions containing various known quantities of the sought-for constituent.

2. The unknown is prepared and a comparison of its color is made with the colors of the known solutions, viewing all tubes vertically with the same light source.

3. When an unknown solution matches one of the standards, its concentration is taken to be the same as that of the standard.

4. When the color is found to lie between the colors of two standard solutions, a new series of standards more closely matching the unknown may be prepared, or the concentration of the unknown can be estimated.

Colored glass standards may be substituted for standard solutions where their use is satisfactory.

*Duplication Method.* This method involves the following steps.

1. The solution containing the unknown is placed in a Nessler tube, filling it up to the mark.

2. All solutions needed to develop the color, except the constituent being determined, are put into another Nessler tube.

3. A solution of known concentration of the sought-for constituent is run from a buret into the tube.

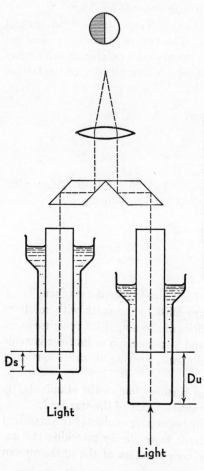

4. When the colors in both tubes almost match, the known solution is diluted nearly to the mark.

5. The final quantity of known solution is run in.

6. The concentration of sought-for constituent will be identical in both tubes, the concentration in the known tube being calculated from the volume of standard needed to prepare it.

THE COLORIMETER. The instrument shown in Fig. 30 is a Duboscq colorimeter which places the transmitted light from two solutions side by side, so that both may be viewed by a single eye. In this way any difference in hue or intensity can be seen to cause a line of demarcation between two halves of a disk.

The colorimeter provides a convenient way of matching colors and measuring accurately the depth of both the known and the unknown solutions. It is assumed that equal amounts of the constituent sought are in both solutions through which the colors of transmitted light beams match. Thus, where:

Fig. 30. Diagram of the Duboscq Colorimeter. $D_s$ is the depth of the standard solution, and $D_u$ is the depth of the unknown solution.

$C_s$ is the concentration of the standard solution,
$C_u$ is the concentration of the unknown solution,
$D_s$ is the depth of the standard solution,

$D_u$ is the depth of the unknown solution, then:

$$C_uD_u = C_sD_s$$

and:

$$C_u = \frac{C_sD_s}{D_u}. \tag{14-2}$$

**Example.** The concentration of molybdenum thiocyanate is $2 \times 10^{-4}$ molar in a standard solution. The depth or thickness of this solution is read as 8.47 cm. The depth of the matching unknown solution is read as 6.55 cm. What is the molar concentration of the unknown solution?

Step 1. Substitute the given values in Equation (14-2).

$$C_u = \frac{2 \times 10^{-4} \times 8.47}{6.55}.$$

Step 2. Solve for $C_u$.

$C_u = 2.59 \times 10^{-4}$ molar = the concentration of molybdenum thiocyanate in the unknown solution.

**Spectrophotometry.** Spectrophotometry differs from colorimetry in that the absorbance of a solution or substance is determined with only one wave length of light being transmitted and measured. In practice, a narrow band of wave lengths of light is used, rather than a single wave length.

CONSTRUCTION OF THE SPECTROPHOTOMETER. A spectrophotometer always consists of four essential parts:

1. A light source. This is usually a light bulb with a carefully controlled current delivered to it.

2. A monochromator. This part of the instrument may be any one of the following:

a. A filter or set of filters that eliminates all but a narrow band of wave lengths of light.

b. A slit and prism arrangement to allow a slit of light to enter the prism and emerge as a series of hues, a narrow band of which can be selected by a second narrow slit.

c. A grating with slits which functions like the arrangement of the prism.

3. An absorption cell in which the absorbance of known and unknown solutions can be measured.

4. The photocell and galvanometer which make up the light-measuring part of the instrument.

These parts are illustrated diagrammatically in Fig. 31, p. 202.

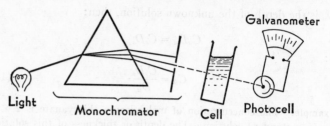

Fig. 31. Diagram of a Spectrophotometer.

OPERATION OF THE SPECTROPHOTOMETER. The basic steps in an analysis with a spectrophotometer are always the same. Slight variations in each step and sometimes the mechanics of operating different instruments may alter the details of procedure somewhat.

Step 1. The absorbance of every solution at any given wave length is found by placing an absorption tube, called a cell or cuvette, in the instrument containing solvent only, adjusting the instrument to read 100% transmittance, then placing the absorption tube containing the unknown constituent in the instrument, and reading the per cent transmittance or the absorbance (optical density).

Step 2. If the absorption spectrum of the substance is not known, it should be determined by measuring the $\%T$ (per cent transmittance) or absorbance (optical density) over a wide range of wave lengths of light. Plotting such values gives curves such as those in Fig. 32.

Step 3. From the absorption spectrum choose a wave length at which the unknown has a high absorbance, or small per cent transmittance. If other substances are present their absorption spectra should be inspected and the wave length at which measurements are made on the unknown should be such as to give little interference by the other substances present. From Fig. 32 it can be seen that at 550 m$\mu$ wave length permanganate is not at its wave length of maximum absorbance. On the other hand, dichromate ions do not interfere as much as they do at 525 m$\mu$, where the absorbance of permanganate is at a maximum. Therefore 550 m$\mu$ would be a better wave length for measuring the absorbance of permanganate from manganese in steel in which chromium might occur.

Step 4. Make a calibration or working curve. Two general ways of plotting calibration curves are used.

a. The concentration-absorbance curve is a straight line if the Beer-

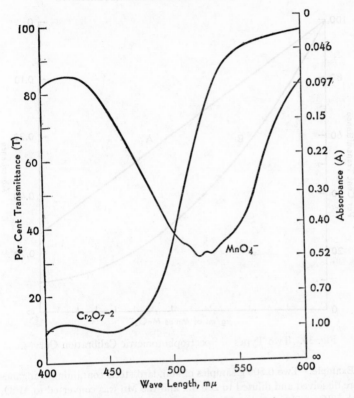

Fig. 32. Absorption Spectrum Curves for
Permanganate and Dichromate.

Lambert law holds for the substance. If such a line is not straight, the curve may still be satisfactory for analytical work. Such a plot is curve $A$ in Fig. 33, p. 204.

b. Another type of calibration curve plots per cent transmittance against concentration. The curve $B$ in Fig. 33 illustrates such a curve for permanganate.

Step 5. Find the absorbance (optical density) or per cent transmittance of the solution containing an unknown quantity of the constituent sought, where the solution was prepared by a procedure identical with that used for finding points on the calibration curve. The absorbance of the unknown solution is found on the calibration or standardization curve, and the corresponding concentration is read from the graph.

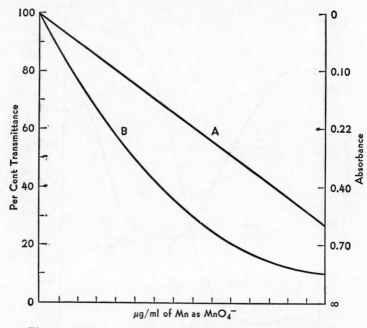

Fig. 33. Two Types of Spectrophotometric Calibration Curves.

**Example.** Two 0.500 g samples of standard steels containing manganese were dissolved and diluted to 250 ml, and the Mn was converted to $MnO_4^-$ with $KIO_4$. The sample with a per cent Mn of 0.628 had an absorbance of 0.688, and the one with 0.507 per cent Mn had an absorbance of 0.556. A 0.500 g sample of an unknown steel, when treated like the standards, had an absorbance of 0.592.

a. Draw a calibration or standardization curve plotting absorbance against micrograms of Mn per ml ($\mu g$ Mn/ml).

b. Find the concentration of Mn in the 250 ml of solution containing the unknown.

c. Find the per cent of Mn in the unknown steel.

Procedures.

a. Calculate the micrograms ($\mu g$) of Mn per ml of each of the 250 ml solutions of the standard steels. One $\mu g$ is one millionth gram, $10^{-6}$ grams.

For sample 1:

$$\frac{0.500 \times 10^6 \times 0.628 \times 10^{-2}}{250} = \mu g \text{ Mn/ml.}$$

$$20 \times 0.628 = 12.56 \ \mu g \text{ Mn/ml in sample 1,}$$

where:

0.500 is the weight of the sample;

$10^6$ converts grams to micrograms ($\mu g$);

$0.628 \times 10^{-2}$ is the % Mn converted to a decimal;

250 is the number of ml in which the Mn is dissolved.

For sample 2:

$$\frac{0.500 \times 10^6 \times 0.507 \times 10^{-2}}{250} = 10.14 \ \mu g \ Mn/ml.$$

b. Several methods are available for finding the concentration of Mn in the unknown.

1. By reading directly off the graph. This gives a value of about 10.7 $\mu g/ml$.

2. By interpolation or extrapolation.

Step 1. Between the concentrations of 10.14 $\mu g/ml$ and 12.56 $\mu g/ml$ there is a difference of 2.42 $\mu g/ml$. For this same difference in concentration there is a difference in absorbance of $0.688 - 0.556 = 0.132$.

Step 2. For any straight line plot, one absorbance unit will equal a certain value in $\mu g/ml$ of Mn. Thus 0.132 unit of absorbance is equal to 2.42 $\mu g/ml$ of Mn. Therefore:

$$\frac{2.42}{0.132} = 18.35 \ \mu g/ml \ of \ Mn \ for \ each \ 1.00 \ unit \ of \ absorbance.$$ Rounding off numbers and dividing by 1000 on both sides of the equation to get numbers of a magnitude that is more useful, we get:

$$0.0184 \ \mu g/ml \ of \ Mn = 0.001 \ unit \ of \ absorbance.$$

Step 3. The difference in absorbance or optical density between sample 1 and the unknown is:
$$0.688 - 0.592 = 0.096 \ unit.$$

The difference in absorbance between sample 2 and the unknown is:
$$0.592 - 0.556 = 0.036 \ unit.$$

Each 0.001 unit is equivalent to 0.0184 $\mu g/ml$ of Mn.

Step 4. Find the concentration of the unknown solution based on the difference in absorbance between the unknown solution and the solution of sample 1.

$$\frac{0.096}{0.001} \times 0.0184 = 1.77 \ \mu g/ml \ Mn$$ difference in concentration between the known sample 1 and the unknown.

$12.56 - 1.77 = 10.79 \ \mu g/ml$ of Mn = the concentration of the unknown solution.

To find the concentration of the unknown, based on the difference in absorbance between the unknown and sample 2, find the difference in absorbance units:

$$0.592 - 0.556 = 0.036 \ unit.$$

Calculate the difference in concentration, as shown above for sample 1:

$$\frac{0.036}{0.001} \times 0.0184 = 0.66 \ \mu g/ml \ Mn \ difference.$$

Add the difference to the concentration of the solution of sample 2:

$$10.14 + 0.66 = 10.80 \ \mu g/ml \ of \ Mn.$$

This method of calculating is quite satisfactory if the concentrations of unknowns and standards do not differ greatly, and if Beer's law holds. It can be seen that differences in calculations result if numbers are rounded off.

Where the per cent transmittance, instead of the absorbance, is measured, this same method of calculating can be applied, but only if the knowns (standards) and unknowns are very nearly the same. It is generally more reliable to read values directly from a graph.

3. A third way of calculating is to use only one standard and Beer's law. If only standard sample 1 and the unknown are run, find the concentration of the unknown, when the absorbance of the standard is 0.688 for a concentration of 12.56 $\mu g/ml$ and the absorbance of the unknown is 0.592.

From the Beer-Lambert law it can be shown that:

$$\frac{a_{unknown}}{a_{standard}} = \frac{c_{unknown}}{c_{standard}}, \quad (14-3)$$

where $a$ is the absorbance and $c$ is the concentration. Substituting in Equation (14-3):

$$\frac{0.592}{0.688} = \frac{c_{unknown}}{12.56 \ \mu g/ml}.$$

$$c_{unknown} = \frac{0.592 \times 12.56}{0.688}$$

$$= 10.80 \ \mu g/ml \ of \ Mn \ in \ the \ unknown \ solution.$$

This method is rapid but there are few checks against possible errors.

c. Calculation of the per cent of manganese in the sample from the concentration, 10.8 $\mu g/ml$, is as follows:

Step 1. Convert $\mu g/ml$ (micrograms per ml) to grams per liter by dividing $\mu g/ml$ by 1000.

$$(10.8 \ \mu g/ml = 10.8 \ mg/liter = 0.0108 \ g/liter.)$$

$$\frac{10.80}{1000} = 0.0108 \ g \ of \ Mn \ per \ liter \ of \ solution.$$

Step 2. Divide the g/liter by 4 to find the grams of Mn in 250 ml ($\frac{1}{4}$ of a liter).

$$\frac{0.0108}{4} = 0.0027 \ g \ of \ Mn \ in \ the \ sample.$$

Step 3. Calculate the per cent of Mn in the 0.5000 g of sample.

$$\frac{0.0027 \times 100}{0.5000} = 0.54\%.$$

## Turbidimetry and Nephelometry

Turbidimetry is the measurement of light that passes through a suspension. Nephelometry is the measurement of light reflected off particles in a suspension. Both turbidimetry and nephelometry are methods of determining the quantities of substances in the form of fine, suspended precipitates.

If all particles suspended in a liquid are the same size and shape, the amount of light either reflected to the side or allowed to go on through the solution is a function of the number of particles per unit volume of the solution.

The preparation of uniform precipitates is a difficult task but, for certain cases, may be worth the trouble for the saving in time. Details of such operations are beyond the scope of this book, however. All instruments useful in absorptiometry may be modified, or used directly, for either nephelometry or turbidimetry methods. Calculations are like those for absorptiometry.

## Fluorimetry

Certain substances absorb light energy of one wave length and re-emit the energy at a longer wave length. The re-emitted light is observed as fluorescence. Measuring the amount of energy re-emitted as light is easily accomplished by use of a spectrophotometer that has been modified for nephelometry. The amount of fluorescence is a function of the amount of material in the solution. Many possible errors and difficulties can be minimized, making such methods quick and fairly precise.

## Emissimetry

Tremendous strides have been made in recent times in applying photographic and photoelectric methods to the measurement of energy emitted by elements at high temperatures.

Fundamentally, most metallic elements, when heated, radiate energy of specific wave lengths when their valence electrons fall back into normal positions after being forced into energy levels more distant from the nucleus. Nonmetals do not readily radiate such energy. If all other conditions are constant, the amount of energy emitted is dependent upon the amount of the element excited. The substance may be excited by heating it in an arc, a spark, or a flame. The amount of energy radiated by any one element is measured either photographically or with a photocell.

If the substance is heated in a flame, the energy of some specific wave length emitted is usually measured with a photocell and the process is called flame spectrophotometry. The excitation of atoms by means of either an arc or a spark is employed in spectrographic analysis. The high temperatures obtained with arcs and sparks make it possible to determine quantities of many elements that cannot be found by flame methods. To arrive at an analysis, standards are compared to an unknown under as nearly identical conditions as possible.

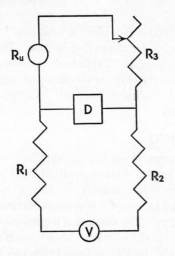

Fig 34. Diagram of a Conductance Bridge.

## Electrometric Methods

New design of many instruments has made various electrical measurements useful in analytical chemistry.

**Conductometric Methods.** Variations in concentrations of ions or in types of ions can result in variations in conductance of solutions.

**Basic Principles.** A great many variables exist in measurements of conductance. Because of this the measurements themselves and their interpretation require care and judgment. Measurements are made with a conductance bridge.

THE CONDUCTANCE BRIDGE. The construction of a bridge for measuring conductance is shown diagrammatically in Fig. 34, where $R_u$ is the resistance of the conductivity cell; $R_1$, $R_2$, and $R_3$ are resistances, $R_3$ being variable; $V$ is the A.C. voltage source; and $D$ is a detector which may be an ear phone, an electronic eye, or an A.C.

milliammeter. The circuit of this instrument is said to be balanced when no response is indicated by the detector. When the circuit is balanced, the following relation is true:

$$\frac{R_u}{R_1} = \frac{R_3}{R_2}. \qquad (14\text{--}4)$$

It is clear that conductance is really measured as a resistance.

IONIC MOBILITIES. The conductance of a solution is the sum of the conductance due to the number and mobility of each ion present. Hydrogen ions have the greatest mobility, hydroxide ions are also very mobile, and sodium and chloride ions are somewhat less mobile. See Table 8 for a comparison of the relative mobilities of several ions.

TABLE 8

RELATIVE MOBILITIES OF IONS

| | |
|---|---|
| $H_3O^+$ | 100 |
| $OH^-$ | 54 |
| $Cl^-$ | 21 |
| $NO_3^-$ | 20 |
| $Ag^+$ | 18 |
| $Na^+$ | 15 |

**Applications of Conductometric Methods.** Although measurement of the over-all concentration of all types of ions in solution, such as in determining the hardness of water, is one application, generally conductance methods are used in neutralization or precipitation titrations involving quite small quantities of materials.

NEUTRALIZATION TITRATIONS. During a neutralization reaction the number and mobilities of ions may change the over-all conductance so that if a graph is made by plotting conductance against volume of base added, a curve can be made such as Fig. 35, p. 210. It shows the neutralization of hydrochloric acid with sodium hydroxide solution. $E$ represents the equivalence or end point of the titration.

Starting at the left in Fig. 35, with hydrochloric acid alone, the conductance is the sum of the conductance of chloride and hydrogen ions. Adding sodium hydroxide reduces the number of hydrogen ions and increases the number of sodium ions, giving an over-all decrease in conductance. After the equivalence point is reached an excess of very mobile hydroxide ions increases the conductance again.

PRECIPITATION TITRATIONS. The conductance of a solution during a precipitation titration indicates an end point in much the same way

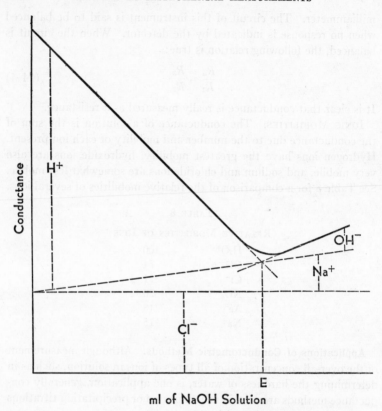

Fig. 35. A conductometric titration curve showing the contribution of each ion to the total conductance during an acid-base titration.

as during a neutralization titration. Fig. 36 plots the conductance during the titration of sodium chloride solution with silver nitrate solution. The addition of silver ions and nitrate ions together adds nitrate ions as the chloride ions are precipitated out. Nitrate and chloride have about the same mobility, so that no change in conductance occurs until the equivalence point is reached. When this occurs the excess of silver ions increases the conductivity. $E$ in Fig. 36 is the equivalence point.

Conductivity analyses can be very precise, even with minute quantities of materials. Some applications of conductance methods are the very accurate titration of sulfate in sea water, and titration of chloride in many very dilute solutions. Many other conductometric

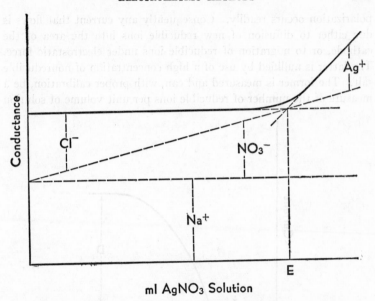

Fig. 36. A conductometric titration curve showing the contribution of each ion to the total conductance during a precipitation titration.

determinations have also been found useful. See H. T. S. Britton, *Conductometric Analysis*, Chapman and Hall, 1934, for applications.

**Polarography.** The polarograph has become a valuable instrument for determining very small quantities of impurities in metals and for analyzing traces of metals.

Only a small current will flow if two inert electrodes such as platinum or mercury are immersed in a solution containing $Pb^{+2}$ ions where the potential applied is insufficient to reduce the $Pb^{+2}$ to Pb at the cathode. This is called the residual current. If the voltage is increased until it is just large enough to reduce $Pb^{+2}$ to Pb, those lead ions near the cathode will be reduced whereas those farther away will not, since they are not in contact with the cathode. The reduction at the cathode surface reduces the concentration of lead ions near the cathode, and the flow of current soon becomes very small. The electrode is said to be polarized because its potential cannot be determined by applying the Nernst equation but can be determined by other factors proportional to the change in concentration. Such polarization is called concentration polarization.

With minute cathodes, such as a drop of mercury, concentration polarization occurs readily.   Consequently any current that flows is due either to diffusion of new reducible ions into the area of the cathode, or to migration of reducible ions under electrostatic force. The latter is nullified by use of a high concentration of nonreducible salt.   The former is measured and can, with proper calibration, be a measure of the number of reducible ions per unit volume of solution

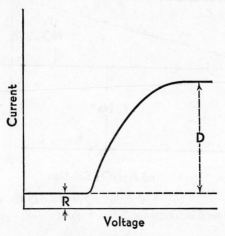

Fig. 37.   Type of Curve Obtained with a Polarograph.

that are capable of diffusion into the cathode area.   It is obvious that the higher the concentration of such ions, the greater the diffusion current.

A typical polarographic curve is shown in Fig. 37, where $D$ is the diffusion current and $R$ is the residual current.   $D$ is proportional to the concentration of reducible ions at the potential given along the voltage axis.

For further information about the polarographic method of analysis see Willard, Merritt, and Dean, *Instrumental Methods of Analysis*, Van Nostrand, 1951.

## Density Methods

Rapid, accurate analyses can be made by comparing the density of a solution of known constituents but of unknown percentage composition with densities of similar solutions of known percentage composition.   Alcohol content of liquors, strengths of acid solutions, etc. are quickly found by measuring the density and consulting tables.

For a brief but excellent summary of these methods see M. G. Mellon, *Quantitative Analysis*, Crowell, 1955, p. 305.

## Refractometry Methods

Quite precise analyses can be made quickly, in much the same way as in density methods, by comparing the index of refraction of unknowns with standards. For a summary of these methods see Mellon, *op. cit.*, p. 313.

### Review Questions and Problems

1. Define: transmittance, absorptivity, monochromator, calibration curve, absorbance, nephelometry, turbidimetry, diffusion current.
2. Explain why the conductivity of a solution of hydrochloric acid in water changes as it is titrated with sodium hydroxide solution.
3. Describe three methods of optical analysis which use Nessler tubes and a colorimeter.
4. State Beer's law, mathematically.
5. Draw a rough diagram of a spectrophotometer, labeling the essential parts.
6. a. From Fig. 32, at what wave lengths in millimicrons ($m\mu$) will (a) a solution of permanganate and (b) a solution of dichromate absorb light most strongly?
   b. At which wave length, 500 $m\mu$, 525 $m\mu$, or 550 $m\mu$, will dichromate have the least absorbance when one is measuring the absorbance of permanganate?
   c. At which wave length, 450 $m\mu$, 475 $m\mu$, or 500 $m\mu$, will permanganate cause the least interference when measuring the absorbance or transmittance of dichromate?
7. Draw a diagram of a conductance bridge and state how it operates.
8. A standard steel is known to contain 0.705 per cent Mn. One sample (sample No. 1), weighing 0.1558 g, produces 250 ml of a permanganate solution (solution No. 1) that has an absorbance or optical density of 0.215. Sample No. 2 of the standard steel, weighing 0.2131 g, produced 250 ml of a solution (solution No. 2) with an absorbance of 0.294. A sample of unknown steel, weighing 0.1998 g, produced 250 ml of a solution (solution No. 3) with an absorbance of 0.262.
   a. Calculate, in micrograms per ml ($\mu g/ml$), the concentration of Mn per ml in solutions 1 and 2.
   b. Draw a standardization curve (an absorbance-concentration curve).
   c. By using the graph, find the concentration of Mn in $\mu g/ml$ in solution No. 3.

d. Calculate, by interpolation, the weight of Mn in $\mu g/ml$ in solution No. 3.
e. From the value found in d calculate the per cent of manganese in the unknown steel.
f. Calculate the molar absorptivity of solution No. 2, assuming a cell thickness of 1 cm, and a per cent $T$ (transmittance) of 50.8.

# 15

# Analysis of Complex Substances

The complete analysis of complex materials is beyond the scope of this book, but a few outlines of the steps needed to accomplish an analysis may be helpful as examples. The analysis of brass is discussed in Chap. 11 (p. 169). The analysis of calcium in limestone is given in Chap. 10 (p. 144). The outline of a proximate analysis of limestone is given in this chapter. The analysis of steels, minerals, and other complex materials is available in many standard works.

## Limestone Analysis

More complete directions for this analysis are available in such volumes as I. M. Kolthoff and E. B. Sandell, *Textbook of Quantitative Inorganic Analysis*, 3rd ed., Macmillan, 1952, and W. F. Hillebrand and G. E. F. Lundell, *Applied Inorganic Analysis*, Wiley, 1929. The outline of the analysis given here contains only the essential steps, not the details of procedure.

**Outline of Limestone Analysis.** The outline on p. 216 gives a condensed picture of the limestone analysis.

**Loss on Ignition.** The sample of about 1 g of limestone should be dried at about 110° C, weighed into a crucible (platinum is most satisfactory), and heated slowly to about 950°–1000° C either in an electric furnace or over a Meker burner. If a furnace is used, start with it cold. The crucible and contents are repeatedly heated, cooled, and weighed until a constant weight is attained. The loss in weight is largely due to loss of $CO_2$ when carbonates of calcium and magnesium decompose to leave the oxides. This "loss on ignition" is calculated in per cent as follows:

$$\frac{\text{Loss in weight} \times 100}{\text{Weight of sample}} = \text{per cent loss on ignition.} \quad (15\text{-}1)$$

## LIMESTONE ANALYSIS

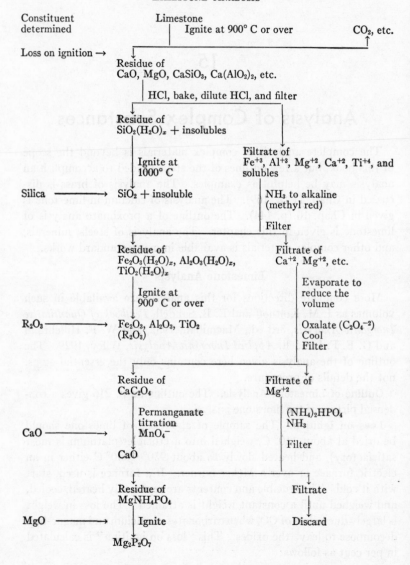

Constituent determined

Limestone — Ignite at 900° C or over      $CO_2$, etc.

Loss on ignition →

Residue of
CaO, MgO, CaSiO₃, Ca(AlO₂)₂, etc.

   HCl, bake, dilute HCl, and filter

Residue of
$SiO_2(H_2O)_x$ + insolubles

Filtrate of
$Fe^{+3}$, $Al^{+3}$, $Mg^{+2}$, $Ca^{+2}$, $Ti^{+4}$, and solubles

Silica     Ignite at 1000° C → $SiO_2$ + insoluble

NH₃ to alkaline (methyl red)

Filter

Residue of
$Fe_2O_3(H_2O)_x$, $Al_2O_3(H_2O)_x$, $TiO_2(H_2O)_x$

Filtrate of
$Ca^{+2}$, $Mg^{+2}$, etc.

Ignite at 900° C or over

Evaporate to reduce the volume

$R_2O_3$ → $Fe_2O_3$, $Al_2O_3$, $TiO_2$ ($R_2O_3$)

Oxalate $(C_2O_4^{-2})$
Cool
Filter

Residue of
$CaC_2O_4$

Filtrate of
$Mg^{+2}$

Permanganate titration $MnO_4^-$

$(NH_4)_2HPO_4$
NH₃
Filter

CaO → CaO

Residue of
$MgNH_4PO_4$

Filtrate

MgO → Ignite → $Mg_2P_2O_7$

Discard

**Example.** Some limestone was dried and a sample weighing 0.9817 g was placed in a platinum crucible which had been heated to constant weight at 950° C. After igniting the crucible containing the sample to constant weight, the residue in the crucible weighed 0.5924 g. Find the per cent loss on ignition.

Step 1. Find the loss in weight of the sample by subtracting the weight of sample after ignition from that before ignition.

$$0.9817 - 0.5924 = 0.3893 \text{ g loss on ignition.}$$

Step 2. Find the per cent of loss on ignition by dividing the loss in weight by the weight of the original sample and multiplying by 100.

$$\frac{0.3893 \times 100}{0.9817} = 39.66\% \text{ loss on ignition.}$$

**Silica.** The residue from the loss on ignition is treated with HCl solution, evaporated, and baked at about 110° C; all the soluble materials are then dissolved in dilute HCl solution. The insoluble residue of silica and other insoluble materials is filtered off and washed thoroughly, the paper is burned off, and the silica is heated to constant weight at the highest temperature that a burner or furnace can reach. The weight of the silica and insoluble residue is calculated as a per cent of the original sample weight.

$$\frac{\text{Weight of silica} \times 100}{\text{Weight of sample}} = \text{per cent silica.} \tag{15-2}$$

**Example.** What is the per cent of silica in the sample if the residue from the loss on ignition, as found in the example above, is extracted with acid, and the silica is heated to constant weight and found to weigh 0.04102 g? The sample weighed 0.9817 g.

Divide the weight of silica by the weight of the sample and multiply by 100.

$$\frac{0.04102 \times 100}{0.9817} = 4.18\% \text{ silica.}$$

**The $R_2O_3$.** The $R_2O_3$ is a mixture of $Fe_2O_3$, $Al_2O_3$, $TiO_2$, and other materials in the natural mineral that are made insoluble by the addition of ammonia. The solution obtained by extracting the silica with acid is made barely alkaline to methyl red, by adding dilute (1:2) ammonia solution. The precipitate formed is filtered off and placed in a crucible that has been heated to constant weight at about 950° C, and the paper is burned off at as low a temperature as possible. The crucible and contents are then heated to constant weight at 950° C. The weight of residue in the crucible is the weight of the $R_2O_3$. The per cent of $R_2O_3$ is calculated in exactly the same way as the per cent of silica.

$$\frac{\text{Weight of } R_2O_3 \times 100}{\text{Weight of sample}} = \text{per cent of } R_2O_3. \qquad (15\text{-}3)$$

**The CaO.** This material is determined as previously explained in detail in Chap. 10 (p. 144).

**The MgO.** The filtrate from the precipitation of the calcium as $CaC_2O_4$ (calcium oxalate) is evaporated with nitric acid to destroy the excess of $NH_4^+$ by the reaction:

$$NH_4^+ + NO_3^- \rightarrow N_2O + 2H_2O.$$

The solution is diluted; diammonium hydrogen phosphate and then ammonia solution are added until a strongly alkaline solution is obtained. The precipitate is filtered off, redissolved in HCl solution, and reprecipitated, using the same procedure as for the first precipitation. The precipitate is then filtered off and placed in a weighed crucible (heated to constant weight at 600° C or higher), and the crucible and its contents are heated to constant weight at 600° C. The precipitate is $MgNH_4PO_4$ which, upon ignition, becomes $Mg_2P_2O_7$ thus:

$$2MgNH_4PO_4 \rightarrow Mg_2P_2O_7 + 2NH_3 + H_2O.$$

The weight of MgO in the sample is calculated by finding the gravimetric factor of MgO in $Mg_2P_2O_7$, and multiplying the weight of residue in the ignited crucible by this factor:

$$\frac{MgO}{Mg_2P_2O_7} = \frac{80.64}{222.59}$$

$$= 0.3622, \text{ the gravimetric factor for MgO in } Mg_2P_2O_7.$$

$0.3622 \times$ weight of $Mg_2P_2O_7$ residue = the weight of MgO in the sample.

The per cent of MgO is found by dividing the weight of MgO by the weight of the sample and then multiplying by 100.

$$\frac{\text{Weight of MgO} \times 100}{\text{Weight of sample}} = \text{per cent of MgO in the sample.} \quad (15\text{-}4)$$

**Example.** If a sample weighing 0.9817 g produces an ignited precipitate of $Mg_2P_2O_7$ weighing 0.1238 g, what is the per cent of MgO in the sample?

Step 1. Using the gravimetric factor, find the weight of MgO in the sample by multiplying the weight of the residue ($Mg_2P_2O_7$) by the gravimetric factor, 0.3622.

$$0.1238 \times 0.3622 = 0.04484 \text{ g of MgO in the sample.}$$

Step 2. Find the per cent of the MgO in the sample by dividing the weight of MgO in the sample by the weight of the sample, and then multiplying by 100.

$$\frac{0.04484 \times 100}{0.9817} = 4.568\% \text{ MgO in the sample.}$$

Steps 1 and 2 can be combined:

$$\frac{0.1238 \times 0.3622 \times 100}{0.9817} = 4.568\% \text{ MgO.}$$

## Review Questions and Problems

1. Define: (a) loss on ignition, (b) $R_2O_3$.
2. After drying, a sample of limestone was measured out and found to weigh 0.8847 g. It weighed 0.6239 g after being ignited. The residue was treated with acid and the insoluble material was filtered out, ignited, and found to weigh 0.0391 g. Ammonia solution was added to the filtrate from the silica until the solution was alkaline to methyl red. The resultant precipitate of $R_2O_3$ was filtered, washed, ignited, and found to weigh 0.0514 g. From the remaining solution, calcium oxalate and then magnesium ammonium phosphate were precipitated. When the phosphate was ignited and weighed, it was found to weigh 0.1927 g. Calculate: (a) The per cent loss on ignition. (b) The per cent of silica. (c) The per cent of $R_2O_3$. (d) The per cent of MgO in the sample.

# APPENDIX I

## Answers to Problems

**Chapter 2.**

1. +0.9 scale divisions
2. 15.5305 g
3. 13.3754 g
4. 3.0032 g
5. 21.7228 g
6. Sample 0.4202 g
   Precipitate 1.1217 g
   No, the correction on the sample is only approximately 1 part in 2000 and that on the precipitate is approximately 1 part in 14,000.
7. 249.87 ml uncorrected for buoyancy
   250.13 ml corrected
8. 1 g is 1.0000
   2 g is 2.0013
   5 g is 5.0006
   10 g is 10.0002

**Chapter 4.**

4. a. 23.18% average
   b. Sample No.

   | 1 | 2 | 3 | 4 |
   |---|---|---|---|

   Deviation
   −0.16  +0.23  −0.03  −0.06
   c. 0.12 average deviation
   d. 0.17 standard deviation
   e. Sample No. 2 should be discarded because 4 × 0.05 = 0.20 which is less than 0.31.
   f. Sample No.

   | 1 | 2 | 3 | 4 |
   |---|---|---|---|

   Relative error in parts per 1000
   3.46  13.45  2.16  0.866

**Chapter 5.**

1. 2.182% sulfur
   0.1374 sulfur — barium sulfate factor

2. 4.91% tin
   0.7877 tin — tin oxide factor
3. 17.37% phosphorus
   86.98% calcium phosphate
   0.2785 phosphorus — magnesium pyrophosphate factor
   1.394 calcium phosphate — magnesium pyrophosphate factor
4. a. 1.15% silica
   b. 4.49% $R_2O_3$
   c. 48.26% CaO
5. $1 \times 10^{-8}$ molar solubility
   $1 \times 10^{-16}$ solubility product
6. $2.93 \times 10^{-2}$ molar solubility
   $1.0 \times 10^{-4}$ solubility product
7. $1.52 \times 10^{-3}$ molar solubility
   0.700 g per liter
8. 0.0533 g per 100 ml
9. $K_e = \dfrac{[C][D]^2}{[A][B]^3}$
10. 0.5870 g lead sulfate should be found.
    0.0063 g lost during precipitation
    0.0048 g lost by washing
    0.0111 g total of losses
    78.70% reported, after losses
11. $2.04 \times 10^{-4}$ g calcium ion in 100 ml of solution
    $1.04 \times 10^{-7}$ g calcium ion in 100 ml of 0.01 M oxalate
    $2.26 \times 10^{-2}$ g magnesium ion in 100 ml of solution
    $2.12 \times 10^{-2}$ g magnesium ion in 100 ml of 0.01 M oxalate
12. $0.09 = \mu$
13. 0.0373 g calcium ion in acid
    0.00204 g calcium ion in water
    Calcium oxalate is about 18 times as soluble in pH 2 as in water.

## Chapter 6.

21. 41.21% sulfur
22. 21.15% chloride
    33.80% $CaCl_2$ (chloride basis)
23. 49.08% $SO_3$
    98.95% $ZnSO_4$
    If first weighing is taken,
    48.90% $SO_3$
    98.59% $ZnSO_4$
24. 8.82 ml of $BaCl_2$ solution
    9.70 ml if 10% excess is added
25. 0.0346% sulfur
26. 0.106% phosphorus
27. 9.89% $R_2O_3$
    6.99% iron
28. 0.3083 g $Al_2O_3$
29. 0.1846 g AgCl
30. 15.04% $P_2O_5$

## Chapter 7.

1. a. 0.5846 g
   b. 0.8569 g
   c. 0.5550 g
   d. 1.6989 g
   e. 0.3267 g
   f. 0.6302 g
3. 0.1386 N
   721.4 ml
4. 0.0728 N
5. 29.52 ml
6. 0.2046 N
7. 0.09885 N
8. 0.0971 N
9. 0.005574 NaOH titer
   0.007819 KOH titer
   0.007385 $Na_2CO_3$ titer
10. 40.31% Fe
11. 55.43% $As_2O_3$.
12. 9.13% Ag
13. 0.1052 N
14. 0.0874 g

## Chapter 8.

3. a. 1.787 volts
   b. 1.67 volts
   c. 1.492 volts
   d. 1.628 volts
4. a. 0.288 volts
   b. 0.64 volts
   c. 1.387 volts
   d. 1.53 volts
5. a. $\frac{[Ti^{+4}]}{[Ti^{+3}]} = 10^{4.2}$
   b. $\frac{[Sn^{+4}]}{[Sn^{+3}]} = 10^{16.3}$
   c. $\frac{[Fe^{+3}]}{[Fe^{+2}]} = 10^{10.4}$
   d. $\frac{[Fe^{+3}]}{[Fe^{+2}]} = 10^{8.3}$
6. a. $10^{8.4}$
   b. $10^{49.5}$
   c. $10^{62.5}$

## Chapter 9.

3. a. 13.30
   b. 12.82
   c. 12.35
   d. 11.30
   e. 10.30
   f. 3.70
4. 0.1021
5. 2.93
6. 5.07
7. 4.55
8. 4.77
9. 2.72
10. a. 6.13
    b. 6.06
11. 4.15
12. Concentration of ion form and
    molecular form must be equal.

## Chapter 10.

1. 0.09076 N
   0.003218 chloride titer

2. 0.1260 N
3. 48.93% chloride
5. 0.09071 N
   0.009781 silver titer
6. 25.80% silver
11. 0.1231 N
12. 51.31% sodium carbonate
13. 12.30% potassium acid phthalate
16. 0.008069 iron titer
17. 30.83% iron
22. 0.002798 CaO titer
    0.09978 N
27. 20.13% Mn
28. 9.019% Cu

## Chapter 11.

2. a. 804.9 coulombs
   b. 98.63 coulombs
   c. 2290 coulombs
3. a. 0.8945 g Ag
   b. 0.2634 g Cu
   c. 0.6626 g Br
4. 0.785 volts
5. a. 0.311 volts
   b. 0.281 volts
   c. 0.193 volts
10. a. 1.955% Sn
    b. 80.62% Cu

c. 8.211% Pb
d. 9.214% Zn
11. a. 5370 seconds
    b. 1200 seconds

## Chapter 13.

12. 5.135% $CN^-$
13. 166 ppm of $CaCO_3$

## Chapter 14.

6. a. Permanganate absorbs most
      strongly at about 525 m$\mu$.
      Dichromate absorbs most
      strongly at about 450 m$\mu$.
   b. 550 m$\mu$
   c. 450 m$\mu$
8. a. 4.29 $\mu$g/ml in solution No. 1
      6.01 $\mu$g/ml in solution No. 2
   c. Approximately 5.33 $\mu$g/ml of
      Mn in solution No. 3
   d. 5.31 $\mu$g/ml of Mn
   e. 0.664% Mn
   f. 2.7 $\times$ 10$^3$

## Chapter 15.

2. a. 29.48% loss on ignition
   b. 4.42% silica and insoluble
   c. 5.81% $R_2O_3$
   d. 7.89% MgO

# APPENDIX II

### Weight of One Ml of Water, Weighed in Air with Brass Weights, Contained in Glass Vessels

| Temp C° | Weight of one ml of water | Temp C° | Weight of one ml of water |
|---------|---------------------------|---------|---------------------------|
| 17 | 0.99766 | 24 | 0.99638 |
| 18 | 0.99751 | 25 | 0.99617 |
| 19 | 0.99735 | 26 | 0.99594 |
| 20 | 0.99718 | 27 | 0.99570 |
| 21 | 0.99700 | 28 | 0.99545 |
| 22 | 0.99681 | 29 | 0.99519 |
| 23 | 0.99661 | 30 | 0.99492 |

# APPENDIX III

## Solubility Product Constants

| Substance | Formula | $k_{sp}$ |
|-----------|---------|----------|
| Arsenious sulfide | $As_2S_3$ | $1.1 \times 10^{-33}$ |
| Barium carbonate | $BaCO_3$ | $5 \times 10^{-9}$ |
| Barium chromate | $BaCrO_4$ | $1.2 \times 10^{-10}$ |
| Barium sulfate | $BaSO_4$ | $1.1 \times 10^{-10}$ |
| Calcium carbonate | $CaCO_3$ | $5 \times 10^{-9}$ |
| Calcium fluoride | $CaF_2$ | $4 \times 10^{-11}$ |
| Calcium oxalate | $CaC_2O_4$ | $2.6 \times 10^{-9}$ |
| Calcium sulfate | $CaSO_4$ | $6 \times 10^{-5}$ |
| Lead chloride | $PbCl_2$ | $1 \times 10^{-4}$ |
| Lead fluoride | $PbF_2$ | $4 \times 10^{-8}$ |
| Lead iodide | $PbI_2$ | $1.4 \times 10^{-8}$ |
| Lead sulfate | $PbSO_4$ | $1.1 \times 10^{-8}$ |
| Magnesium ammonium phosphate | $MgNH_4PO_4$ | $2.5 \times 10^{-13}$ |
| Magnesium oxalate | $MgC_2O_4$ | $8.7 \times 10^{-5}$ |
| Silver bromide | $AgBr$ | $7.7 \times 10^{-13}$ |
| Silver chloride | $AgCl$ | $1.2 \times 10^{-10}$ |
| Silver chromate | $Ag_2CrO_4$ | $1.15 \times 10^{-12}$ |
| Silver cyanide | $AgCN$ | $3 \times 10^{-12}$ |
| Silver iodide | $AgI$ | $1 \times 10^{-16}$ |
| Silver thiocyanate | $AgCNS$ | $2 \times 10^{-12}$ |
| Zinc carbonate | $ZnCO_3$ | $1 \times 10^{-10}$ |
| Zinc sulfide | $ZnS$ | $1 \times 10^{-23}$ |

# APPENDIX IV

## Ionization Constants of Acids and Bases

| Acid | Equilibrium Reaction | | $k_A$ |
|------|---------------------|---|-------|
| Acetic | $HC_2H_3O_2 + H_2O \rightleftarrows H_3O^+ + C_2H_3O_2^-$ | | $1.8 \times 10^{-5}$ |
| Arsenic | (1) $H_3AsO_4 + H_2O \rightleftarrows H_3O^+ + H_2AsO_4^-$ | $K_1$ | $2.8 \times 10^{-4}$ |
| | (2) $H_2AsO_4^- + H_2O \rightleftarrows H_3O^+ + HAsO_4^{-2}$ | $K_2$ | $7 \times 10^{-8}$ |
| | (3) $HAsO_4^{-2} + H_2O \rightleftarrows H_3O^+ + AsO_4^{-3}$ | $K_3$ | $1 \times 10^{-12}$ |
| Carbonic | (1) $H_2CO_3 + H_2O \rightleftarrows H_3O^+ + HCO_3^-$ | $K_1$ | $3.1 \times 10^{-7}$ |
| | (2) $HCO_3^- + H_2O \rightleftarrows H_3O^+ + CO_3^{-2}$ | $K_2$ | $4.2 \times 10^{-11}$ |
| Hydrocyanic | $HCN + H_2O \rightleftarrows H_3O^+ + CN^-$ | | $1 \times 10^{-9}$ |
| Hydrofluoric | $HF + H_2O \rightleftarrows H_3O^+ + F^-$ | | $1.7 \times 10^{-5}$ |
| Hydrogen sulfide | (1) $H_2S + H_2O \rightleftarrows H_3O^+ + HS^-$ | $K_1$ | $5.9 \times 10^{-8}$ |
| | (2) $HS^- + H_2O \rightleftarrows H_3O^+ + S^{-2}$ | $K_2$ | $1 \times 10^{-15}$ |
| Lactic | $HC_3H_5O_3 + H_2O \rightleftarrows H_3O^+ + C_3H_5O_3^-$ | | $1.4 \times 10^{-4}$ |
| Oxalic | (1) $H_2C_2O_4 + H_2O \rightleftarrows H_3O^+ + HC_2O_4^-$ | $K_1$ | $5 \times 10^{-2}$ |
| | (2) $HC_2O_4^- + H_2O \rightleftarrows H_3O^+ + C_2O_4^{-2}$ | $K_2$ | $3 \times 10^{-5}$ |
| Phosphoric | (1) $H_3PO_4 + H_2O \rightleftarrows H_3O^+ + H_2PO_4^-$ | $K_1$ | $7.5 \times 10^{-3}$ |
| | (2) $H_2PO_4^- + H_2O \rightleftarrows H_3O^+ + HPO_4^{-2}$ | $K_2$ | $6.2 \times 10^{-8}$ |
| | (3) $HPO_4^{-2} + H_2O \rightleftarrows H_3O^+ + PO_4^{-3}$ | $K_3$ | $2 \times 10^{-12}$ |
| Phthalic | (1) $H_2C_8H_4O_4 + H_2O \rightleftarrows H_3O^+ + HC_8H_4O_4^-$ | $K_1$ | $1.29 \times 10^{-3}$ |
| | (2) $HC_8H_4O_4^- + H_2O \rightleftarrows H_3O^+ + C_8H_4O_4^{-2}$ | $K_2$ | $3.8 \times 10^{-6}$ |

| Base | | $k_B$ |
|------|---|-------|
| Ammonia (ammonium hydroxide) | $NH_3 + H_2O \rightleftarrows NH_4^+ + OH^-$ | $1.8 \times 10^{-5}$ |
| Aniline | $C_6H_5NH_2 + H_2O \rightleftarrows C_6H_5NH_3^+ + OH^-$ | $2.7 \times 10^{-10}$ |
| Diethylamine | $(C_2H_5)_2NH + H_2O \rightleftarrows (C_2H_5)_2NH_2^+ + OH^-$ | $8.92 \times 10^{-4}$ |
| Hydrazine | $N_2H_4 + H_2O \rightleftarrows N_2H_5^+ + OH^-$ | $3 \times 10^{-6}$ |
| Triethylamine | $(C_2H_5)_3N + H_2O \rightleftarrows (C_2H_5)_3NH^+ + OH^-$ | $6.5 \times 10^{-4}$ |

# APPENDIX V

## Table of International Atomic Weights (1961)

| Element | Symbol | Atomic No. | Atomic Weight | Element | Symbol | Atomic No. | Atomic Weight |
|---|---|---|---|---|---|---|---|
| Actinium | Ac | 89 | | Mercury | Hg | 80 | 200.59 |
| Aluminum | Al | 13 | 26.9815 | Molybdenum | Mo | 42 | 95.94 |
| Americium | Am | 95 | | Neodymium | Nd | 60 | 144.24 |
| Antimony | Sb | 51 | 121.75 | Neon | Ne | 10 | 20.183 |
| Argon | Ar | 18 | 39.948 | Neptunium | Np | 93 | |
| Arsenic | As | 33 | 74.9216 | Nickel | Ni | 28 | 58.71 |
| Astatine | At | 85 | | Niobium | Nb | 41 | 92.906 |
| Barium | Ba | 56 | 137.34 | Nitrogen | N | 7 | 14.0067 |
| Berkelium | Bk | 97 | | Nobelium | No | 102 | |
| Beryllium | Be | 4 | 9.0122 | Osmium | Os | 76 | 190.2 |
| Bismuth | Bi | 83 | 208.980 | Oxygen | O | 8 | 15.9994[a] |
| Boron | B | 5 | 10.811[a] | Palladium | Pd | 46 | 106.4 |
| Bromine | Br | 35 | 79.909[b] | Phosphorus | P | 15 | 30.9738 |
| Cadmium | Cd | 48 | 112.40 | Platinum | Pt | 78 | 195.09 |
| Calcium | Ca | 20 | 40.08 | Plutonium | Pu | 94 | |
| Californium | Cf | 98 | | Polonium | Po | 94 | |
| Carbon | C | 6 | 12.01115[a] | Potassium | K | 19 | 39.102 |
| Cerium | Ce | 58 | 140.12 | Praseodymium | Pr | 59 | 140.907 |
| Cesium | Cs | 55 | 132.905 | Promethium | Pm | 61 | |
| Chlorine | Cl | 17 | 35.453[b] | Protactinium | Pa | 91 | |
| Chromium | Cr | 24 | 51.996[b] | Radium | Ra | 88 | |
| Cobalt | Co | 27 | 58.9332 | Radon | Rn | 86 | |
| Copper | Cu | 29 | 63.54 | Rhenium | Re | 75 | 186.2 |
| Curium | Cm | 96 | | Rhodium | Rh | 45 | 102.905 |
| Dysprosium | Dy | 66 | 162.50 | Rubidium | Rb | 37 | 85.47 |
| Einsteinium | Es | 99 | | Ruthenium | Ru | 44 | 101.07 |
| Erbium | Er | 68 | 167.26 | Samarium | Sm | 62 | 150.35 |
| Europium | Eu | 63 | 151.96 | Scandium | Sc | 21 | 44.956 |
| Fermium | Fm | 100 | | Selenium | Se | 34 | 78.96 |
| Fluorine | F | 9 | 18.9984 | Silicon | Si | 14 | 28.086[a] |
| Francium | Fr | 87 | | Silver | Ag | 47 | 107.870[b] |
| Gadolinium | Gd | 64 | 157.25 | Sodium | Na | 11 | 22.9898 |
| Gallium | Ga | 31 | 69.72 | Strontium | Sr | 38 | 87.62 |
| Germanium | Ge | 32 | 72.59 | Sulfur | S | 16 | 32.064[a] |
| Gold | Au | 79 | 196.967 | Tantalum | Ta | 73 | 180.948 |
| Hafnium | Hf | 72 | 178.49 | Technetium | Tc | 43 | |
| Helium | He | 2 | 4.0026 | Tellurium | Te | 52 | 127.60 |
| Holmium | Ho | 67 | 164.930 | Terbium | Tb | 65 | 158.924 |
| Hydrogen | H | 1 | 1.00797[a] | Thallium | Tl | 81 | 204.37 |
| Indium | In | 49 | 114.82 | Thorium | Th | 90 | 232.038 |
| Iodine | I | 53 | 126.9044 | Thulium | Tm | 69 | 168.934 |
| Iridium | Ir | 77 | 192.2 | Tin | Sn | 50 | 118.69 |
| Iron | Fe | 26 | 55.847[b] | Titanium | Ti | 22 | 47.90 |
| Krypton | Kr | 36 | 83.80 | Tungsten | W | 74 | 183.85 |
| Lanthanum | La | 57 | 138.91 | Uranium | U | 92 | 238.03 |
| Lead | Pb | 82 | 207.19 | Vanadium | V | 23 | 50.942 |
| Lithium | Li | 3 | 6.939 | Xenon | Xe | 54 | 131.30 |
| Lutetium | Lu | 71 | 174.97 | Ytterbium | Yb | 70 | 173.04 |
| Magnesium | Mg | 12 | 24.312 | Yttrium | Y | 39 | 88.905 |
| Manganese | Mn | 25 | 54.9380 | Zinc | Zn | 30 | 65.37 |
| Mendelevium | Md | 101 | | Zirconium | Zr | 40 | 91.22 |

[a] The atomic weight varies because of natural variations in the isotopic composition of the element. The observed ranges are boron, ±0.003; carbon, ±0.00005; hydrogen, ±0.00001; oxygen, ±0.0001; silicon, ±0.001; sulfur, ±0.003.

[b] The atomic weight is believed to have an experimental uncertainty of the following magnitude; bromine, ±0.002; chlorine, ±0.001; chromium, ±0.001; iron, ±0.003; silver, ±0.003. For other elements the last digit given is believed to be reliable to ±0.5.

# APPENDIX VI

## Table of Logarithms

| N | 0 | 1 | 2 | 3 | 4 | 5 | 6 | 7 | 8 | 9 | Proportional Parts | | | | |
|---|---|---|---|---|---|---|---|---|---|---|---|---|---|---|---|
| | | | | | | | | | | | 1 | 2 | 3 | 4 | 5 |
| 10 | 0000 | 0043 | 0086 | 0128 | 0170 | 0212 | 0253 | 0294 | 0334 | 0374 | 4 | 8 | 12 | 17 | 21 |
| 11 | 0414 | 0453 | 0492 | 0531 | 0569 | 0607 | 0645 | 0682 | 0719 | 0755 | 4 | 8 | 11 | 15 | 19 |
| 12 | 0792 | 0828 | 0864 | 0899 | 0934 | 0969 | 1004 | 1038 | 1072 | 1106 | 3 | 7 | 10 | 14 | 17 |
| 13 | 1139 | 1173 | 1206 | 1239 | 1271 | 1303 | 1335 | 1367 | 1399 | 1430 | 3 | 6 | 10 | 13 | 16 |
| 14 | 1461 | 1492 | 1523 | 1553 | 1584 | 1614 | 1644 | 1673 | 1703 | 1732 | 3 | 6 | 9 | 12 | 15 |
| 15 | 1761 | 1790 | 1818 | 1847 | 1875 | 1903 | 1931 | 1959 | 1987 | 2014 | 3 | 6 | 8 | 11 | 14 |
| 16 | 2041 | 2068 | 2095 | 2122 | 2148 | 2175 | 2201 | 2227 | 2253 | 2279 | 3 | 5 | 8 | 11 | 13 |
| 17 | 2304 | 2330 | 2355 | 2380 | 2405 | 2430 | 2455 | 2480 | 2504 | 2529 | 2 | 5 | 7 | 10 | 12 |
| 18 | 2553 | 2577 | 2601 | 2625 | 2648 | 2672 | 2695 | 2718 | 2742 | 2765 | 2 | 5 | 7 | 9 | 12 |
| 19 | 2788 | 2810 | 2833 | 2856 | 2878 | 2900 | 2923 | 2945 | 2967 | 2989 | 2 | 4 | 7 | 9 | 11 |
| 20 | 3010 | 3032 | 3054 | 3075 | 3096 | 3118 | 3139 | 3160 | 3181 | 3201 | 2 | 4 | 6 | 8 | 11 |
| 21 | 3222 | 3243 | 3263 | 3284 | 3304 | 3324 | 3345 | 3365 | 3385 | 3404 | 2 | 4 | 6 | 8 | 10 |
| 22 | 3424 | 3444 | 3464 | 3483 | 3502 | 3522 | 3541 | 3560 | 3579 | 3598 | 2 | 4 | 6 | 8 | 10 |
| 23 | 3617 | 3636 | 3655 | 3674 | 3692 | 3711 | 3729 | 3747 | 3766 | 3784 | 2 | 4 | 5 | 7 | 9 |
| 24 | 3802 | 3820 | 3838 | 3856 | 3874 | 3892 | 3909 | 3927 | 3945 | 3962 | 2 | 4 | 5 | 7 | 9 |
| 25 | 3979 | 3997 | 4014 | 4031 | 4048 | 4065 | 4082 | 4099 | 4116 | 4133 | 2 | 3 | 5 | 7 | 9 |
| 26 | 4150 | 4166 | 4183 | 4200 | 4216 | 4232 | 4249 | 4265 | 4281 | 4298 | 2 | 3 | 5 | 7 | 8 |
| 27 | 4314 | 4330 | 4346 | 4362 | 4378 | 4393 | 4409 | 4425 | 4440 | 4456 | 2 | 3 | 5 | 6 | 8 |
| 28 | 4472 | 4487 | 4502 | 4518 | 4533 | 4548 | 4564 | 4579 | 4594 | 4609 | 2 | 3 | 5 | 6 | 8 |
| 29 | 4624 | 4639 | 4654 | 4669 | 4683 | 4698 | 4713 | 4728 | 4742 | 4757 | 1 | 3 | 4 | 6 | 7 |
| 30 | 4771 | 4786 | 4800 | 4814 | 4829 | 4843 | 4857 | 4871 | 4886 | 4900 | 1 | 3 | 4 | 6 | 7 |
| 31 | 4914 | 4928 | 4942 | 4955 | 4969 | 4983 | 4997 | 5011 | 5024 | 5038 | 1 | 3 | 4 | 6 | 7 |
| 32 | 5051 | 5065 | 5079 | 5092 | 5105 | 5119 | 5132 | 5145 | 5159 | 5172 | 1 | 3 | 4 | 5 | 7 |
| 33 | 5185 | 5198 | 5211 | 5224 | 5237 | 5250 | 5263 | 5276 | 5289 | 5302 | 1 | 3 | 4 | 5 | 6 |
| 34 | 5315 | 5328 | 5340 | 5353 | 5366 | 5378 | 5391 | 5403 | 5416 | 5428 | 1 | 3 | 4 | 5 | 6 |
| 35 | 5441 | 5453 | 5465 | 5478 | 5490 | 5502 | 5514 | 5527 | 5539 | 5551 | 1 | 2 | 4 | 5 | 6 |
| 36 | 5563 | 5575 | 5587 | 5599 | 5611 | 5623 | 5635 | 5647 | 5658 | 5670 | 1 | 2 | 4 | 5 | 6 |
| 37 | 5682 | 5694 | 5705 | 5717 | 5729 | 5740 | 5752 | 5763 | 5775 | 5786 | 1 | 2 | 3 | 5 | 6 |
| 38 | 5798 | 5809 | 5821 | 5832 | 5843 | 5855 | 5866 | 5877 | 5888 | 5899 | 1 | 2 | 3 | 5 | 6 |
| 39 | 5911 | 5922 | 5933 | 5944 | 5955 | 5966 | 5977 | 5988 | 5999 | 6010 | 1 | 2 | 3 | 4 | 6 |
| 40 | 6021 | 6031 | 6042 | 6053 | 6064 | 6075 | 6085 | 6096 | 6107 | 6117 | 1 | 2 | 3 | 4 | 5 |
| 41 | 6128 | 6138 | 6149 | 6160 | 6170 | 6180 | 6191 | 6201 | 6212 | 6222 | 1 | 2 | 3 | 4 | 5 |
| 42 | 6232 | 6243 | 6253 | 6263 | 6274 | 6284 | 6294 | 6304 | 6314 | 6325 | 1 | 2 | 3 | 4 | 5 |
| 43 | 6335 | 6345 | 6355 | 6365 | 6375 | 6385 | 6395 | 6405 | 6415 | 6425 | 1 | 2 | 3 | 4 | 5 |
| 44 | 6435 | 6444 | 6454 | 6464 | 6474 | 6484 | 6493 | 6503 | 6513 | 6522 | 1 | 2 | 3 | 4 | 5 |
| 45 | 6532 | 6542 | 6551 | 6561 | 6571 | 6580 | 6590 | 6599 | 6609 | 6618 | 1 | 2 | 3 | 4 | 5 |
| 46 | 6628 | 6637 | 6646 | 6656 | 6665 | 6675 | 6684 | 6693 | 6702 | 6712 | 1 | 2 | 3 | 4 | 5 |
| 47 | 6721 | 6730 | 6739 | 6749 | 6758 | 6767 | 6776 | 6785 | 6794 | 6803 | 1 | 2 | 3 | 4 | 5 |
| 48 | 6812 | 6821 | 6830 | 6839 | 6848 | 6857 | 6866 | 6875 | 6884 | 6893 | 1 | 2 | 3 | 4 | 4 |
| 49 | 6902 | 6911 | 6920 | 6928 | 6937 | 6946 | 6955 | 6964 | 6972 | 6981 | 1 | 2 | 3 | 4 | 4 |
| 50 | 6990 | 6998 | 7007 | 7016 | 7024 | 7033 | 7042 | 7050 | 7059 | 7067 | 1 | 2 | 3 | 3 | 4 |
| 51 | 7076 | 7084 | 7093 | 7101 | 7110 | 7118 | 7126 | 7135 | 7143 | 7152 | 1 | 2 | 3 | 3 | 4 |
| 52 | 7160 | 7168 | 7177 | 7185 | 7193 | 7202 | 7210 | 7218 | 7226 | 7235 | 1 | 2 | 2 | 3 | 4 |
| 53 | 7243 | 7251 | 7259 | 7267 | 7275 | 7284 | 7292 | 7300 | 7308 | 7316 | 1 | 2 | 2 | 3 | 4 |
| 54 | 7324 | 7332 | 7340 | 7348 | 7356 | 7364 | 7372 | 7380 | 7388 | 7396 | 1 | 2 | 2 | 3 | 4 |
| N | 0 | 1 | 2 | 3 | 4 | 5 | 6 | 7 | 8 | 9 | 1 | 2 | 3 | 4 | 5 |

## Table of Logarithms

## (continued)

| N | 0 | 1 | 2 | 3 | 4 | 5 | 6 | 7 | 8 | 9 | Proportional Parts | | | | |
|---|---|---|---|---|---|---|---|---|---|---|---|---|---|---|---|
| | | | | | | | | | | | 1 | 2 | 3 | 4 | 5 |
| 55 | 7404 | 7412 | 7419 | 7427 | 7435 | 7443 | 7451 | 7459 | 7466 | 7474 | 1 | 2 | 2 | 3 | 4 |
| 56 | 7482 | 7490 | 7497 | 7505 | 7513 | 7520 | 7528 | 7536 | 7543 | 7551 | 1 | 2 | 2 | 3 | 4 |
| 57 | 7559 | 7566 | 7574 | 7582 | 7589 | 7597 | 7604 | 7612 | 7619 | 7627 | 1 | 2 | 2 | 3 | 4 |
| 58 | 7634 | 7642 | 7649 | 7657 | 7664 | 7672 | 7679 | 7686 | 7694 | 7701 | 1 | 1 | 2 | 3 | 4 |
| 59 | 7709 | 7716 | 7723 | 7731 | 7738 | 7745 | 7752 | 7760 | 7767 | 7774 | 1 | 1 | 2 | 3 | 4 |
| 60 | 7782 | 7789 | 7796 | 7803 | 7810 | 7818 | 7825 | 7832 | 7839 | 7846 | 1 | 1 | 2 | 3 | 4 |
| 61 | 7853 | 7860 | 7868 | 7875 | 7882 | 7889 | 7896 | 7903 | 7910 | 7917 | 1 | 1 | 2 | 3 | 4 |
| 62 | 7924 | 7931 | 7938 | 7945 | 7952 | 7959 | 7966 | 7973 | 7980 | 7987 | 1 | 1 | 2 | 3 | 3 |
| 63 | 7993 | 8000 | 8007 | 8014 | 8021 | 8028 | 8035 | 8041 | 8048 | 8055 | 1 | 1 | 2 | 3 | 3 |
| 64 | 8062 | 8069 | 8075 | 8082 | 8089 | 8096 | 8102 | 8109 | 8116 | 8122 | 1 | 1 | 2 | 3 | 3 |
| 65 | 8129 | 8136 | 8142 | 8149 | 8156 | 8162 | 8169 | 8176 | 8182 | 8189 | 1 | 1 | 2 | 3 | 3 |
| 66 | 8195 | 8202 | 8209 | 8215 | 8222 | 8228 | 8235 | 8241 | 8248 | 8254 | 1 | 1 | 2 | 3 | 3 |
| 67 | 8261 | 8267 | 8274 | 8280 | 8287 | 8293 | 8299 | 8306 | 8312 | 8319 | 1 | 1 | 2 | 3 | 3 |
| 68 | 8325 | 8331 | 8338 | 8344 | 8351 | 8357 | 8363 | 8370 | 8376 | 8382 | 1 | 1 | 2 | 3 | 3 |
| 69 | 8388 | 8395 | 8401 | 8407 | 8414 | 8420 | 8426 | 8432 | 8439 | 8445 | 1 | 1 | 2 | 3 | 3 |
| 70 | 8451 | 8457 | 8463 | 8470 | 8476 | 8482 | 8488 | 8494 | 8500 | 8506 | 1 | 1 | 2 | 2 | 3 |
| 71 | 8513 | 8519 | 8525 | 8531 | 8537 | 8543 | 8549 | 8555 | 8561 | 8567 | 1 | 1 | 2 | 2 | 3 |
| 72 | 8573 | 8579 | 8585 | 8591 | 8597 | 8603 | 8609 | 8615 | 8621 | 8627 | 1 | 1 | 2 | 2 | 3 |
| 73 | 8633 | 8639 | 8645 | 8651 | 8657 | 8663 | 8669 | 8675 | 8681 | 8686 | 1 | 1 | 2 | 2 | 3 |
| 74 | 8692 | 8698 | 8704 | 8710 | 8716 | 8722 | 8727 | 8733 | 8739 | 8745 | 1 | 1 | 2 | 2 | 3 |
| 75 | 8751 | 8756 | 8762 | 8768 | 8774 | 8779 | 8785 | 8791 | 8797 | 8802 | 1 | 1 | 2 | 2 | 3 |
| 76 | 8808 | 8814 | 8820 | 8825 | 8831 | 8837 | 8842 | 8848 | 8854 | 8859 | 1 | 1 | 2 | 2 | 3 |
| 77 | 8865 | 8871 | 8876 | 8882 | 8887 | 8893 | 8899 | 8904 | 8910 | 8915 | 1 | 1 | 2 | 2 | 3 |
| 78 | 8921 | 8927 | 8932 | 8938 | 8943 | 8949 | 8954 | 8960 | 8965 | 8971 | 1 | 1 | 2 | 2 | 3 |
| 79 | 8976 | 8982 | 8987 | 8993 | 8998 | 9004 | 9009 | 9015 | 9020 | 9025 | 1 | 1 | 2 | 2 | 3 |
| 80 | 9031 | 9036 | 9042 | 9047 | 9053 | 9058 | 9063 | 9069 | 9074 | 9079 | 1 | 1 | 2 | 2 | 3 |
| 81 | 9085 | 9090 | 9096 | 9101 | 9106 | 9112 | 9117 | 9122 | 9128 | 9133 | 1 | 1 | 2 | 2 | 3 |
| 82 | 9138 | 9143 | 9149 | 9154 | 9159 | 9165 | 9170 | 9175 | 9180 | 9186 | 1 | 1 | 2 | 2 | 3 |
| 83 | 9191 | 9196 | 9201 | 9206 | 9212 | 9217 | 9222 | 9227 | 9232 | 9238 | 1 | 1 | 2 | 2 | 3 |
| 84 | 9243 | 9248 | 9253 | 9258 | 9263 | 9269 | 9274 | 9279 | 9284 | 9289 | 1 | 1 | 2 | 2 | 3 |
| 85 | 9294 | 9299 | 9304 | 9309 | 9315 | 9320 | 9325 | 9330 | 9335 | 9340 | 1 | 1 | 2 | 2 | 3 |
| 86 | 9345 | 9350 | 9355 | 9360 | 9365 | 9370 | 9375 | 9380 | 9385 | 9390 | 1 | 1 | 2 | 2 | 3 |
| 87 | 9395 | 9400 | 9405 | 9410 | 9415 | 9420 | 9425 | 9430 | 9435 | 9440 | 0 | 1 | 1 | 2 | 2 |
| 88 | 9445 | 9450 | 9455 | 9460 | 9465 | 9469 | 9474 | 9479 | 9484 | 9489 | 0 | 1 | 1 | 2 | 2 |
| 89 | 9494 | 9499 | 9504 | 9509 | 9513 | 9518 | 9523 | 9528 | 9533 | 9538 | 0 | 1 | 1 | 2 | 2 |
| 90 | 9542 | 9547 | 9552 | 9557 | 9562 | 9566 | 9571 | 9576 | 9581 | 9586 | 0 | 1 | 1 | 2 | 2 |
| 91 | 9590 | 9595 | 9600 | 9605 | 9609 | 9614 | 9619 | 9624 | 9628 | 9633 | 0 | 1 | 1 | 2 | 2 |
| 92 | 9638 | 9643 | 9647 | 9652 | 9657 | 9661 | 9666 | 9671 | 9675 | 9680 | 0 | 1 | 1 | 2 | 2 |
| 93 | 9685 | 9689 | 9694 | 9699 | 9703 | 9708 | 9713 | 9717 | 9722 | 9727 | 0 | 1 | 1 | 2 | 2 |
| 94 | 9731 | 9736 | 9741 | 9745 | 9750 | 9754 | 9759 | 9763 | 9768 | 9773 | 0 | 1 | 1 | 2 | 2 |
| 95 | 9777 | 9782 | 9786 | 9791 | 9795 | 9800 | 9805 | 9809 | 9814 | 9818 | 0 | 1 | 1 | 2 | 2 |
| 96 | 9823 | 9827 | 9832 | 9836 | 9841 | 9845 | 9850 | 9854 | 9859 | 9863 | 0 | 1 | 1 | 2 | 2 |
| 97 | 9868 | 9872 | 9877 | 9881 | 9886 | 9890 | 9894 | 9899 | 9903 | 9908 | 0 | 1 | 1 | 2 | 2 |
| 98 | 9912 | 9917 | 9921 | 9926 | 9930 | 9934 | 9939 | 9943 | 9948 | 9952 | 0 | 1 | 1 | 2 | 2 |
| 99 | 9956 | 9961 | 9965 | 9969 | 9974 | 9978 | 9983 | 9987 | 9991 | 9996 | 0 | 1 | 1 | 2 | 2 |
| N | 0 | 1 | 2 | 3 | 4 | 5 | 6 | 7 | 8 | 9 | 1 | 2 | 3 | 4 | 5 |

# Index

229